CONFLUENCE
The Story of Greeley Water

Gregory J. Hobbs, Jr.

Michael Welsh

Foreword by Reagan Waskom

Preface by Roy Otto

City of Greeley Colorado

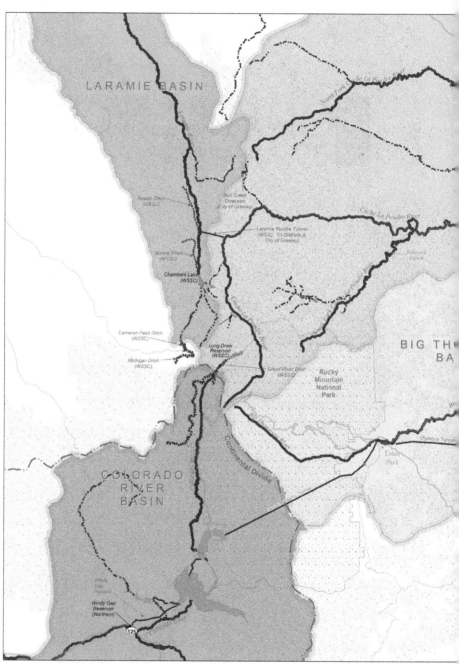

The Greeley Water system map was created by the staff of the City of Greeley, Geographic Information Systems Department.

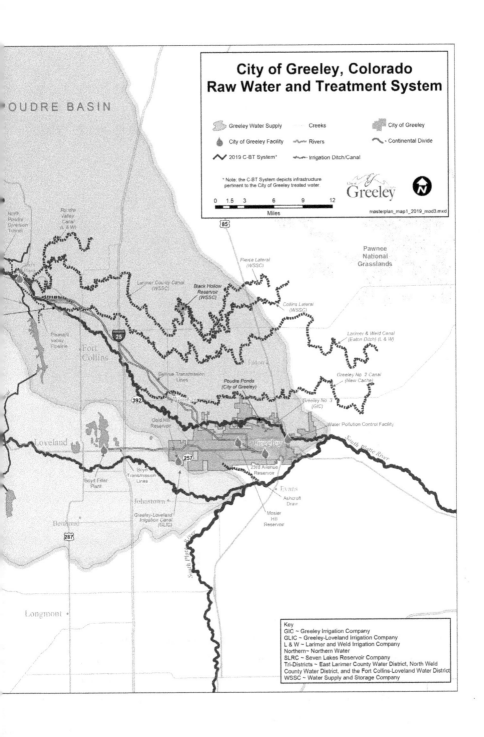

City of Greeley, Colorado
Raw Water and Treatment System

Greeley Water Supply	Creeks	City of Greeley
City of Greeley Facility	Rivers	Continental Divide
2019 C-BT System*	Irrigation Ditch/Canal	

* Note: the C-BT System depicts infrastructure
pertinent to the City of Greeley treated water.

0   1.5   3   6   9   12
Miles

masterplan_map1_2019_mod3.mxd

POUDRE BASIN

Pawnee
National
Grasslands

North
Poudre
Diversion
Tunnel

Poudre
Valley
Canal
(L & W)

Pierce Lateral
(WSSC)

Larimer County Canal
(WSSC)

Black Hollow
Reservoir
(WSSC)

Collins Lateral
(WSSC)

Pleasant
Valley
Pipeline

Larimer & Weld Canal
(Eaton Ditch) (L & W)

Fort
Collins

Eaton

Bellvue Transmission
Lines

Poudre Ponds
(City of Greeley)

Greeley No. 2 Canal
(New Cache)

Greeley No. 3
(GIC)

Gold Hill
Reservoir

Water Pollution Control Facility

Loveland

South Platte River

Greeley

Boyd
Transmission
Lines

23rd Avenue
Reservoir

Boyd Filter
Plant

Johnstown

Evans

Ashcroft
Draw

Greeley-Loveland
Irrigation Canal
(GLIC)

Mosier
Hill
Reservoir

Berthoud

South Platte River

Longmont

Key
GIC ~ Greeley Irrigation Company
GLIC ~ Greeley-Loveland Irrigation Company
L & W ~ Larimer and Weld Irrigation Company
Northern~ Northern Water
SLRC ~ Seven Lakes Reservoir Company
Tri-Districts ~ East Larimer County Water District, North Weld
County Water District, and the Fort Collins-Loveland Water District
WSSC ~ Water Supply and Storage Company

ISBN: 978-0-578-63416-6

Contents

Illustrations

Foreword

"In the West, when you touch water, you touch everything."
—Congressman Wayne Aspinall

GREELEY'S 150-YEAR QUEST for a sustainable water supply reminds us of the immortal words of West Slope Congressman Wayne Aspinall, as water touches virtually every aspect of Greeley's history. This is a story that, while unique, could describe the development of many western communities forged from a dry landscape by hard work and vision. Simply stated, water development and community building progressed together in the arid lands. Greeley's history informs our understanding of European settlement beyond the 100th Meridian, where human ingenuity is required to overcome the hydrologic vagaries of the region.

It is fitting that western history scholars and prolific authors Justice Gregory J. Hobbs, Jr., and University of Northern Colorado History Professor Michael Welsh, in collaboration with well-known Colorado water author Tom Cech as executive editor, and Greeley Water and Sewer Board Chairman Harold Evans, worked to bring this book to life. A former Colorado Supreme Court Justice and a university historian collaborating on a scholarly history of a midsized western water utility! Is there something of wider interest here? Indeed there is. The authors' insight and knowledge of Colorado history, the development of our legal framework and institutions, the indigenous West, and our rivers run through the chapters, shining light on how place and people interact to build community.

This is a book about individuals and organizations that built an extraordinarily resilient water infrastructure and a city on the dry plains of northern Colorado.

The book crosses generations, like Michener's *Centennial*, but in this case the actors and the circumstances are historically accurate. Easterners who had lived through the Civil War epoch imagined a better life in the West and set out to build it. Our stories define us—they are borne of places, such as Greeley, but transcend time and space as they show us who and what we are. But real stories such as these are messy, with failures and conflict, containing multiple viewpoints, and are unfinished, with the next chapter yet to unfold. This book does not present a varnished, gauzy look back at an idealized and charming past; it is a gritty tally of shovels and sweat and money that helps us understand what it took to become the agricultural capital of Colorado, if not the region.

Greeley's central story is one of a deliberate undertaking to build a utopian temperance colony of individuals who were "of good character, financially solvent, and skilled in diverse trades and professions." Although they strategically founded their colony at the junction of the Cache la Poudre and South Platte Rivers, their knowledge of hydraulic engineering was rudimentary and the struggle with water began immediately. Canal construction commenced just two weeks after the colonists arrived and they quickly discovered that there was either too much water, or not enough. Water was an unruly resource that they learned to love and fear. One colonist noted their experiences with water "have taken hold on us, have sunk deeply in our hearts." Our authors, sensitive to word play, have documented the poetry in the words of early settlers' accounts, quoting one exuberant colonist describing how the "water came dancing through the flumes like ministering angels, scattering blessings all along its path."

The reality was less poetic, as hailstorms, bitter winds, blizzards, dust, locusts and droughts plagued the colonists. Economic hard times, two world wars, loss and setbacks such as the Number 3 canal breach, or Delph Carpenter's failed strategy in the Laramie River lawsuit just spurred greater efforts. Failure was an idea so unreasonable that the early settlers did not countenance it. They came with a can-do spirit and attitude to find a way through each challenge. They trusted Divine Providence but invested in technical expertise. The idea of a self-governing utopian frontier community may seem idealistic or even quaint from the distance of 150 years, but the Union Colonists built and sustained community just as we do today—through shared vision, leadership and collaboration.

Hobbs and Welsh remind us of well-known historical Colorado figures such as

Nathan Meeker, Benjamin Eaton, Delph Carpenter, W.D. Farr, and Senator Hank Brown as they cross these pages, but also bring us the legacies of lesser-known heroes such as General Robert Cameron, Burton D. Sanborn, David Boyd, Milton Seaman and William R. Kelly. *Greeley Tribune* publisher Charles Hansen is described quietly coaxing all parties to cooperate on projects almost too grand to contemplate, such as the 13-mile tunnel under Rocky Mountain National Park to bring Colorado River water to northeast Colorado. We see the cycle of western water development to accommodate growth, followed by shortage, then conservation, water quality concerns, then further water development that temporarily alleviates shortage and facilitates continued growth. The cycle continues to this day, but in the context and constraints of the time, and the never-ending need for infrastructure repair and updating of transmission, treatment and storage. Necessity forced water conservation very early in Greeley's history and the city continues to lead in conservation strategies and messaging to this day.

What can we take of wider interest from the iterative struggle to grow and build and maintain a municipal water system? The authors describe how technical expertise, vision and political will enabled key community leaders in each era to understand the challenges before them and to craft and sell solutions. It only looks easy if you gloss over the endless meetings, multiple layers of governance, constraints in financing, state and federal laws, and competing interests. Welsh and Hobbs take you into the details while telling the broader story and historical context, giving a glimpse of civic engagement across time from settlement to current day. Lessons of leadership, community and Colorado's water history emerge from this account, such as the need for a long view, build coalitions, practice careful stewardship of resources, pursue a collaborative strategy, but be willing to fight if you must.

We tend to think the challenges facing society today are somehow unique and more daunting than past problems. Hobbs and Welsh remind us that virtually all of today's issues have been seen before, from the Great Depression and the sense of an uncertain climate future during the Dust Bowl era, to the shortages of materials and labor during World War II, to the cultural upheaval of the environmental era. Resources and funding for water projects are almost always scarce, yet our modern civilization rests on the improbable comforts and benefits of water and sanitary engineering.

Although Greeley has built a vast and resilient infrastructure covering four river basins, the work goes on as we arrive at the 150th anniversary of the founding of the Union Colony. One writer in the 1920s stated, "Greeley is an idea . . . a philosophy of community life, including agriculture, home building, schools, civilization and religion." Greeley's quest for adequate water has had long-lasting impacts on the development of water in Colorado and the West, helping shape water law and administration. Our authors have crafted a beautiful Colorado narrative that enriches our understanding of a people who were not only concerned with their survival or their personal enrichment; these were a people building something to last that encompassed the seventh generation in their foresight. Were the politics tough, the disagreements bitter, and the stakes high? You bet. They fought to solidify what became the bedrock of Colorado water law, the first in time, first in right doctrine of prior appropriation. The seminal idea of interstate river compacts was born from a son of the Union Colony, as was the Colorado-Big Thompson project, Wild and Scenic designation for the Poudre, Shared Vision Planning process for reservoir permitting, and the value of preserving agriculture in an urbanizing region.

It has been 150 years since Greeley's idealistic start on the banks of the Cache la Poudre River. The sons and daughters of the Union Colony were tempered in the crucible of hard summers and uncertain winters. They saw the splendid alchemy of sunshine and river water spilt on the dry prairie soil. They grew and prospered through a shared vision of what could be. The Greeley legacy of human ingenuity and persistence still manifests in today's leadership, as the community continues building towards a future vision. These leaders bring the gift of this book, written by Justice Hobbs and Professor Welsh, to those wanting a deeper understanding of this place we call Colorado.

—Reagan Waskom
Director of the Colorado Water Center at Colorado State University
Fort Collins, Colorado

Preface

HISTORY—OR RATHER the stories and lessons that come alive through history—offer rare moments for reflection and enlightenment. The stories of our history allow us to imagine what it was like to live during a particular period of time. What character in the story are we most like? What character is not anything like me? Can I learn from them, and apply the lessons in their stories to my life?

There is a quote often attributed to the Spanish writer/philosopher George Santayana: "Those who cannot remember the past are condemned to repeat it." This quotation certainly sets an ominous tone, and stresses the importance and relevance of paying attention to our local history and stories. The context of his remarks are rooted in the perpetual relationship between man and conflict—specifically armed conflict. His remarks suggest that humankind has a way of repeating history and that we too often end up in armed confrontations.

Does this hold true for conflicts or disagreements over water? Are we to have water wars? It is said that the Union Colonists, the original residents of Greeley, uttered the words "Every man to his tent, to his rifle and cartridges!" during the summer of 1874 when they found their irrigation ditch was dry. Their belief was that neighbors to the northwest, in Fort Collins, were stealing their water. Time for a good gunfight, after all, in the West, whiskey is for drinking but water is for fighting over.

We are fortunate that cooler heads prevailed during that parched summer of 1874, and instead of bloodshed, ink was put to paper and Colorado water law, "first in time, first in right," was created. That same law governs water today. The foresight and diplomacy of our early settlers created a legacy for Greeley and all northern Colorado. I submit that this law and early alliances demonstrate that the Cache la Poudre River flows on the power of relationships. What appeared, initially, to be toxic, ultimately became collaborative and the result is a blessing to many.

Greeley's water history outlines two very important themes that I hope we are "doomed to repeat" as we face a critical time in our community's history. The first lesson is that we have a legacy of resolving water disagreements through collaboration. Yes, there is conflict as people disagree over the use of water, but we have a tradition of working toward collaborative solutions. As we try to balance the need for vital water supplies to grow our cities, we compete with environmental and recreational interests to keep water in the river.

In the pages that follow, you will learn how this challenge was addressed through bypass flow agreements to ensure that the Cache la Poudre River maintains a healthy habitat for fish. You will learn how Greeley's Hank Brown reached across the political aisle in Washington, D.C., to designate the upper 76-mile portion of the Cache la Poudre River as a National Wild and Scenic River, from Poudre Lake at the headwaters, to near the mouth of the Cache la Poudre River northwest of Fort Collins. The Cache la Poudre River National Heritage Area would later be created from the eastern edge of the Roosevelt National Forest downstream to the confluence of the South Platte River east of Greeley. Greeley's water people get things done.

Today, individuals from a variety of interest areas, who all share a common passion for the river, have formed the Poudre Runs Through It Committee to collaborate and find solutions to problems. Their collective desire is to ensure that the Poudre River be known as the world's premier example of a healthy working river. In some circles, Greeley is known as the State Capitol of Agriculture. As such, we intentionally work with the agricultural industry to ensure that water is available for their success. This is critical for Greeley, northern Colorado and the State of Colorado's economic success.

You will read how Charles Hansen led a collaborative effort to establish the Colorado-Big Thompson Project during the devastating drought of the 1930s. Recently, Hansen's work directly resulted in Greeley being ranked as the 8th most dynamic metropolitan area in the United States. Northern Colorado, Larimer and Weld Counties are consistently ranked among the fastest growing areas in the country. I believe this prosperity would not be possible if not for the collaborative effort to build the Colorado-Big Thompson water supply project. You will also learn about the Windy Gap Project and collaboration between the communities of Greeley, Estes Park, Longmont, Boulder, Loveland and Fort Collins.

Today we are about to construct the Chimney Hollow Reservoir just west of Carter Lake in Loveland. This partnership will improve the yield of these important water rights of the Windy Gap Project. It is humbling to serve as Greeley's current city manager and member of the Greeley Water and Sewer Board as we put the finishing touches on Windy Gap. This project was initiated in 1970 when the Northern Water Municipal Subdistrict was created. You must be patient when working in water.

The second historic theme I hope we repeat is that Greeley has an established record of one generation working to meet the water demands of the next generation. Harold Evans, the current and long-time chairman of the water and sewer board, and the champion of this book, is always reminding anyone who will listen that we are benefitting from the investments of our founders—and each generation that follows. Harold is at the forefront of challenging the current generation to do the same for the next—whether it be Gen X, Y, millennials, or Generation 6G residents. Greeley's future success depends on the investments we make in water.

Harold recently provided me with the following quote as he was researching this important history project. On March 29, 1941, a group of Greeley businessmen ran an advertisement in the *Greeley Tribune* concerning Greeley's water future. The one quote that stood out was: "Look ahead and plan for others as others have planned for you." To no surprise, two of the men named as part of the group were Charles Hansen and W.D. Farr. Words of wisdom from over 75 years ago. We are motivated today by this same wisdom. I can only hope that this book and the history of water and collaboration inspire future generations. May they repeat these lessons and be motivated to pay it forward.

As I write this, I am flying over Colorado's Rocky Mountains and can see reservoirs from my window—many of which are referenced in the pages of this book. This panoramic view provides me with a great opportunity to reflect and ponder about Greeley's water challenges. Water is, in my opinion, our most important piece of infrastructure. We need it to support our collective municipal, agricultural, industrial, environmental and recreational interests.

The challenges we face today are daunting. The Colorado-Big Thompson Project may not yield as much water in the future as some of our Colorado River water may be needed to ensure that the Lower Basin States (Arizona, California and Nevada—parties to the Colorado River Compact) have their legal share of water. Years of drought in the southwestern United States have depleted the amount of water stored in Lake Powell and Lake Mead. There are concerns that the impacts of climate change will only make the problem worse.

In northern Colorado, there is considerable conflict over the construction of much-needed reservoirs to meet the region's future growth. The growing Denver metro area is looking to divert water in the Cache la Poudre Basin to meet their needs. As developers and municipalities buy and dry agricultural water supplies, the viability of this important economic sector is in doubt. These threats and challenges create stress. I can hear the faint call of "Every man to his tent, to his rifle and cartridges!"

Nevertheless, I am hopeful. I believe that our water history will, indeed, repeat itself. Our rich history teaches us to collaborate and invest in the next generation. I hear loud and clear the inspiring Greeley water history in the challenges facing today's water leaders as they plan for Greeley's water future. We will collaborate. We will invest in the next generation as generations in the past have invested in us. I add my voice to this call as well. I would like to amend my prior statement that water is the most important piece of our infrastructure. In truth, it is the people that collaborate, innovate, and invest in the future that we must look to. WE are the most important piece of our infrastructure. As we collaborate, we become a civic infrastructure that is more than capable of developing and using water wisely.

As you read this book, I ask you to consider, what will our legacy be? Will we continue the legacy and collaborate to find solutions to our challenges? Will we invest in the future just as many did in the past for us? It has never felt better to be "doomed to repeat history."

—Roy Otto
City Manager
City of Greeley, Colorado

Introduction

At the Confluence

A BOOK ABOUT a water agency in the western United States is not the first topic that comes to mind when we look for a good book to read. Our first inclination is that it will be dry (pun intended); it will be a chore to read through the details of pipes and projects, and construction programs and endless meetings. On the contrary, that is not the theme of this book.

Greeley, Colorado, has the distinction of being one-of-a-kind. Its roots stretch all the way back to New York City and the newspaper publisher Horace Greeley. In 1870, shortly after the Civil War ended, hundreds of fledgling adventurers settled along the confluence of the Cache la Poudre and South Platte Rivers in Colorado Territory. These were cosmopolitan travelers, the type that would quit their office jobs today and start a new business in Alaska, or move east to take their chances in a big city like New York or west to Los Angeles. The story of the Union Colonists and Greeley is one for the movies—and James Michener did just that in the 1970s with his book, and a later mini-series, called *Centennial*.

Mining camps came and went as towns sprang up out of sagebrush and farm ground. It became clear that Greeley's most precious heritage consisted of its four main watersheds—the Cache la Poudre, Big Thompson, Colorado, and the South Platte. Before the gold and silver miners, and the rest of us, came onto these lands of Colorado, the Arapaho, Cheyenne, Ute, Navajo, and Hispanos were here—prior to them, the ancestral Pueblo people of southwestern Colorado. They had constructed cisterns, interceptor ditches and reservoirs to survive in the arid lands of the Mesa Verde. Across the region, all of these peoples had to invent water-sharing customs for their own communities, to nurture families and sustain dwelling places the best they could.

The founders of the Union Colony cast themselves in the image and likeness of Abraham Lincoln, a man of their generation. He so dearly dreamed "that this nation under God shall have a new birth of freedom, and that government of the people, by the people, for the people shall not perish from the earth." Soldiers of the civil war, utopian community organizers, and city dwellers in search of newer opportunities were the primary instigators in settling the Union Colony in 1870 and onward. Through the years, Greeley has developed and defended its essential water supplies—as a growing municipality and supporter of surrounding agricultural environs—collaboratively. City Manager Roy Otto explains this relationship well in his *Preface* to this book.

So why should you read this literary work? Authors Michael Welsh and Greg Hobbs are students of this heritage, and have a long history of working together. In their lifetimes of teaching and learning, the authors have spoken with many who savor Colorado water history. Michael and Greg first worked together in preparation of the *Citizen's Guide to Colorado's Water Heritage*, designed by Emmett Jordan and published by the Colorado Foundation for Water Education in 2005 (now known as Water Education Colorado). Emmett also designed the initial set of ten water law guides for Water Education Colorado, including the *Citizen's Guide to Colorado Water Law*, which Greg authored in 2003, now in its 4th edition. Michael is a Professor of History in the College of Humanities and Social Sciences at the University of Northern Colorado in Greeley, with a doctorate from the University of New Mexico. A distinguished historian, he authored *U.S. Army Corps of Engineers, Albuquerque District, 1935-1985* published by the University of New Mexico; which includes the Arkansas River in Colorado.

For six years, from 2006-2012, Michael and Greg participated in "The Middle Ground Project in American History and Civics Education." It was part of the Congressionally-funded Presidential Academies for American History and Civics Education Program, the brainchild of U.S. Senator Lamar Alexander of Tennessee. There were only two awards made for that program in 2005: one to the University of Northern Colorado and the Navajo Education Technology Consortium for Navajo teacher workshops at locations throughout the Navajo Reservation; the other to the Ashbrook Center for Public Affairs at Ashland University, Ohio.

The purpose of the presidential program was to engage middle school and high school teachers in a six-year program concentrating on American History and Civics education. Over the program period it would serve a network of 23 reservation school districts in the isolated Four Corners region of Colorado, New Mexico, Arizona and Utah. The scope was huge—85,000 students and 125 novice and veteran teachers.[1]

Greg and Michael have threaded their expertise and passions throughout this co-authored work. Greg was primarily the water law and policy discussion lead, with a perspective gleaned from four years with the Colorado Attorney General's Office, 17 years as an attorney for the Northern Colorado Water Conservancy District, nearly 20 years as a Justice of the Colorado Supreme Court, and four years as Senior Water Judge for Colorado Courts and Co-Director of the University of Denver's Environmental and Natural Resources program.

Others who assisted with this book project for the City of Greeley include Emmett Jordan of Jordan Design as designer, Tom Cech of Metropolitan State University of Denver as project manager and lead editor, Peggy Ford Waldo of the City of Greeley Museums as reviewer and editor, and Harold Evans serving in the role of publisher for this book. Harold is chair of Greeley's Water Board, and states that this book might be viewed as the "third Greeley water book." The first was Professor Dan Tyler's *Silver Fox of the Rockies, Delphus E. Carpenter and Western Water Compacts*, and the second *W.D. Farr, Cowboy in the Boardroom*. Greg and Michael would surely add Tyler's *The Last Water Hole in the West, The Colorado-Big Thompson Project and the Northern Colorado Water Conservancy District* to this quartet of stories.

Generally, less-celebrated in literature, film, scholarship and novels have been the stories of municipal water utilities in the West. The movie *Chinatown* does come to mind, and water acquisition, delivery, and intrigue were central to its story. Michener's *Centennial* is another work, with a mosaic of settlement and conflict etched on the Colorado Plains. As the mid-sized city of Greeley enters its 150th year of existence, it's time again to learn our story of how urban and rural life intersected with one of the most unique water systems in the United States.

Greeley is located in a land of "extremes." Mountain snows melt and flow eastward onto the plains, where good soil, a temperate climate, and dry air combine to allow for cultivation of all manner of water-intensive crops. Livestock flourish in these conditions, elevating Greeley and its surrounding farms and ranches to a high ranking among the most-productive counties in the nation.

What makes the story of Greeley water most compelling, however, are the people. We learn how the residents from 1870 forward expected the best that nature could sustain. The colony's founders had promised water that was abundant, secure, reasonable in price, and clean. Today, the citizenry still holds its water and wastewater department accountable to these standards, which says much about the past 150 years. No matter the vagaries and fickleness of nature, economics, politics, or social and cultural change, the river that flows through the heart of Greeley has given all who called it home a water supply that few of its peers can claim. This is the reason for our book—*Confluence: The Story of Greeley Water.*

CHAPTER ONE

The Land and People Before 1870

Desert or Garden

THE STORY OF the Greeley water system owes much to Horace Greeley, 19th century publisher of the *New York Tribune*. He is often credited with the famous quote: "Go West young man, go West and grow up with the country." A journalist and visionary, Greeley advocated for westward expansion, a common view of other prominent political and civic leaders of the mid-19th century. Greeley viewed the fertile farmland west of the Mississippi River as the ideal place for families to succeed—if they were willing to work hard. His commentary, in America's most-read newspaper at the time, contributed to the post-Civil War surge across the continent. It also helped establish the modern history of Colorado, encouraging the early settlers of the Union Colony to leave their homes, and planted the seeds for the remarkable chronicle of Greeley Water.

This narrative of water supply, distribution, and growth of an urban society on the edge of the Great Plains fits well with Colorado's reputation as a "land of extremes"—for its mountains and plains, its climate and seasons, plants and animals, and its historic cultural diversity. Horace Greeley envisioned the region as a "land of opportunity" 150 years ago, and today it is home to nearly six million people who value Colorado's beauty, natural resources, and outdoor recreational opportunities. Like their predecessors, these optimistic and energetic residents share the spirit and determination of the first generation of motivated settlers. Led by Nathan Meeker, *New York Tribune* agricultural editor, they established an experimental society (based upon temperance and farming) a few miles west of the confluence of the Cache la Poudre and South Platte Rivers.

Greeley is also a place of extremes, where the French-named Cache la Poudre River can drop to a trickle during dry summer months, creating troubles for irrigators, town dwellers, and other water users. A critical challenge for the Union Colonists was to transform the semi-arid "desert" of the region into an "irrigated garden" by diverting water from the Cache la Poudre. Initially experiencing hard setbacks, they were ultimately successful and laid the groundwork for the next century of planning and hard work.

IN 1820, MAJOR Stephen Harriman Long, a 36-year-old topographical engineer, career U.S. Army officer and explorer, journeyed along the South Platte River with his expedition. Long's assignment was to continue the transcontinental journeys of the Lewis and Clark Expedition of 1804-1806. Much like the ill-fated excursion of Lieutenant Zebulon Pike in 1806-1807 through the Arkansas River Valley to the south, the Long party described the 700-miles of treeless expanse, between the Missouri River to the east and the Rocky Mountains to the west, as a "Great Desert" (later expanded to the "Great American Desert").

Long and his expedition members saw the Platte and South Platte River Basins of Colorado and Nebraska as "almost entirely destitute of woodlands, scarcely a tree, bush, or even a shrub, making its appearance." The only inhabitants of this landscape, wrote Long, were "roving bands of Indians who have no fixed place of residence but roam from place to place in quest of game." The Army major advised his superiors: "I do not hesitate in giving the opinion, that it is almost wholly unfit for cultivation, and of course uninhabitable by a people depending upon agriculture for their subsistence."[1]

Long conceded that "tracts of fertile land considerably extensive are occasionally to be met with." Yet "the scarcity of wood and water, almost uniformly prevalent," prophesied Long, "will prove an insuperable obstacle in the way of settling the country."[2] This harsh description of the Front Range and eastern Colorado stuck, and discouraged permanent settlement of the region for decades.

In the late 1860s, nearly two generations after Major Long came West, the agricultural editor of the *New York Tribune* described a much brighter future for the Cache la Poudre Valley of northern Colorado. Nathan C. Meeker, a well-traveled 52-year-old journalist, had convinced his employer, the famed publisher Horace Greeley, to endorse what Meeker described as "a Western

Colony . . . in Colorado Territory." In 1869, the first sentences of Meeker's "Call" to head West attracted an audience of eager Easterners.

It was a cold December night. The overflowing room of prospective Union Colonists was full of interested and excited people. They met in the Cooper Union Building in downtown New York City, unsure of their future but curious to form a new community in the Colorado Territory. The call of "Go West!" resonated strongly in their hearts and souls. Eager individuals responded for many reasons, including the post-war stress of Civil War veterans, opportunities not always available in the rapidly growing Eastern cities, and the dream of owning a family farm on land provided through the 1862 Homestead Act.

Many of these curious individuals had read the writings of Nathan Meeker with keen interest. Tragic Civil War experiences still loomed, but the opportunity to participate in an organized venture with like-minded individuals conjured up untold possibilities. Meeker beseeched a panacea: "A location which I have seen," Meeker had written in the *New York Tribune*, "is well watered with streams and springs. There are beautiful pine groves, the soil is rich, the climate healthful, grass will keep stock the year round, coal and stone are plentiful, and a well-traveled road runs through the property." Meeker told his *Tribune* readers: "The Rocky Mountain scenery is the grandest, and the most enchanting in America." Water would be the key. "A colony which can control water in that country will be master of the situation for all time."[3] This vision of an irrigated garden took years of ripening for the new town of Greeley.

It was an "extreme" shift of attitudes and imagery—from the dire descriptions of the Long Expedition of 1820 to the exuberance of Meeker's 1869 meeting in New York City—and reflected the unpredictable and erratic nature of Colorado's semi-arid environment. In 1983, William Cronon, considered by many as the preeminent environmental historian of his generation, wrote that "all human groups consciously change their environments to some extent . . ." Cronon's perspective was that humans could alter their local environment to make it suitable for settlement, even considering the vagaries of the semi-arid environment at the Union Colony in Colorado. This human characteristic would be vital for the settlers Meeker needed. The Call from New York City went out to find a group of people with the necessary characteristics, to develop and anchor his vision of a new community in the West. It was answered by many.

THE LIFEBLOOD OF the new settlement would be water diverted from the Cache la Poudre River. The river was named by 19th century French fur trappers who "cached" or stored their pelts, gunpowder ("poudre") and other supplies near the river's bank. The Poudre River begins as a high mountain stream along the east face of the Continental Divide. The headwaters flow downslope for 126 miles, intersecting with the South Platte River east of present-day Greeley. Enroute, the Cache la Poudre descends from over 12,000 feet in altitude at the peaks of the Rocky Mountains to an elevation of 6,700 feet in just 20 miles.[4] High-water flows in the springtime give way to low flows during the hot and dry summer months. Melting winter snow provides the early runoff, and summer thunderstorms may, at times, replenish the river. It is a vital source of water that the early settlers tapped, treasured and dubbed "liquid gold," as it was their most precious resource.

Scholars of the region's ancient climate have identified periods of abundance and scarcity that appeared after the last Ice Age (12,000-10,000 years ago). As the glaciers melted and receded, vegetation and large game animals flourished on the High Plains. Hunters followed, such as the Clovis People (12,000-9,750 years ago) and the Folsom People (11,000-8,700 years ago).[5] Elliott West wrote that the climate changed for the worse around 5,000 B.C., entering a 2,500-year cycle of "mega-drought" that archaeologists have called the "Altithermal" period (literally, the "high heat"). At the far western edge of the dry plains, however, a natural phenomenon occurred that offered refuge for nomadic peoples and the future Union Colony settlers alike. West described an "erosional trough" formed between the Front Range and the high ridge of the plains, some 80 miles to the east. The latter stood at 6,500 feet above sea level, while the base of the foothills fell to about 5,000 feet.

Streams flowed in each direction into the river valley the French would later call the La Rivière Plate ("flat river"). It was a "double drainage," said West, supporting "lush pasture that in turn lures whatever grazers the plains are allowing at the time." This topography also meant "nice stands of timber," which offered "superb shelter and resources for people and animals during the plains' bitter winters." Concluded West: "From the first human habitation to the present, this coincidence of traits has made the foot of the Front Range some of the most appealing terrain in an often-demanding region."[6] This is the location of our story.

Two phenomena—one natural, one cultural—converged to bring people back onto the High Plains of Colorado, and to make it possible for the Union Colonists to settle there. A 400-year "wet cycle" began around 1600 A.D. in the interior of North America; one that scientists of the early 21st century described as among the "wettest" on record. Native societies (such as the Cheyenne, Arapaho and Ute) took advantage of this climatic shift, and more than a dozen distinct tribal groups moved to Colorado's mountains and plains in search of a more secure and stable food supply.

As the climate tempered, Spanish explorers arrived around the early 1700s. French and American fur trappers and traders later joined them. As the wet cycle advanced into the 1800s, interest in the Far West attracted U.S. Army expeditions. This was followed by the discovery of gold in California in 1848-1849, and a decade later in the Colorado Rockies. Thus, by 1870, the Cache la Poudre River Valley would host the latest wave of occupation; this time based upon irrigated agriculture, displacing the nomadic existence of so many groups that had come before.

In spite of the temperate climate, members of Meeker's new community were unaware of and unprepared for the fickleness of the seasons and the fluctuating water supplies. These climatic traits created serious water management challenges, which regional water managers still confront today.

DESPITE THEIR EARLY presence in the Southwest, the Spanish (who would give the name *Colorado* to the multi-hued landscape) showed little interest in traveling north of their 17th century settlements of Santa Fé and Taos. The great distances from New Mexico, the high altitude of the Rocky Mountains, and the aridity of the Four Corners and High Plains regions posed chronic challenges to Spanish exploring parties. Only one expedition, that of Pedro de Villasur in 1720, traveled into the South Platte River Valley (which the Spanish called *El Rio de Jesus Maria*) to its confluence with the Cache la Poudre River, and then east. Villasur had been sent north by Spanish government officials who feared the presence of the French along the Platte River in Nebraska. A group of Pawnee Indians, joined by soldiers dressed in

French uniforms, attacked Villasur in eastern Nebraska (near present-day Columbus), killing two-thirds of the Spanish force. That military defeat ended the Spanish government's interest in the northern regions of Colorado.

As the 19th century dawned, events far from the future state of Colorado initiated a cycle of change. In 1803, the French emperor Napoléon Bonaparte (eager to raise money to wage war on Great Britain) accepted an offer of $15 million ($350 million today) from the United States to purchase 826,000 square miles of land between the Mississippi River and the Rocky Mountains. President Thomas Jefferson acquired the "Louisiana Purchase" which included the eastern lands of the future state of Colorado (the Western Slope remained part of the Kingdom of Spain until 1821, when it was ceded to Mexico).

In 1804-1806, the U.S. Army's Corps of Discovery, led by Captains Meriwether Lewis and William Clark, traveled north of Colorado and returned with descriptions of adventure on their journey to reach the Pacific Ocean.[7] They did not venture south into Colorado on their trip, but Army Lieutenant Zebulon Pike did arrive in 1806, on a separate mission, to study the southern boundaries of the Louisiana Purchase that reached to the Arkansas River.[8]

Major Stephen H. Long was the last of the early Rocky Mountain explorers. While Long's proclamations that the region was the "Great American Desert" may have discouraged settlement along the Front Range of Colorado for decades, his 1820 expedition did achieve some measure of success with its scientific reports. In addition, sketches by 19-year-old naturalist, Titian Ramsay Peale provided remarkable images of the region. Peale and Samuel Seymour, a fellow artist on the expedition, gave the nation its first glimpses of the extraordinary Rocky Mountains through their paintings and sketches (which served as that era's version of transportable cameras).

Long's written descriptions of the natural landscape of the South Platte Valley and the Cache la Poudre River included references to abundant wildlife, including bison. On June 30, 1820, he noted in his journal the sighting (near present-day Wiggins, Colorado) of "a high Peake [that] was plainly to be distinguished towering above all others as far as the sight attended." Long gave the mountain no name, even though French fur trappers would call it *Les Deux Oreilles* (the "two ears") for its double peaks.

The U.S. Army Major, whose name would later grace the "two ears" mountain west of Longmont, then continued with his diary entry for that day: "The whole range had a beautiful and sublime appearance to us, after having been so long confined to the dull uninteresting monotony of prairie country." Three days later, Long's expedition came upon three large streams entering the South Platte River— the future-named Cache la Poudre, the Big Thompson, and St. Vrain Creek. Long camped at the mouth of the St. Vrain, at the confluence of the South Platte, where 17 years later the French fur trapper Ceran St. Vrain would establish a trading post west of present-day Platteville. Long offered no description of the Cache la Poudre River, nor does it appear that his party ventured upstream to reconnoiter it.[9]

IN THE 1820S, with no interference from the Mexican government, it would be left to fur trappers of American and French descent, such as Ceran St. Vrain, Jim Bridger and A.P. Chouteau, to seek beaver pelts from the South Platte River Basin. These were in high demand among stylish men and women of New York, Philadelphia, London and Paris. The fur traders of the day were part of either French or British businesses that made handsome profits from the wildlife they harvested.

Beaver trapping was a way of life for rugged, independent individuals who knew the land, interacted fairly successfully with native peoples, and prided themselves on lifesaving survival skills. Westward travel was difficult, however, and no permanent settlements existed along Colorado's Front Range. In addition, environmental obstacles of mountains and arid plains, and the control of the indigenous nations like the Comanche, Cheyenne, Arapaho, Ute, and Pawnee over non-native visitors, made trapping difficult and served as effective barriers to westward migration of settlers and other adventurers.

In 1824, the Rocky Mountain Fur Company, under the auspices of the mountain man William Ashley, brought a party of 22 men from the upper Missouri River in modern-day Montana to northeastern Colorado. Ashley's 1825 report spoke of ascending the South Platte River to the base of the Front Range mountains. They found the confluence of the Cache la Poudre River and followed it upstream to the Laramie Plains of south-central Wyoming, most likely by way of the Poudre's North Fork. From there the Ashley party headed west to seek the Green River in far western Wyoming.[10]

By 1835, the lucrative fur trade generated another U.S. Army expedition, this one led by Colonel Henry Dodge. He followed the Platte River in Nebraska and journeyed west to the South Platte River of eastern Colorado. Dodge had assembled an impressive group of men which he called the "First Regiment of Mounted Dragoons." They included Lieutenant Colonel Stephen W. Kearny, commander of the "Army of the West" a decade later in the War with Mexico; Major Richard B. Mason, the first military governor of California after its 1849 gold rush; Captain Nathan Boone, youngest son of the famed pioneer Daniel Boone; First Lieutenant Jefferson Davis, who later became the U.S. Secretary of War in 1853 and then President of the Confederate States of America; Lieutenant Lancaster Lupton, who would resign his commission after the 1835 expedition and return to Colorado to open a trading post at the junction of the South Platte and Adobe Creek, the site of today's town of Fort Lupton; and Jesse Chisholm, a guide and interpreter who blazed a cattle trail through Texas and Kansas that bears his name.

On July 18, 1835, the group reached the confluence of the Cache la Poudre River, which Dodge described as "a large stream, emptying into the [South] Platte on the opposite side, with timber on its banks." The colonel marveled at the "enormous" quantities of bison along the creek. For himself, Dodge would note that the name of this stream was the "Cache de la Poudre," while his assistant, Captain Ford, called it the "Powder River."[11] Dodge and his expedition members were standing near the future site of Greeley, the agricultural settlement that would be established 35 years later by members of the Union Colony of Colorado.

While Dodge, First Lieutenant Jefferson Davis, Captain Nathan Boone and the rest of his party surveyed the Front Range, Louis (or Luis) Vasquez and Andrew Sublette established Fort Vasquez near present-day Platteville, Colorado, to compete for the trade generated by nearby Forts Lupton and St. Vrain. Farther to the north, travelers from the East and Midwest began appearing on the famed "Oregon Trail" on their way to the Pacific Northwest. By 1842, the volume of traffic became so great that the federal government ordered the U.S. Army Corps of Topographical Engineers to survey the popular route, and create detailed maps for future settlers.

The Age of Exploration would bring Lieutenant John C. Frémont, leader of three surveys, to the Rocky Mountain West between 1842 and 1845.[12] His companions included Christopher ("Kit") Carson, by then the most-heralded frontiersman in the West, Lucien Maxwell, William Gilpin, and Thomas ("Broken

Hand") Fitzpatrick. Seeing snowmelt spilling from the east side of the Great Divide, from what is now Rocky Mountain National Park, Frémont dispelled Long's Great American Desert theme. One journal entry described a rich and fertile land: "July 11, 1843. The soil of this country is excellent, admirably adapted to agricultural purposes, and would support a large agricultural and pastoral population. The plain is watered by many streams."[13]

Frémont also cautioned that drought could devastate the fertile plains. Just the year before, his journal entry of July 28, 1842, declared: "The present year has been one of unparalleled drought, both forks of the Platte have entirely failed." Expedition member Lucien Maxwell's claim to fame would be his future ownership of the largest Mexican land grant in the Southwest, nearly two million acres in modern-day Colfax County, New Mexico.[14] That is where the future Weld County settler, entrepreneur and investor, Benjamin Eaton (the largest landowner in the Cache la Poudre and South Platte River Valleys) would learn about irrigation techniques indigenous to the Pueblo/Spanish/Mexican Southwest, later sharing his knowledge with the early settlers of the Union Colony.[15] Eaton's familiarity with *acequias* (Spanish irrigation ditches or canals) of northern New Mexico inspired the early water development in Colorado.[16]

FRÉMONT'S REPORTS ABOUT the challenges and opportunities awaiting those who ventured into the Cache la Poudre Valley touched the young nation at a critical time in its history. Frémont's father-in-law, Thomas Hart Benton, was a powerful U.S. senator from Missouri and a strong proponent of westward expansion. The senator's support of his son-in-law's expedition helped initiate a generation coming of age in 1845-1870. Among these were the Union Colonists who witnessed changes as exhilarating and daunting as at any other time in American history.

Historian Bernard DeVoto labeled 1846 as "The Year of Decision."[17] From the acceleration of travel along the Oregon Trail to the campaigns of American soldiers to explore new lands, the leaders of the United States, and their constituents alike, put in motion a process of conquest and settlement across the American West. For the first time since the signing of the Louisiana Purchase,

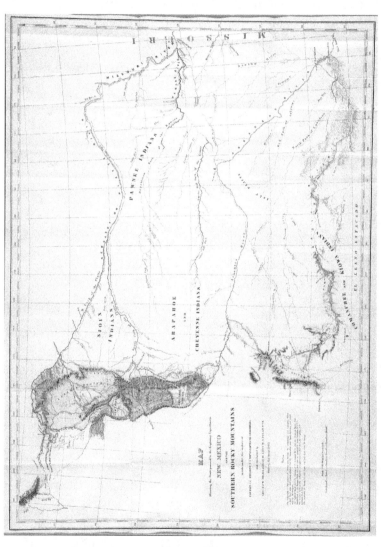

Figure 1.1 Captain John Charles Frémont, U.S. Topographical Engineers, and Lieutenants J.W. Abert and W.G. Peck were members of the U.S. Army expedition that produced this map of *New Mexico and the Southern Rocky Mountains* in 1845. Major rivers and their tributaries flow east across the seemingly endless plains, inhabited by Native peoples. The confluence of the Cache la Poudre and South Platte Rivers, seen here, would become the site of Greeley, Colorado Territory in April 1870. Image courtesy of Gregory J. Hobbs, Jr., private collection.

the land that would become Colorado drew increased attention, followed by permanent settlement, under the ambitious rubric of "Manifest Destiny." New adventurers joined the ranks of explorers, traders and entrepreneurs to seek out wild experiences in a rough but exhilarating new land.

In July 1846, a summer of travel awaited a young graduate of Harvard College in Massachusetts. Francis Parkman joined a party of fur trappers leaving Fort Laramie (Wyoming) for the Arkansas River trading post at Pueblo in southern Colorado. Parkman, who became one of the most-popular historians of the 19th century, had come west at the age of 22 to follow the massive migration of pioneers and adventurers along the Great Platte River Road. Parkman probably wondered if tales of the Great American Desert were indeed true.

The most troubling situation for Parkman and his companions was the lack of water in midsummer. Five days south from Fort Laramie, they came upon "what we supposed to be a considerable stream," most likely the Cache la Poudre. "Upon approaching it," Parkman recalled, "we found to our mortification nothing but a dry bed of sand, into which the water had sunk and disappeared." Despite dividing their party and riding along the riverbanks, they "found no traces of water, not even so much as a wet spot in the sand." Parkman provided a vivid description of the challenges that would later face settlers in the region.

Three years later in 1849, the surge of gold seekers traveling to California only added to the volume of traffic along the Platte River Road. Excited gold miners accompanied optimistic farmers who would continue on to Oregon Territory. Mormons, seeking refuge in their promised land of Deseret, traveled apart from the others along their route to the Great Salt Lake Valley of Utah. Through the 1848 Treaty of Guadalupe Hidalgo, the United States had annexed a large portion of Mexican Territory extending from the south bank of the Arkansas River across the desert Southwest to California.[18] Together with the 1845 annexation of Texas and the 1846 Oregon Treaty, the shape and extent of the American West was completed to the Pacific Ocean.[19]

To Native Americans, it must have seemed that foreigners were everywhere. In 1851, the U.S. government had negotiated the Treaty of Fort Laramie with dozens of Native American Tribes from the northern and central plains. The tribes promised to avoid the immigrant trails of the Platte River Valley in exchange for annuities and payments from the federal government. The U.S. government made promises in return that, too often, were not honored.

This increasing wave of settlers ultimately destroyed the way of life for Native Americans. In 1850, estimates of the volume of travel along the North Platte River Valley through Fort Laramie exceeded 50,000 pioneers. Four years later, Congress passed the Kansas-Nebraska Act. This measure encouraged settlers to further populate these territories to achieve statehood.[20] The Northern Arapaho, under the leadership of Warshinun (also known as Chief Friday), were the last band of Native Americans to inhabit the Cache la Poudre River Valley. Before being forced out in the late 1860s, he had requested a reservation on the north bank of the Poudre River, but was denied. In 1868, Friday's band would be removed to the Wind River Reservation in Wyoming.[21]

Economic crisis had affected the United States during the "Panic of 1857," even as heated debates between Northern and Southern states (regarding the expansion of slavery into the West) brought violence to "Bloody" Kansas (a term popularized by newspaper editor Horace Greeley). A year later, gold discoveries along the tributaries of the South Platte River lured an estimated 100,000 treasure-seekers to the Colorado Rockies.[22] This brought chaos, controversy, and the threat of the expansion of slavery into Colorado. Locals feared the South might seize control over the valuable goldfields, but the election of President Abraham Lincoln blocked this from happening.

THE COLORADO GOLD rush became a nationwide sensation in 1859, prompting intensive migration and settlement of the Rockies. Always the journalist, Horace Greeley, publisher of the *New York Tribune*, came west in the spring of 1859. He hoped to capture the excitement of the mining frontiers of the Colorado Rockies while reporting on the legacy of the California Gold Rush. To learn about this migration, Greeley traveled by train, stagecoach and horse from the streets of Manhattan to the Clear Creek gold diggings of Colorado. His journey then took him north along the Front Range, across the Cache la Poudre and Laramie Rivers, and then west to California. Greeley's articles and reports, *An Overland Journey from New York to San Francisco in the Summer of 1859*, highlighted Colorado's and California's economic potential that sprouted from the mining booms.

Horace Greeley also provided the most thorough descriptions of the Cache la Poudre River to date. His stagecoach had crossed "near its mouth, where, like nearly all of these streams, it is broader and shallower than where it issues from the Rocky Mountains." Like Parkman in 1846, Greeley passed by "St. Vrain's [deserted] Fort" and ventured up "Thompson Creek." There he saw "a caravan moving from Missouri to California, which reminded me of the days of Abraham and Lot." Greeley chronicled the triumphs and hardships of this surge of immigrants across the high desert plains, leading him to comment: "Was there ever another such vagrant, restless, discontented people, pretending to be civilized, as ours!"[23]

Greeley's colorful images of the Cache la Poudre Valley in 1859 inspired Nathan Meeker, one of the correspondents Greeley would hire later during the Civil War. Meeker shared with Greeley his long-cherished desire to build a utopian community of good citizens in the Rocky Mountain West. The *New York Tribune* publisher's descriptions of Colorado's northern Front Range, as "the center of the antelope country," were intriguing. Said Greeley: "There are no settlements, save a small beginning just at this ford [the town of Laporte], as yet hardly three months old, between Denver, seventy miles on one side, and Laramie, one hundred and thirty on the other."[24]

When Greeley looked to the east, he saw "the high prairie on either side [as] thinly grassed, being of moderate fertility at best." This landscape was "full of pebbles of the average size of a goose-egg, and apparently doomed to sterility by drought." At this point, Greeley acknowledged that the Cache la Poudre Valley, "though inferior in soil, and less smooth in surface, is not dissimilar in its topography to Lombardy." Like the region he had visited in northern Italy, the New Yorker predicted that the Cache la Poudre River Valley "will in time be subjected to systematic irrigation, should the Rocky Mountain gold mines prove rich and extensive."

Nathan Meeker took note of the New York publisher's belief that "some of the streams crossed by our road might easily be so dammed at their egress from the mountains as to irrigate miles in width to the South Platte River, forty or fifty miles distant." Greeley further speculated that "at the prices which vegetables must always command here should the gold mines prove inexhaustible, the enterprise would pay well."[25] He knew the value that miners placed on fresh food—especially fresh vegetables.

During the summer of 1859, Greeley claimed to have witnessed some 5,000 people per week flooding into the foothills near Denver. Population estimates that summer surged to 100,000 residents. In the 1860 U.S. Census Bureau report, however, the actual count was a third of that number (34,277 people). Of these, a mere 12 percent resided in "Denver City," with the remainder scattered in dozens of mining camps from Boulder in the foothills to Oro City, renamed "Leadville" during the silver boom.

As Horace Greeley continued on his journey to California, his newspaper articles heralded the need for irrigation, food production, gardens, women, and railroad routes across the West. These turned out to be prophetic key elements responsible for the success of the Union Colony and Greeley after its establishment in 1870. The *New York Tribune* publisher would return later to check on the progress of his namesake community.

THE CALIFORNIA GOLD Rush would have a profound effect on future water law development in Colorado, and in particular, on the soon-to-be-established Union Colony. Prompted by the 1848-1849 rush of gold seekers to the Sierras, a series of California Supreme Court decisions held in favor of the "prior appropriation water use doctrine," also known as "first in time, first in right."[26] Prior to California statehood in 1850, prospectors had simply started mining on public lands and diverted water to wherever it was needed. This often meant constructing flumes (artificial channels generally made of wood) to transport water many miles away from a stream.

This was contrary to the water use practices of the eastern United States and in England where the "riparian water law" prevailed. Also known as the "common law," riparian law restricted water diversions and use to only those landowners with property that abutted a natural watercourse. "A riparian right is not gained by use, nor generally lost by disuse, but is part and parcel of the land."[27] Under that doctrine, the natural flow of a river is shared, between upstream and downstream land owners, on a correlative reasonable use basis. No preference is given for a prior-established use right during times of water shortages

The California miners, however, didn't own riparian lands prior to 1850 (the U.S. government did), and nobody could gain access to a riparian right. Many gold mining claims also lay beyond the banks of a stream. Under these circumstances, the right to sever a water-use interest from that of property ownership was of paramount concern in the new State of California. The state's supreme court found a solution and ruled that the United States had "acquiesced" in the creation of prior appropriation water use rights on public lands. That meant that the extent of a water right would be measured by actual water use, and would prevail over and be senior to later appropriations, when not enough water was available to all comers. This became known as "first in time, first in right."

A decade later, several Colorado mining camps adopted codes containing rules tracking the California precedent. In the Clear Creek Basin west of Denver, for example, Section 9 of the 1860 Lincoln District Mining Code[28] stated that the senior claimant "shall have a priority of right to the use of water" when there is insufficient water for all uses. Section 14 of this Code provided for a right-of-way to build a structure to carry water "over any claim, road or ditch, provided the water shall be guarded as not to interfere with any vested right."

Other mining codes intermixed prior appropriation and common law principles. For example, Section 11 of the January 22, 1861, code for the Spanish Bar District also in Clear Creek,[29] provided that "all mill privileges, on either side of Clear Creek, shall be entitled to half the water in the creek." This was inconsistent with prior appropriation principles and must have created confusion. Colorado wouldn't settle its water law exclusively in favor of prior appropriation until adoption of the 1876 Colorado Constitution.

Water was not the only challenging issue enveloping the region. The expansion of slavery threatened to spread into the Kansas and Nebraska Territories (which included part of the future state of Colorado). In February 1861, soon after Kansas became a state, the U.S. Congress created the trapezoidal Colorado Territory to include all possible gold-bearing country between Wyoming and New Mexico.[30] The value of gold in this area was promising, and the resource was highly prized by both the Northern-controlled Congress and the Southern Confederacy.

Abraham Lincoln had been elected President and opposed the spread of slavery into the public domain lands of the West. The Union Congress agreed with Lincoln, and intended to hold the gold fields against the Confederates.[31] Lincoln's 1860 Republican platform also included the Homestead Act, the Land Grant College Act, and the Railroad Act, all of which the Union Congress proceeded to enact in 1862.

These momentous Congressional acts afforded Colorado and the West three of the most basic means to attract settlers—land, transportation, and education.[32] Above all, however, was the need for adequate water to grow food for miners, their camps, and growing towns. "Agricultural sufficiency became the goal."[33] Consequently, immigration increased into Colorado and across the West following the Civil War. Irrigation of farms became important features of settlement, and Congress confirmed in the 1866 Mining Act that water would be allocated and managed under whatever laws, including prior appropriation, the territories and states had enacted or would enact in their legislatures. This law also authorized settlers to use federal lands to construct irrigation ditches and reservoirs to grow food to increase agricultural sufficiency and self-reliance in the new lands.[34] These new laws were vital to the success of the future Union Colony.

In September 1861, Colorado's first Territorial Legislature met on the block that is now Denver's Larimer Square, and began addressing the subject of water law. They declared initially that the common law of England would prevail "until repealed by legislative authority."[35] Within a scant two months, however, Colorado began its departure from riparian water law. The November 5, 1861, Act[36] allowed irrigation ditches to be constructed across intervening public or private lands to move water to locations not adjacent to a stream. Three years later, Colorado explicitly invoked prior appropriation as a guiding principle.[37] Irrigation ditch companies ". . . shall not interfere with any other ditch whose rights are prior . . . Nor shall the water of any stream be directed from its original channel to the detriment of any miner, mill-men, or others along the line of said stream, who may have a priority of right."

This law benefitted new appropriators like Benjamin Eaton—a frustrated Colorado '59 gold seeker who later permanently settled in Colorado. In 1864, Eaton and his new bride, Rebecca ("Becky"), traveled from Iowa by freight wagons and a smaller covered wagon to settle along the Cache la Poudre River (near the future town of Windsor) where they dug a small irrigation ditch. Eaton would later help the nascent Union Colony get a foothold in the Poudre River Valley. However, he also looked keenly upstream with British investment partners to develop a much larger irrigation system, one that threatened the very livelihood of the downstream Union Colony settlers that he had most recently invested in and helped develop.

THE CIVIL WAR ended in the spring of 1865, but the nation faced another set of challenges altering Colorado's fate. Before his assassination in April 1865, President Lincoln had called for policies to "bind up the nation's wounds;" a strategy that became known as "Reconstruction." While Congress debated the best methods to bring the defeated Southern states back into the Union, it also looked to the West for new lands to settle, resources and markets to develop, and a national identity to create.

In his Pulitzer Prize winning book, historian William Goetzmann explains how science and art helped lead the way into the future. "As the settlers reached out into ever more remote regions, a demand arose for data concerning mountain passes, transportation routes, Indian strongholds, river courses, resources for farmer, miner, and railroader, and even such prosaic things as the degree of annual rainfall."[38]

To meet this demand for information, the U.S. Army dispatched a former Civil War officer, General John W. Pope, to study the Rocky Mountain region of Colorado. Accompanying Pope on this expedition was Thomas Worthington Whittredge, considered by American art historians as the most accomplished member of the postwar generation of the Hudson River School (a mid-19th century American artistic movement of landscape artists who embraced romanticism in their works). As with the Long Expedition of 1820, Pope's 1865 party would have a profound impact on the future settlement of the American West, and the Union Colony of Colorado, in particular, because of its use of art and artists.

In his autobiography, Whittredge recalled a sense of awe and wonder at seeing the Colorado plains for the first time; this after a 2,000 mile journey on horseback that extended from June 1865 to October 1866 (just prior to completion of the transcontinental railroad).[39] After a youth spent in Germany, Italy, and as a young adult artist in New York City, Whittredge often remarked about the diverse landscapes of the American West. "They [the Colorado plains] impressed me deeply," wrote Whittredge in 1905. "I cared more for them than the mountains," he proclaimed. "Whoever crossed the plains at that period," before the arrival of the railroad, "notwithstanding its herds of buffalo and flocks [sic] of antelope, its wild horses, deer and fleet rabbits, could hardly fail to be impressed with its vastness and silence, and the appearance everywhere of an innocent, primitive, existence."[40]

Then as now, it would be the artists' renditions of such landscapes that intrigued Easterners and Europeans who were curious about the grandeur of the West. Whittredge's friendship with Albert Bierstadt also shaped his vision of Colorado. Unlike Bierstadt, the famed German-American landscape artist who glorified the natural landscapes of the American West and fueled European emigration, Whittredge included Native peoples, such as the Arapaho and Cheyenne, in his iconic painting, *Indians Crossing the Platte River* (1866). Where many Americans feared or viewed indigenous people as obstacles to progress, Whittredge, in the words of his biographer, "depicts them as living in an ideal state of nature similar to that enjoyed by the pioneers." Given Whittredge's desire to be inspiring as well as authentic in his representations of the plains, it is not surprising that the Cache la Poudre and South Platte Rivers lured him back to Colorado. He made two more trips West, in 1870 and 1871, to improve upon sketches drawn while sojourning with General Pope.

His first rendering of the tranquility of the Colorado plains (*Indians Crossing the Platte River*) did not please Whittredge, as "the trees did not suit me." Instead, he recalled "a group [of cottonwoods] I had seen on the Cache la Poudre River, fifty miles from Denver, which I thought would suit my picture better." In 1870, Whittredge and his traveling companions, Sanford Gifford and John Kensett of the Hudson River School, left Denver to ride northwest to the mining camp of Boulder.[41] There, Whittredge painted a scene of the iconic Flatirons, calling it the "Valmont Valley" for the Valmont Butte, a winter camp and sacred site of the Southern Arapaho and other tribes of the region. Whittredge later created a painting of Major Long's Peak west of present-day Longmont.

The group of Hudson River School artists then entered the Cache la Poudre River Valley, following it downstream to the new community of Greeley. Whittredge found a grove of cottonwood trees near the river "which I thought would suit my picture better [to complete the painting]." Biographer Anthony Janson recognized that this excursion "proved of major importance in [Whittredge's] career because "his landscapes of the next six years are remarkable for their ability to capture even the most transient effects of light and mood."[42]

The lure of the American West continued to call. In the summer of 1871, Whittredge traveled one last time to northern Colorado. Arriving by train, he hoped to reconsider what Janson considered Whittredge's finest work: *On the*

Figure 1.2 *On the Cache la Poudre River, Colorado, 1876.* American artist Thomas Worthington Whittredge (1820-1910) delighted in Colorado's incomparable scenery and the success of the new town of Greeley. The massive cottonwood trees, which framed the river in Island Grove Park, became the perfect pastoral setting for Whittredge to sketch and paint in the summers of 1870 and 1871. Amon Carter Museum of American Art, Fort Worth, Texas.

Cache la Poudre River (1876). The artist added to his sketch the cottonwood trees growing adjacent to what is now Island Grove Regional Park and the Poudre River Trail in north Greeley, "much to its improvement."[43] One can only imagine the thinking of early Union Colonists, who arrived the previous year and were struggling to build their homes and irrigation systems, when they came across a group of artists from the East searching for "the right group of cottonwood trees" to sketch and paint.

In 1876, Whittredge displayed his masterful work, *On the Cache la Poudre River,* at the Philadelphia Centennial Exposition. There the "Century Association" (a prestigious group of artists and intellectuals) purchased the painting to hang in their gallery in New York City. Janson called it "unquestionably the masterpiece among Whittredge's western landscapes." Colorado, said Janson, had "replaced Newport [Rhode Island] and upstate New York as Whittredge's favorite subjects." Today, Whittredge's painting is at the Amon Carter Museum of American Art in Fort Worth, Texas, and other works are in the collections of the Smithsonian American Art Museum in Washington, D.C., the Metropolitan Museum of Art in New York, and the Louvre Museum in Paris.

The influence of Worthington Whittredge on Nathan Meeker, and others interested in the Union Colony experiment, factored heavily in the early settlement of the community. In the spring of 1871, Whittredge corresponded with Meeker, now the editor of the *Greeley Tribune* (first published in November 1870 and making use of its *New York Tribune* namesake for its masthead), to acknowledge the benefits of reading the *Greeley Tribune* in anticipation of his third and final visit to Colorado.

The artist called Meeker's publication a "bright little paper," one that "contains information both useful to me, and quite inspiring." Whittredge conceded that "being an artist, I take a particular interest in whatever relates to the appearance of the landscape round about you." He also acknowledged "having never seen the Rocky Mountains at this season." Yet Whittredge had devoted "two or three summers in making sketches near Greeley." From these he "had obtained several pictures . . . which I have found produced considerable interest from the public."[44]

Personal correspondence between newspaper editor Meeker and renowned artist Whittredge revealed a dynamic symmetry. Ever the perfectionist, Whittredge thanked the publisher of the *Greeley Tribune* for his advice about seeing the landscape in new ways. "Your position in regard to the distance from the snowy range is an admirable one," wrote Whittredge in May 1871, "being, according to my judgment, just far enough away from them to get sufficient intervening plain." At the same time, said the artist, "to see the mountains in that mysterious detail . . . to me, is so captivating."

Readers of the *Greeley Tribune*, contemplating their first year in the Union Colony, learned that spring of Worthington Whittredge's endorsement of their good fortune through the commentary of Nathan Meeker. "Whittredge, a New York artist of no little celebrity," wrote the *Tribune* editor, "has been stopping several weeks in our town, making sketches of mountain and river scenery."

Meeker noted reluctantly that "the view of the mountains has been obstructed most of the time by a smoky atmosphere." Yet he could report to his fellow colonists: "With rare good judgment . . . Whittredge has lingered lovingly along the Cache la Poudre, the Thompson, the St. Vrain and Platte."

The Hudson River School artist, in Meeker's opinion, "has reproduced some of their loveliest aspects." The editor conceded that "there are many rare nooks, vales and points which he [Whittredge] has been unable to visit." Echoing the late-20th century campaign in Greeley, to preserve the best of the river corridor through the designation of the Cache la Poudre River National Heritage Area, Meeker concluded: "For all time, this valley region, between Greeley and Platte Canyon, and the mountains, must furnish favorable points where artists shall delight to take their stand."[45] The beauty of the Cache la Poudre River, and the artwork of New York City artist Worthington Whittredge, came together to inspire people to look West for a confluence of new ideas and opportunities.

IN THE SPRINGTIME of 1870, the valley of the Cache la Poudre River awaited the first group of Union Colonists to arrive. It was a location that had experienced great climatic and cultural changes over the centuries. Nomadic tribes—the Arapaho, Cheyenne, and Ute—had recently lived and hunted on these lands, and in earlier years the region had experienced a mega-drought, the "high heat." Now the landscape had a flowing stream coursing through it, the Cache la Poudre, which was increasingly providing water to new settlers.

The colonists were excited, and ready to begin new lives to prosper as families and community builders in the new Colorado Territory. They had received a circular published by the Union Colony organizers listing the provisions and supplies needed in the West. Most brought adequate resources to survive, but many were unprepared for the vagaries, dangers and challenges of their new environment.

Lifestyle changes would be demanded immediately. In the East, the 1870s ushered in a "Gilded Age" of reforms, the rapid expansion of municipal hospitals, improved waste and sanitation systems, curbed and guttered streets, municipal railways, fine restaurants, opera houses and good schools. In contrast, the Union Colonists were tasked with transforming a "desolate plain" of buffalo grass, cacti, prairie dogs, and rattlesnakes into a model utopian western agricultural community. This work would continue despite early failures in irrigation ditch construction, high interest rates due to the Financial Panic of 1873, four years of locust plagues that decimated crops, expensive ditch and fence repairs, hail, blizzards and drought.

Irrigation, of necessity, became the first order of business. Urban lawns and gardens were planted, irrigated and tilled, and sufficient food sources were secured. Accordingly, from the beginning, water would shape the heart, soul, and fortunes of the Greeley, Colorado Territory, experiment.

CHAPTER TWO

1870-1880
The Union Colony and its Quest for Water

The Promise

ON DECEMBER 4, 1869, readers of the *New York Tribune* encountered an intriguing proposition. The agricultural editor and former Civil War correspondent, Nathan C. Meeker, had editorialized on the front page: "A Western Colony." The publication reached 350,000 or more patrons, allowing Meeker to recruit adventurers like himself to create a new community in the postwar American West.

Needing settlers and investors for his idea, Meeker said little about the harsh judgment of the Great Plains made in 1820 by U.S. Army Lieutenant Stephen Long. Instead, he borrowed from the Romantic-era prose of Captain John C. Frémont, whom Meeker had admired for his descriptions a generation earlier of the beauty of the Rocky Mountains. "A location which I have seen," Meeker informed his newspaper audience, "is well watered with streams and springs." For farmers, said the *Tribune* columnist, "the soil is rich." For the afflicted, he wrote, "the climate is healthful." For ranchers, "grass will keep stock the year round."[1] Meeker's "Call" for a new western colony reached far and wide, and generated hundreds of letters of interest from readers enamored with his proposal.

Meeker appealed to the "proper persons" who would follow him to the fertile valley of the Cache la Poudre River in Colorado, so recently praised by Army explorers and Hudson River School artists alike. Yet it was Meeker's dream of what he called a frontier "utopian community" that found favor with many readers. Similar communal towns had emerged in New England and the Midwest in the years prior to the Civil War. Many were seeking escape from the rigors of urban life and sought refuge with like-minded souls. Communities like Brook Farm near Boston, Oneida in upstate New York, and New Harmony, Indiana, had failed due to the residents' lack of farming skills or their unwillingness to embrace hard work. Meeker hoped that his "Western Colony" would look more like the established town of Northampton, Massachusetts, or communities like Painesville, Ohio, and Lincoln, Nebraska.

In each case, said Meeker, newcomers would find "easy access to schools and to public places, meetings, lectures, and the like." Where the pioneer spirit had celebrated individualism, only to succumb to isolation and often loneliness, Meeker promised that "society can be had at once." This would make the Union Colony more inviting and successful than previous experiments because the founding principles would be a confluence of temperance, religion, education, agriculture, irrigation, cooperation, and family values.[2] Meeker did embellish and exaggerate the ease of community building, ". . . while smoothing away flaws like Colorado's inherent aridity."[3]

THE HEADLINE IN the *New York Tribune* achieved its goal when three weeks later, on December 23, 1869, Meeker convened a public meeting at the famed Cooper Union building in downtown Manhattan. Hundreds of readers rallied to Meeker's Call, yearning for a new start out West. The name "Union Colony" and a joint investment enterprise were established that evening "to unite with the proper persons in establishing a colony in Colorado Territory." This collaborative effort drew its inspiration from the concept of a nation reunited after the tragedy of war; hence the name *Union Colony*, ". . . the honor of first proposing this name belonging to John Leavy."[4] He would become one of the first to pitch his tent at the Greeley townsite.

At Meeker's gathering in New York City, 59 attendees paid the $5 initiation fee (about $100 in 2020 dollars), and others contributed $155 ($3,000 in 2020) each to establish a "purchase fund," to acquire property in Colorado. The "Union Colony Corporation" would have Nathan Meeker elected as President; General Robert Cameron, Vice-President; and Horace Greeley, Treasurer. Cameron, A.C. Fisk, and Meeker formed a committee to travel to Colorado to survey land for the new town site.

In February 1870, Meeker and his associates arrived in Colorado Territory, bearing money and subscriptions in hand. This locating committee first traveled to the Pikes Peak region with ex-Territorial Governor Alexander Hunt, thinking this would be the site for their agrarian paradise, but the land area was "too small, and the water supply too limited for the large agricultural community which it was now necessary to provide for."[5] They also visited but chose not to settle along the Arkansas River upstream of Pueblo. The committee then met with Territorial Governor John Evans, who was also a member of the Denver Pacific Railway's board of directors, who advised them to "look up the country around the town bearing his name." They did, but then rejected Evans as a town site because "the remains of a railroad building population" was in place and the whole site could not be controlled so as to keep out intoxicating liquors by forfeiture clauses in the deeds."

Benjamin Eaton, the local pioneer, farmer and entrepreneur who lived with his wife, Becky, and two sons near present-day Windsor, recommended the Box Elder Creek area, a tributary of the Cache la Poudre River near Laporte and the Overland Trail. It was also near Eaton's own land. Meeker and the committee declined his suggestion as it could only encompass 50 farms, far fewer than the number of colonists expected.

The locating committee then learned from William Byers, publisher of Denver's *Rocky Mountain News*, about a large area of public land the Denver Pacific had for sale; with the right combination of potential farmland and access to water. Byers was also the manager for the National Land Company, a wholly-owned subsidiary of the railway company. The search was over, and the Union Colony committee purchased 9,324 acres of railway lands (for $3-$5 an acre) four miles upstream of the confluence of the Cache la Poudre and South Platte Rivers.

A major challenge for the railway company, and its real estate division, was the legal requirement that construction of the rail line between Cheyenne and Denver had to proceed before title could be transferred from the federal government to interested buyers. When the Denver Pacific's board could not secure adequate construction funding to commence work between Evans and Denver, Governor John Evans resigned from the company's board of directors and agreed to build and complete the railroad project himself. In return, Evans received a sizable share of the company's capital stock. Meeker's timing was good as he also negotiated the acquisition of up to 60,000 acres of public domain lands from the U.S. General Land Office for $3 per acre, about $300 per acre in 2020 dollars.[6] The site for the new western colony had been located and secured.

Much has been written about the arrival of the Union Colonists at their new home in April 1870, not all of it complimentary. The land was dry, trees were scarce, and prairie dogs were more than plentiful. Some wide-eyed colonists barely stepped off the train before they abruptly turned around and re-boarded for their homes back East, angrily leaving their money with Meeker. He had collected more than 3,000 inquiries (letters and applications) from prospective colonists, and from these Meeker had chosen 737 individuals he deemed the most desirable to become Union Colony members. Some were merely investors, like Phineas Taylor (P.T.) Barnum of circus fame who whole-heartedly supported the concept of a temperate, utopian community with no drinking allowed. (Barnum never actually settled in Greeley.) Ninety members (a little over 10 percent) demanded that their money be refunded. Approximately 500 individuals occupied the town-site by the fall of 1870. One journalist wrote that "Greeley looks like so many dry goods boxes scattered across the plains of the Almighty."[7] It was an inauspicious beginning for the new town of Greeley, Colorado.

Prior to settlement, many of the Union Colonists wanted to call the town "Meeker" for its founder. Nathan Meeker would hear none of this, wishing to honor Horace Greeley (and also to utilize the name recognition of the country's best known newspaper editor) to promote the town. Horace Greeley was delighted, and he would visit the new town in its first year.[8]

The desolate settlement, however, was a far cry from the comfortable surroundings settlers had left behind. For about one-third of the settlers, the journey West began in the bustling urban landscape of New York City, followed by a short ferry boat ride across the Hudson River to Hoboken, New Jersey. From there, colonists boarded trains that connected with the recently completed Union Pacific transcontinental railroad for the three-to-four day cross-country journey to Cheyenne, Wyoming. They then transferred to the southbound Denver Pacific line, reaching the desolate Greeley location or Evans a few hours later.

For those who disembarked at Evans, it would have appeared as a rough outpost of bars and off duty railroad workers. Meeker had stated in his "Western Colony" article that the location of the new settlement would be "in the shadow of the Rocky Mountains." Instead, when the first colonists disembarked from the train at Greeley, they were greeted only by wide open spaces, unsettling solitude, tents instead of solid homes, and the mountains 25 miles away.

Figure 2.1 Greeley, Colorado Territory, in the summer of 1870. After the Denver-Pacific Railway was completed from Cheyenne to Denver in June 1870, workers who resided at Evans, during the winter and spring of 1869-1870, were happy to sell their humble and easily moveable "homes" to new arrivals—the Union Colonists. The tent in the foreground was the temporary home of Job and Martha A. Brownell. City of Greeley Museums, Permanent Collection, 1971.20.0004.

ON APRIL 25, 1870, settler Robert Orr used his horse-drawn plow to delineate the streets of the future town of Greeley. Similar plows, along with slips, Fresno scrapers, shovels and a great deal of man and horse power, were used to construct the first irrigation ditch, the Greeley Number 3. (Fortunately, Orr's plow was preserved as a Union Colony "relic," and today is on permanent exhibit at the Greeley History Museum.) Four ditches were planned, aligned from north to south and parallel to the Cache la Poudre River. Two irrigation ditches were constructed—the Number 3 followed by the Greeley Number 2. These irrigation systems became the lifeblood of the community, bringing water to urban gardens, town landscapes, and budding croplands.

Figure 2.2 Irrigation was the solution to transform the "Great American Desert" into a bountiful "Oasis." Patents for scrapers and dredging devices, pulled by horse or oxen teams, appeared in the 1870s. In 1883, a Californian, James Porteous, patented his "Fresno scraper" and thousands were manufactured and used to construct canals and ditches. The name and location of the irrigation ditch seen here is unknown. City of Greeley Museums, Permanent Collection, 1970.22.0021.88.

Construction was complicated by inexperience and a general lack of knowledge regarding irrigation development.

The Greeley Number 3 Ditch (also known as the Union Colony Canal No. 3, Greeley Ditch No. 3, Ditch No. 3, Number 3 and the Town Ditch—and still at the heart of the Greeley water system today) first delivered water to the town on June 10, 1870. It was a 10-mile-long cut across virgin prairie, six to eight feet wide and 15 inches deep, insufficient to carry the anticipated volume of irrigation water. To the dismay of the colonists, the inexperienced canal builders had to enlarge and expand it several times at great expense.

In 1871, William E. Pabor, another early colonist, wrote the first and only annual report of Colony activities.[9] Hailing "the magic touch of water," he described the Number 3 Ditch as "ten miles long, and capable of being extended two miles further." Using the water measurement method of the gold rush era

Figure 2.3 Lincoln Park, Greeley, Colorado Territory, July 4, 1870, Main Street looking east from the intersection near 10ᵗʰ Avenue. Water from the Greeley Number 3 Ditch, eight blocks south of the park, was diverted into smaller ditches, called "laterals," throughout the town. This enabled the Union Colonists to flood irrigate their yards, gardens and Lincoln Park. City of Greeley Museums, Permanent Collection, AI-0007.

called the "miner's inch," Pabor calculated the ditch was "carrying twenty-five hundred inches of water, and capable of irrigating five thousand acres, including the town site." Pabor's calculations may have been some of the first fact-based estimates of the town's water supply system. By June 10ᵗʰ of that first year, the Greeley Number 3 Ditch was completed, and Pabor saw it with water "running through all the streets of the town." This much-needed improvement included a provision that 3/8 (approximately 37 percent of the ditch water) was dedicated for irrigation of town gardens and the cultivation of house lots, flowers, lawns, trees, and for the homes of Greeley families.[10]

The Number 3 Ditch did provide some water for the new colonists that initial summer, and was the first irrigation system for this stretch of dry land. Meeker had claimed the system would irrigate 5,000 acres within the town boundaries, but was a wildly inaccurate estimate. Only 200 acres were watered the first year, much of it applied to newly planted trees to create a buffer zone against the relentless and dusty winds.[11]

To alleviate the frustration of community building, residents quickly learned that irrigation and water management were a full time task. J. Max Clark, one of the original colonists and later the editor of the *Greeley Tribune,* recalled some three decades later that "during the day, if the weather was pleasant, the larger share of us were at work on our own houses and in our gardens, for pride in the garden was one of the first evidences of attachment to the new country." When the settlers turned their attention to the Greeley Number 2 Ditch (also known as Union Colony Canal No. 2, Greeley Ditch No. 2, Ditch No. 2, Number Two and the Farmers' Ditch), they soon realized the difficult task of canal building.

Construction of the latter facility began in the fall of 1870, and posed a formidable engineering enterprise from the start. This was the first attempt by Colorado farmers to irrigate "bench lands" that rose higher and farther away from the bottom lands of the Cache la Poudre River. The Greeley Number 2 Ditch headgate was located more distant upstream of the Union Colony to allow water to move by gravity from the river to the bench lands to be irrigated. The ditch had to curve around hills, bypass gullies, meander and wind its way across dozens of miles of semi-arid prairie—destined to irrigate the newly cultivated farm land.

It was a significant engineering challenge, and maintenance costs were high. This intrepid project, tackled by the inexperienced Union Colony irrigators, was eventually sold to a group of more knowledgeable farmers and irrigation experts. They formed the Cache la Poudre Irrigation Company, known today as the New Cache la Poudre Irrigating Company located in Lucerne north of Greeley.[12]

"THE FIRST ATTEMPT at general farm cultivation," wrote Clark in 1902, "resulted in blank failure to a large majority of those immediately interested in production." Clark admitted that "I had made a complete failure that year, owing to a lack of water and a lack of experience combined." The colonists, whose descendants would later take pride in the quality of their water system and the value of their agricultural production, subsisted in the early 1870s "almost entirely on wild game for the meat they consumed, instead of patronizing the butcher's stalls."[13] The future robust agricultural economy of the region was barely a seed sprouting from the ground during this first decade of settlement.

Water remained the top priority for the Colony, as they sought a steady supply of irrigation water for their village and its outlying fields. They also learned to their chagrin that their founder, Nathan Meeker, had overstated the ease of cultivating the "Great American Desert." "When Mr. Meeker was writing for the *New York Tribune*," recalled Clark, "and told his Eastern readers how the waters of irrigation wobbled down the furrows after a man like a little dog at his heels, how that pleasing description must have interested the citizen of that densely populated city." Unfortunately, water management and water delivery were not that simple. "What wonder, then," wrote Clark, "that many of our experiences with ditches and water and the water supply, have taken a deep hold on us, have sunk deeply in our hearts." That view would embrace those who followed, leading Clark to invent and patent an improved irrigation shovel to lessen the physical strain of this work.[14] Clark's talent for innovation would mirror that of later generations of water managers in Greeley and northern Colorado.

In May 1870, David Boyd arrived on the scene to join the irrigation enterprise. Looking back two decades later, the Civil War veteran and University of Michigan graduate recalled that, beyond the initial cost of a $155 "membership fee" in the enterprise, "many paid an extra $75 for water rights to [irrigate] 80 acres of government land, which they were able to take on their certificates by paying this sum." He considered this "cheap water, if it had been sufficient to irrigate the whole." Yet for the first settlers, wrote Boyd in 1890, "it was not, even after the first enlargement, sufficient to irrigate more than twenty acres of an eighty-acre lot." Instead, colonists had received "a proportionate share in the ditch, with the privilege of going on and making it large enough as they became able."[15]

The Union Colony had originally proposed four major irrigation ditches—Numbers 1 through 4. The Greeley Number 3 Ditch was constructed first, followed by the Greeley Number 2. The Greeley Number 1 Ditch was to be located on the Cache la Poudre River upstream of the Number 2, but the Union Colony did not build it. Insufficient funds and inexperience with irrigation ditch construction prevented the colonists from constructing all of these planned irrigation ditches. Instead, the Greeley Number 1 Ditch, as proposed by the Colony, became the location of the 1879 Larimer and Weld Canal, a for-profit venture financed by "foreign capitalists" of the Colorado Mortgage and Investment Company of London, England (also known as the "English Company").

The Larimer and Weld Canal later became a mutual ditch company in which the City of Greeley today owns shares. The Number 4 Ditch would have diverted water from the Big Thompson River west of Greeley, but like the Number 1 Ditch, was too costly for the Colony to build. However, in 1881 its proposed route became the Greeley and Loveland Canal, financed by the English Company. (Today it is owned by the Greeley and Loveland Irrigation Company, and provides water to farms in the area. The City of Greeley is now the company's majority shareholder based on historic agreements developed in the 1960s.)

The original Union Colony property deeds included important clauses about water shares and abstinence from alcohol. Property owners would "flood irrigate" their outdoor greenery with water redirected onto privately-owned town lots. Excess irrigation water was channeled to flow downhill to smaller collecting channels. Deeds also stated that the Colony's trustees could not be sued for damages from those who did not monitor and regulate their excess "flood irrigation" water. The temperance clause stated that property could be taken from landowners if they were found consuming, selling, or distributing liquor on their premises. This provision was never actually litigated in a court of law.[16]

At the center of the new village, a "Plaza or Square of ten acres," was laid out, replete with two miniature lakes, *Luna* (named for its crescent shape like the moon) and *Auricular* (shaped like an ear). Colony planners imported trees from a nursery in Bloomington, Illinois, by train to grace the downtown square and "throughout the public streets." To the northwest, said Pabor, "an island in the [Cache la Poudre] river gave ample ground for a public park, and this land, comprising about 48 acres was reserved and denominated 'Island Grove Park.'"[17] From its inception, urban planning was an important trait of the new community.

A native of New York City, Pabor was an accomplished poet, and spoke expressively about the day when irrigation ditch water first arrived in the heart of Greeley. Said Pabor, "water came dancing through the flumes like a ministering angel [as indeed it was], scattering blessings all along its path." Pabor was well known in the East as dozens of his poems were published in prominent journals of the day, including *Godey's Lady's Book*. Ever the verse maker, Pabor watched as the waters of the Greeley Number 3 Ditch "ran over the parched land, and blade and blossom awoke to a new beauty." Soon "trees were planted," said Pabor, and "active, earnest, true-hearted men, women, and children went to work with a spirit that deserved and achieved success."

The Union Colony secretary then compared the miracle of irrigation water to "the poem of the Sleeping Princess in the Woods, who waited for the coming of the Fortunate Prince." Calling the town of Greeley the "slumbering Princess of the Plains," Pabor concluded his fairy tale: "And at the magic touch of water, lo! the powers lying dormant for unnumbered ages suddenly awoke, and from out of the tap of nature flowed abundant evidence that these were fertile instead of sterile plains."[18]

Soon after Pabor's eloquent praise for Greeley's future was penned, environmental and economic realities forced the colony to reassess its plans. In July 1871, a severe hailstorm damaged gardens and crops. This was followed by the bitter winters of 1872 and 1873 that delayed the start of spring planting. Nathan Meeker's attempts to grow hundreds of fruit trees, on the harsh semi-arid plains, were being hampered by the severe weather. "It never occurred to Mr. Meeker," wrote David Boyd in 1890, "or the other members of the locating committee that this could be other than a fruit country."

Having gained invaluable experiences in the Union Colony, Pabor and his peers used their knowledge of colonization strategies to create their own "models" for other experimental communities in the territory. Among these would be the Fort Collins Agricultural Colony and the Fountain Colony which Pabor, as its secretary, renamed "Colorado Springs" in the promotional brochures he wrote. In 1883, Pabor traveled to Colorado's West Slope to reorganize the Grand River Project and then established Fruita, a community he called an "agricultural paradise."[19] The magic touch of water was spreading across Colorado.

ON OCTOBER 12, 1870, Horace Greeley made his only appearance in his namesake town.

Greeley had a "most enthusiastic reception" when he arrived, and the *Daily Rocky Mountain News* reported on the event:

"As the train approached the station the platform was found crowded with people whilst scores were unable to get standing room thereon. As he alighted a call was made by somebody for three cheers which were given with a will and repeated. Many crowded around to shake hands and a numerous escort accompanied him up town and to the office of the *Greeley Tribune*. Flags were flying from numerous houses. A meeting was immediately arranged for 1:30 p.m. and workmen began the erection of a stand and seats in front of the printing office. After an hour's walk about the town, buggies were procured and a small party drove up the river to the head of the [Greeley Number 3] ditch, so that he could see with his own eyes the irrigation system that was the life-blood of this new community on the semi-arid plains of Colorado."[20]

That afternoon, according to the *Denver Daily Colorado Tribune*, Greeley told the colonists, "Our people were habitually gregarious and too fond of flocking to our cities and villages, where they help to swell the ranks of squalid misery and every manner of crime, and pestilence, and want, and all the evils that infest our densely populated places everywhere."

As proof of Horace Greeley's vision, the Denver correspondent described the colony as a "town laid out in regular order, with wide streets and water flowing in little *acequias* [community irrigation ditches used in Spain and later Mexico], to all parts of the village." The reporter marveled at how the colonists had "planted around their dwellings and along their *acequias*, several thousand maple trees, which look remarkably well." The water was "inexhaustible," and the soil was of "surprising fertility." Concluded the *Daily Colorado Tribune* reporter: "I have already learned that there is no such word as 'fail' in their vocabulary; they will not permit themselves to entertain an idea so unreasonable."[21]

The Union Colonists appeared well positioned to build the community they envisioned on that winter's night in New York City in 1869. Conditions in Greeley in the 1870s, however, were harsh and the population grew slowly, from 1,155 residents in 1871 to only 1,298 by 1880—an increase of little more than 140 people. The Greeley Number 3 Ditch had been a disappointment, needing three expensive upgrades by 1873. This included a new diversion dam on the Cache la Poudre River which cost about $25,000 (nearly $500,000 in 2020 dollars).

In 1897, Boyd reported that "the ditch was small and poorly constructed, and without the dam at its head in the river to divert the low flow of water into it, . . . not much water could be obtained for this small area." Future water facilities requiring money and labor would be needed. At times, controversy surrounded the plans of town trustees, who debated at length the lack of water.

In September 1873, Isabella Bird, the famed English traveler, stopped at the "Greeley Temperance Colony," having been encouraged to do so as "my starting point for the mountains." Bird, who had reached Colorado via train from San Francisco, encountered a community "founded lately by an industrious class of emigrants from the East." She mistakenly believed that the colony had "already a population of 3,000," whom she described as "all total abstainers, and holding advanced political opinions." Greeley was "asleep at an hour when other places were beginning their revelries" and "altogether free from laziness or crime." Water was distributed "on reasonable terms," wrote Bird, even as she was "amazed that people should settle here to be dependent on irrigating canals, with the risk of having their crops destroyed by grasshoppers."[22]

If the Union Colony experiment perplexed a worldly-wise traveler like Isabella Bird, it had the opposite effect two years earlier in 1871 on another author, Grace Greenwood, the pen name of Sara Jane Lippincott. She had been the first woman reporter for the *New York Times* with assignments as diverse, in the 1850s and 1860s, as a correspondent from European capitals, and also championed social causes including abolition, women's suffrage, and improved medical care for Civil War soldiers and veterans. Her curiosity about the American West paralleled that of Isabella Bird. Lippincott's cross-country trip to California in 1871 gave her an entirely different view of the Union Colony of Colorado.

Gardens constituted an important feature of the lives of early settlers of Greeley, and irrigation appeared to Greenwood to be almost an obsession. In her book, *New Life in New Lands*, she wrote about traveling by train across Colorado. She said passengers in her parlor car from Cheyenne urged her not to stop in Greeley because

> ". . . you'll die of dullness in less than five hours. There is nothing
> there but irrigation. Your host will invite you out to see him irrigate
> his potato patch; your hostess will excuse herself to go and irrigate

her pinks and dahlias [flowers]. Every young one has a ditch of his
own to manage; there is not a billiard saloon in the whole camp,
nor a drink of whiskey to be had for love or money. The place is
humbug. Its morality and Greeleyisms will bust it up some day."[23]

Greenwood did elect to pause in Greeley, and later praised the character of
its citizens and their progress in transforming the "Great American Desert" into
a "Garden of Eden."[24] Greenwood informed her *New York Times* readers: "The
settlement of most interest to me, after Dogtown [the prairie dog colonies that
would later irritate Bird], on this road, was Greeley."[25] Sparing few words, the
Times columnist considered the year-old community "a really wonderful place."
Greenwood marveled at how Greeley had been "established on a purely agricultural basis," with "an inexhaustible capital of intelligence, energy, economy and
industry." Irrigation indeed!

GREENWOOD'S OBSERVATION OF the inexhaustible capital of intelligence,
energy, economy and industry of the Greeley community would be sorely
tested by the Colorado Territory's emerging water law system. That same year,
in 1871, three irrigators west of Denver (Jason Yunker, Andrew Nichols and
John Bell) constructed an irrigation ditch from Bear Creek across each other's
lands, and verbally agreed to share the water equally. But Nichols, whose land
bordered the stream, changed his mind and intercepted all of the ditch water for
his own crops. Yunker sued to obtain his share of the irrigation water because
Nichols was acting as if the common law of riparian rights applied in Colorado
Territory. Under that doctrine, only those owning land bordering a stream had
any kind of water right. The case went to trial, and Colorado's three-judge
Territorial Supreme Court ruled in favor of Yunker. Chief Justice Moses Hallett
wrote the lead opinion ruling that Nichols could not withhold water intended
to flow down the ditch to Yunker whose lands did not adjoin the stream.

An Illinois lawyer, Chief Justice Hallett had come to the western limits of
territorial Kansas in 1860 to be a gold miner.[26] When Colorado became a territory
in 1861, Hallett stayed on as a lawyer in private practice. Serving as a member

of the Territorial Council from 1863 to 1866, he was thoroughly familiar with Colorado's public domain heritage. This is apparent in his opinion in *Yunker v. Nichols* where he wrote, "All the lands in the territory which are now held by individuals were derived from the general government." In making the lands available to companies and individuals, the national government "intended to convey to the citizens the necessary means to make them fruitful." This was the same reasoning used by the California Supreme Court in 1852.

These "necessary means" included significant departures from the riparian common law of water management. Unlike England and the eastern states, where "the humidity of the climate is sufficient to supply moisture to plants," it is necessary in "a dry and thirsty land" to divert the waters of a stream "from their natural channels." The "value and usefulness of agricultural lands in this territory depends upon the supply of water for irrigation" and this can be obtained only by "constructing artificial channels often at great length, and rarely within the lands of a single proprietor." Because "all tilled lands, wherever situated, are subject to the same necessity," the laws of nature and of the territory thereby imposed a servitude by necessity for ditch rights-of-ways across intervening public and private lands.[27]

Colorado Territorial Supreme Court Justice Ebenezer Wells, a Civil War veteran and also an Illinois-trained lawyer, added a startling concurring opinion in the *Yunker v. Nichols* case. He declared that any effort by the territorial legislature to nullify ditch rights would itself be a nullity "by force of the necessity arising from local peculiarities of climate." Justice Wells, like Justice Hallett, was thoroughly grounded in the fundamental principles of land and water law Colorado needed to grow and prosper. He had been a member of the territorial legislature in 1866-1867, and later became an influential member of Colorado's constitutional convention in 1876—which cemented water and ditch rights into the state's constitution.[28]

THE NASCENT UNION Colony faced its gravest threat during the dry summer of 1874. Benjamin Eaton and a group of other developers had constructed two new irrigation systems upstream of the Union Colony's diversions: the Larimer County Canal Number 2, completed in 1873, and the Lake Canal Company (also called the Eaton and Abbot Canal) in 1874. The U.S. government had made this possible by decommissioning its Army post at Fort Collins, and then opened farm land to the new Fort Collins Agricultural Colony settlement.

These two new ditches challenged downstream irrigation companies, as they could divert the entire upstream flow of the Cache la Poudre River. During the dry summer of 1874, the companies did exactly that. Water historian Robert Dunbar wrote: "Forest fires raged in the mountains, and grasshoppers appeared on the plains." The river's flow, reported the *Fort Collins Standard*, "was extremely low, the lowest . . . since 1863."

By early July 1874, the crisis had worsened. Union Colony irrigators discovered the river was bone dry at the Greeley Number 3 headgate. They immediately sent Nathan Meeker, Joseph C. Shattuck, and others to ride the 30 miles upstream to Fort Collins to investigate.[29] To their horror, the Greeley delegation saw the upstream ditches running full of "their" Cache la Poudre River water. The *Fort Collins Standard* reported that, "as no one having authority to close the canals was approached on the subject, of course no satisfaction was received and the gentlemen returned to Greeley to hold an inflammatory meeting."

David Boyd recalled later how there "appeared to be great danger that the trees, small fruits, and lawns of our town would be ruined." Tempers flared. The *Fort Collins Standard* reported that the Greeley irrigators proposed to enjoin the Fort Collins canals from diverting water, so "that it might flow to Greeley and leave the trees and crops of Fort Collins to get along as best they might."[30] This enraged the Fort Collins irrigators a great deal.

On July 15, 1874, the dispute drew some 40 irrigators to a meeting at the Whitney schoolhouse (the name used by the Fort Collins newspaper, but referred to as the Eaton schoolhouse by the *Greeley Tribune*). The building was located on Benjamin Eaton's property, equidistant from Fort Collins and Greeley, and southwest of the present-day town of Windsor (most likely near the Whitney Ditch).[31] The evening was hot, the structure was small, and the Greeleyites (among them several Civil War veterans) arrived with their guns.

The Union Colony representatives included Meeker, General Robert Cameron of the 9th Indiana Infantry (previously a member of the Indiana House of Representatives), and Captain David Boyd of the 18th Michigan Infantry (and a native of Ireland). The group emphatically declared that Greeley had "prior rights as against any Fort Collins canals, notwithstanding their canals had been nearly doubled in capacity since they were constructed. The crops of Greeley were perishing for the want of water;" a condition that could only be resolved, said a reporter for the *Fort Collins Standard,* if "the people of Fort Collins should close all their headgates and allow suffering Greeley to dip her nose in the cooling fluid."[32]

This attitude further agitated the delegation from Greeley, who threatened to build more ditches upstream to intercept all of Fort Collins' water. Boyd later recalled: "The Collins parties were told that if their policy of the ditches highest up stream taking what they wanted was the one to be pursued, then we [Greeley] would go above them, and there would be an interminable and exhaustive race in which the greatest number and the largest purses would come out the winner. . ."[33] The Fort Collins water users "would not hear to moderation or justice." For that, said Captain Boyd, "force must meet force."

The *Standard* reported: "One of the Greeley gentlemen was forced to his feet to utter a disclaimer for the Hibernian warrior," a reference to Boyd's Irish heritage. "We outnumbered them," another Union Colony pioneer shot back in return, "and many of us had seen as rough service some ten years ago [during the Civil War] as we were likely to experience in an encounter with these water thieves. Then someone arose and moved an immediate adjournment, and shouted 'Every man to his tent, to his rifle and cartridges!'"[34]

The outcome of the contentious meeting that hot summer night in 1874 changed the future of water law in Colorado and much of the arid West. Guns remained holstered, but the irrigators from Fort Collins initially stood their ground. The *Fort Collins Standard* reported "that the owners of Fort Collins [ditches] would not admit any priority of right in favor of Greeley canals." In addition, the "canal owners of Larimer County would irrigate her crops first and last." This negative response did not sit well with the Greeley contingent, and a legal injunction was lobbed across the schoolhouse floor as a threat to halt the "illegal" upstream water diversions. The Fort Collins contingent fired back that, should the Union Colonists file for an injunction against the unrestricted access to the Cache la Poudre River water, "it would be too late to save the [colony's] crops."

Nathan Meeker then stepped forward and into the fray. From his days as a Civil War reporter, Meeker knew well the dangers of verbal challenges and loaded weapons. He warned that a failure to reach agreement on the Cache la Poudre River could open the door to allow "a heavy capitalist or corporation" to build "a huge canal from the Poudre above La Porte [upstream of both Fort Collins and Greeley] and run it [all of the river's waters] through the Box Elder country." This ditch could "irrigate perhaps 20,000 acres of new land, and—dire result—not leave enough water in the river to fill our canals."[35]

Meeker spoke the truth, because Benjamin Eaton (friend and foe in equal measure to people on both sides of the evening's conflict) had the connections and resources to construct huge upstream water canals. Eaton was independently negotiating with English investors to form the Colorado Mortgage and Investment Company, Ltd. of London. If finalized, the new water diversions would dry up the lower Cache la Poudre River and doom the young downstream communities of both Fort Collins and Greeley.

As the night wore on, the verbal attacks in the sweltering schoolhouse gave way to a compromise. The Union Colonists would drop their threat of legal action. The Larimer County irrigators then agreed to release some water downstream to Greeley. Boyd later acknowledged that "gradually voices of reconciliation were heard above the storm." The *Fort Collins Standard* concluded, a week after the notorious "Whitney school" incident, that the Greeley-based *Sun* newspaper had it right about collaboration over conflict: "What Greeley and Fort Collins want from this squabble over the waters of the Poudre is a friendly combination for mutual protection, not a fight over the knotty problem of 'prior rights' or rights in equity."

A mere five days later, Boyd later recalled: "A general rainstorm [five inches of precipitation] came in and saved us; but from this day forth we had set our hearts on having some regulations looking towards a distribution of the waters of the state in harmony with the principle of priority of appropriation."[36] While not apparent at the time to Union Colony residents, historians would point to the events of 1874 at the Eaton/Whitney schoolhouse as THE watershed moment that changed the State of Colorado, the arid West, and by extension urban water utilities like that of the City of Greeley. Two years later in 1876, Greeley irrigators, lawyers, and engineers worked with their peers in Denver and throughout the state to fashion the water provisions of Colorado's Constitution, which are still in effect today. In his 1879 *Report on the Lands of the Arid Regions of the United States*, John Wesley Powell credited Greeley for pioneering the Colorado Doctrine of Prior Appropriation.[37]

SCHOLARS DALE OESTERLE and Richard Collins call the water provisions of Colorado's 1876 Constitution its "most original provisions." It had taken six constitutional conventions to finally arrive at one which led to statehood.[38] Eighteen years had elapsed between the gold discoveries of 1858 and Colorado's admission into the Union as the Centennial State, one hundred years after the signing of the Declaration of Independence.[39] Fifteen Democrats and 24 Republicans were members of the convention. More delegates were lawyers than any other profession or business. Bankers, merchants, stock raisers, farmers, a newspaper man and miscellaneous businessmen made up the rest of the membership. Among the delegates was Judge H.P.H. Bromwell, who had served as a member of the Illinois Constitutional Convention of 1869-1870, and was one of the signers of the 1870 Illinois Constitution.[40]

Gold had been the magnet that brought about the creation of Colorado Territory in 1861, but irrigated agriculture, town building and associated businesses, epitomized by the Union Colony's success, created the State of Colorado in 1876 and propelled it into the 20th century.[41] In retrospect, it seems that the Greeley-Fort Collins water conflict, on the banks of the Cache la Poudre River in 1874, occurred at exactly the right time. The constitutional convention met from December 20, 1875, to March 15, 1876, and proceeded through committee discussions and reports to produce the constitution's final version. These committees included a nine-member "Committee on Irrigation, Agriculture and Manufactures" (let's call it the "Water Committee") appropriately chaired by S.J. Plumb of Weld County. Its members included a second delegate from Weld County as well as members from Bent, Conejos, Las Animas, Saguache, Fremont, Jefferson, and Arapahoe Counties.[42]

On January 5, 1876, Byron Carr of Boulder sponsored a resolution referring a first draft of the water provision to the Water Committee. However, it contained concepts the committee rejected out-of-hand as insufficient to protect water rights. The State, Carr had proposed, would own water in all Colorado streams; the legislature would decide how to distribute the water; and the legislature could also alter or repeal any water laws approved.[43]

This would not work, and so the Water Committee proceeded in a step-by-step fashion to create enduring water law principles. Its February 18th draft included language dedicating "unappropriated water of the natural streams to public use."[44] But the question still remained: Who owned the water? Five days later the February 22nd draft attempted to answer this question, invoking Colorado's heritage in the public domain. The new draft stated that the "public" owns the water, and its use is subject to prior appropriation: "The water of every natural stream, not heretofore appropriated within the State of Colorado, is hereby declared to be the property of the public, and the same is dedicated to their use as herein provided by this Constitution."[45] Enduring water law was being created.

On March 1, 1876, the Water Committee further drafted a provision to provide that "the right to direct the unappropriated waters of any natural stream to beneficial uses shall never be denied."[46] This reference to "beneficial use" neatly captured a requirement of the Colorado Territorial Legislature, which was meeting at the same time as the constitutional convention. It had already approved this requirement for irrigation ditches on February 9, 1876. In essence, no person could carry more irrigation water through an irrigating ditch than was "absolutely necessary" for irrigation, domestic and stock purposes.[47] This provision carried over into the 1877 General Laws of the new State of Colorado and remains virtually unchanged in today's statutory water provisions.[48]

Further amendments to the Water Committee's draft occurred on March 6th,[49] March 8th,[50] and March 14th,[51] producing the final text of the Colorado Constitution's water provisions set forth in Article XVI, Mining and Irrigation, Sections 5, 6, and 7.[52] Accordingly, from first draft through amendment to final draft, the principle of ownership of water in a natural stream changed from ownership by the State of Colorado to ownership by the public. Unappropriated water was dedicated to the people's use by appropriation for beneficial uses. Priority of appropriation is the means for determining who has the better right. This became known around the world as the Colorado Doctrine of Prior Appropriation. Scholar David Schorr's insightful book, *The Colorado Doctrine*, sets forth its five fundamental principles.[53]

First Principle: The public owns all of the water of the natural streams within the State of Colorado (Colo. Const. Art. XVI, Sec. 5). "The appropriation doctrine is part of a complex of pro-settler and anti-speculation laws" that were "aimed at preventing 'monopoly' control of water supplies." The territorial Grange championed public ownership of the water resource to prevent monopolies, by riparian landowners and speculating appropriators, who could deprive small farmers of water they needed. The assertion of public ownership, as distinguished from state ownership, is important. The framers of the water provisions of the Colorado Constitution urged that the stream should be under the control of the sovereign people and not subject to "crowds of monopolies" at the legislature.[54]

Second Principle: The water is dedicated to the use of the people through appropriation of unappropriated waters (Colo. Const. Art. XVI, Sec. 5). Only a right of use can be obtained, and equal opportunity was the guiding principle. The constitutional framers intended to do away completely with the old doctrine of riparian ownership, so that those who should come here to settle would have equal rights, in the unappropriated water, wherever lands they owned might be located. Widespread distribution of water, to those who need it, was the fundamental reason for recognizing public water ownership.[55]

Third Principle: Actual beneficial use of the public's water resource is required for the establishment of a water right. (Colo. Const. Art. XVI, Sec. 6). "Consistent with the distributive ideologies running through miners' and territorial law, the doctrine was a way of limiting speculation and concentration of wealth in water . . . First, by preventing legislative giveaways of water rights; and second, by limiting the amount that could be acquired by any one irrigator to the amount actually needed to water his or her crops, at the time of the appropriation, as opposed to the amount the ditch was capable of carrying or the amount needed for all of the lands that could be watered by the ditch." Diversion alone, without necessity and use, cannot create or maintain a water right. Beneficial use is a necessary derivative of appropriation as opposed to hoarding for later resale; otherwise, the new regime of water rights would simply replace the riparian monopoly with another speculative monopoly injuring subsequent claimants.[56]

Fourth Principle: When there is not sufficient water to satisfy all use rights, the earlier established right prevails. (Colo. Const. Art. XVI, Sec. 6). "Equality of opportunity to claim water rights was the rule as long as enough water remained to satisfy the needs of all claimants, but not when it would dilute the water rights to the point where they were too small to be sufficient for reasonable use." First in time, first in right is an application of the traditional principle of equity favoring an earlier claimant over a later one in cases of conflicting property claims. However, "The prior right of the earlier claimant was a severely restricted one, subject to the limitations of beneficial use."[57]

Fifth Principle: All persons and corporations, upon payment of just compensation, are entitled to a right of way across private lands of another for the construction and operation of water works for use rights. (Colo. Const. Art. XVI, Sec. 7). "The constitution further invaded private property rights by granting easements for the construction of water works . . . thereby guaranteeing that the policy of equal access to water for all would not be hobbled . . . by recalcitrant riparian landowners."[58]

THE UNION COLONY'S second most important contribution to Colorado and western water law, following the constitution's water provisions, was the General Assembly's codification (systematic arrangement) in 1879 and 1881 of adjudication and administration laws for water rights on Colorado's rivers and streams.[59] Again, on-the-ground experience prompted legal action. Former water adversaries in Greeley and Fort Collins now banded together to seek laws that would implement and enforce the Colorado Doctrine of Prior Appropriation. This would prevent speculative appropriators from constructing new irrigation ditches farther upstream to intercept water belonging to more senior downstream water rights along the Cache la Poudre River.

Greeley water experts were instrumental in Colorado's decision to set up a comprehensive system of water officials to enforce water right decrees along the rivers and streams of the state. It was the first water management system of its kind in the United States, and included a state engineer, division engineers within each of the state's major river basins, and local water commissioners to distribute the public's water in accordance with court decrees. Both the state constitution and state legal statutes were grounded in the Cache la Poudre River experience of Greeley irrigators. As Greeley's David Boyd later wrote, "So there was a general call for a convention of delegates representing the different ditches, to meet in Denver during the last days of December, 1878, to formulate some scheme of irrigation legislation."[60] L.R. Rhodes had just been elected a Senator from Larimer County; he favored the idea that courts would undertake the task of deciding who held what priority and for how much water.

A smaller water committee, chaired by Boyd, considered the proposed bill's contents. The legislative drafting committee included J.S. Stranger, editor of the *Colorado Farmer,* Daniel Witter and I.L. Bond of Boulder, and John C. Abbott of Fort Collins. Henry P.H. Bromwell, a delegate to the 1876 Constitutional Convention, was a member of the Legislature's Committee on Irrigation in the Colorado House of Representatives. As Boyd later recalled, "He [Bromwell] spent night and day every spare hour he had upon this bill, and especially deserves credit for formulating a procedure by which a record could be obtained of the priorities in the different districts."[61] This concerted effort produced the 1879 Adjudication and Administration Act, which was followed by the 1881 Act, to clear up deficiencies in due process procedures highlighted by the Colorado Supreme Court in its *Union Colony v. Elliott* decision.[62]

At the instigation of the Greeley representatives, the Cache la Poudre water district became the first to petition a court for the appointment of a referee (an official of the court) to make a field investigation of ditch headgate diversions for preparation of evidence for a court proceeding. This evidence would include the first day water was diverted and put to beneficial use, and the quantity of water diverted. These were all extremely important facts when tabulating the priority (order and quantity) of water diversions along a river or stream.

In the fall of 1879, Judge Victor Elliott of the Second Judicial District of Colorado appointed H.N. Haynes, son of Judge Haynes of Greeley, as referee. "The spring of 1880 was one of the driest and windiest in our experience, and water was scarce during the early part of the summer," Boyd reported. "So a number of these districts that had been so remiss and indifferent, now awoke to the importance of having some better way than every man help himself and the devil take the 'down streamer.'"[63] The need for a better administrative water rights system was becoming apparent to all, and water experts from Greeley would play a leading role in its creation.

DURING THE DECADE of the 1870s, the Union Colonists established Greeley as an extraordinarily successful agricultural and temperance community. They were also hailed as pioneers and innovators in the development of irrigation ditches, water law, and the management of water resources. Their first achievement was the construction of the Greeley Number 3 irrigation ditch. This was a community-wide effort that initially was not very successful. However, subsequent expansions and improvements made the irrigation system a viable part of the Greeley water system. The year 1874 was pivotal in the initial exploration of a water management system called "first in time, first in right." Two years later, residents of Greeley were instrumental in placing the Doctrine of Prior Appropriation in the Colorado Constitution.

Why was Greeley at the center of water management and water law creation in Colorado and the West? Mostly, it was out of necessity, out of survival to establish and grow the Union Colony community. Others have argued that the water users of Greeley were forward thinking, entrepreneurial and creative—exactly the type of people sought out by Nathan Meeker when he wrote his "Call" soliciting individuals, to become members of "A Western Colony," as proposed in his 1869 article in the *New York Tribune*. Whatever the reasons, the fact remains that Greeley citizens were instrumental in helping to establish a new water management system in a harsh and unforgiving land. That effort blossomed into an irrigated economic powerhouse virtually unrivaled in the United States.

CHAPTER THREE

1880-1900

City of Water: Greeley and the Progressive Era

"A colony which can control water in that country will be master of the situation for all time."[1]
—Nathan Meeker

EXCITING TIMES AWAITED the town of Greeley and its water department as the new century approached. Perseverance and hard work finally bore fruit with three significant achievements. First, the issues of water rights and water management, particularly along the Cache la Poudre River, were developed and enacted into state law through the leadership of Greeley and Weld County's elected officials, and its community of water engineers and attorneys. These innovative laws and water management tools were critical in the development of water rights in the region. Second, declining quality of the city's drinking water supply led to construction in 1888-1889 of Greeley's first "Water Works" plant—a treatment facility that removed harmful pollutants from the town's groundwater well through a sand filtration system. Third was the extensive development of irrigated agriculture in the region which would lead to a close partnership between irrigation companies and Greeley's municipal water system.

BY 1882, A comprehensive judicial system was in place to create decrees for water rights, as well as an extensive system of enforcement (a state engineer, division irrigation engineers, and local water commissioners). Judge Victor

Elliott of the Second Judicial District of Colorado entered the first decree adjudicating priorities for the Cache la Poudre River water rights.[2] Henry P.H. Bromwell (a former member of the Colorado House of Representatives) served as the court's referee and took evidence. Greeley's Number 3 Ditch, for example, gained recognition for "irrigation of lands and for domestic purposes." The court's decree awarded it a priority of April 1, 1870, for 52 cfs (cubic feet per second) of water; plus, a first enlargement priority for 41 cfs dated October 1, 1871; a second enlargement priority for 63.13 cfs dated July 15, 1872; and a third enlargement priority for 16.66 cfs dated May 15, 1873 (for a grand total of 172.79 cubic feet per second with various priority dates). Colonists had earned these additional priorities by increasing the width and depth of the Greeley Number 3 Ditch three times to carry more water and by placing that water to beneficial use.[3] (Note: The term "cubic feet per second" is abbreviated "cfs" and is a rate of flow in streams and rivers. It is equal to a volume of water one foot wide and one foot deep, flowing a distance of one foot in one second. One cfs is equal to 7.48 gallons of water flowing past a given location every second.)

Note the precision of these priorities as to the day, month, and year as well as the flow rates that are calculated to the second decimal, i.e. 63.13 cubic feet per second. The value of water in the West was, and still is, so great that water rights are calculated to within decimal points of a cubic foot per second. As the new laws required in 1881, Judge Elliot ranked the Cache la Poudre River water rights in order of their relative priority with each other.

It is clear from tracking the Colorado Constitution's 1876 water provisions, and through their implementation by statutes and court cases, that the farm and town experiences of Union Colonists produced a rule of law framework involving all three branches of government in Colorado. The people of the Centennial State insisted on public governance principles lodged in its Constitution, and leadership was provided by a host of water experts emanating from Greeley, in cooperation with other regions of the state. Colorado's legislature and the courts responded by setting in place a water rights system fostering beneficial use without waste.

The Colorado Legislature assigned the duty to decree water right priorities to the state's judiciary, and enforcement authority was given to the state and division engineers and the local water commissioners.[4] In 1882, the Colorado Supreme

Court's decision in *Coffin v. Left Hand Ditch Company* confirmed Colorado's abolition of riparian water law: "The common law doctrine giving the riparian owner a right to the flow of water in its natural channel upon and over his lands, even though he makes no beneficial use thereof, is inapplicable to Colorado."[5]

IN 1891, THE Colorado Supreme Court's *Strickler v. City of Colorado Springs*[6] decision held that senior irrigation water right priorities were valuable property rights that a city could purchase and change from their former use—so long as the rights of others "are not injuriously affected thereby." In the early 20th century, Greeley relied on this legal authority to buy and use water rights previously decreed for irrigation through the Whedbee Ditch No. 1[7] and the Boyd and Freeman Ditch.[8] The court decrees for these two water use changes provided Greeley with 12.5 cfs of Cache la Poudre River diversions at the mouth of the Poudre Canyon. There, the water is treated at its Bellvue filter plant and delivered through a 38-mile-long pipeline to users in Greeley.

These innovations in water management and water law gained nationwide attention. At the turn of the century in 1901, the U.S. Department of Agriculture published Edwin S. Nettleton's report on the reservoir and exchange system operating in the Poudre Valley.[9] This report, from the former Greeley resident, emphasized the importance of irrigation seepage, return flow, and groundwater in augmenting river flows at times of the year when natural streamflow would not otherwise be present.

Nettleton, an original member of the Union Colony who later became Colorado's second State Engineer, explained to the nation how Colorado's water management experience and legal system forged a cooperative union which extended the availability of water through a common interest in reservoir storage.

> "The plan of exchange or 'trading round' water was conceived, agreed
> to and carried on by the people themselves without legislative enact-
> ments, court decrees, or legal counsel or advice. It was simply the
> outcome of necessity to dispose of water profitably that could be
> utilized on lands in one locality by transferring it to another, thus

benefiting one and often both of the parties to the exchange. It was
first brought about by practical men, getting together in a friendly,
neighborly, and businesslike manner, and consolidating the rights
each might have under existing laws into one common interest in the
storage of water . . . It has been necessary, however, to have a uniform
method of determining quantities used in the exchange; also to have
someone delegated to act as a sort of public gager."[10]

It was a confluence of ideas growing out of practical need and experience. As
always, the magic touch of water was the sustaining force of a community. Use
of the public's groundwater and surface water within a state and interstate, for
the needs of the people and the environment, continues to be one of the most
profound virtues of Colorado. In this, Greeley has played and continues to play
a leading role in water governance.

IN ITS FIRST years, Greeley's residents diverted water from the Cache la
Poudre River through the Greeley Number 3 Ditch for irrigation purposes,
while shallow groundwater wells provided supplies for daily domestic use.
Sixty miles to Greeley's south, Denver's population relied upon a similar irrigation system, known as the "City Ditch," to convey South Platte River flows
along Denver streets for urban uses in Colorado's capital city.

Patricia Limerick, author of a recent history of the Denver Water system, noted
that most of Colorado's 19th century communities had experienced significant water
quality issues. Generally, this was due to declining water quantities and from contamination from animals and land uses. Said the University of Colorado professor:
"Quality and quantity were proving to be connected; the quality worsened when the
quantity diminished."[11] Greeley residents encountered this same dilemma when their
wells became contaminated by animal waste and runoff from irrigated gardens and
outlying farm fields. Drought was also a major factor. Residents agreed that Greeley
urgently needed to improve the quantity and quality of its potable (drinkable) water.

By the late 1800s, in response to water quality concerns, the citizens of Greeley
endorsed construction of a domestic water treatment system similar to those of

major urban centers in the East and in Europe. Martin Melosi, author of *The Sanitary City*, wrote of the parallels between urban density and illnesses, such as cholera and typhoid, most often attributed to polluted drinking water.[12] Historically, open ditches carried wastes from homes, businesses, industries, and animals. As indoor "water closets" came into use, more effluent (contaminated water) seeped from ditches and other settling areas into shallow aquifers that provided drinking water.

Until the "bacteriological revolution" of the late 19th century, when chemically treated water became a standard practice, communities large and small believed that disease could be avoided by passing the effluent through town to a downstream river. Another option was dilution: a process that required greater volumes of water to meet increased disposal of waste. Children and the elderly were most susceptible to waterborne diseases, as were neighborhoods occupied by the poor that had few options other than to drink contaminated water.

ONE MAJOR SOURCE of potable water in Greeley was known as the "Colony Well," dug in the early 1870s at the intersection of 9th Avenue and 8th Street. Residents could fill cans and buckets with fresh water, at no cost, for their homes from this reliable well. As David Boyd wrote of those early years: "It was one of the fortunate things in the selection of the town site that good well water (groundwater) was easily obtained." Gravel, which served to trap particulates in the stream, said Boyd, "is reached at from four to fifteen feet, and at some seasons of the year water is up to the top of the gravel." This gave the community a natural filtration system for their wells, as Boyd observed. Increases in local irrigation, however, led to "more inorganic impurities when the stream is partly fed by return waters draining into [wells] from lands on either bank [of the Cache la Poudre River]."[13] It would only be a matter of time before groundwater contamination became a serious health problem, and forced the development of other water options.

With the deterioration of Greeley's well water quality, business travelers of the day spoke disparagingly of the poor taste and color of water in Greeley. Promoters of settlement in Grand Junction and the Grand Valley of western Colorado cited Greeley's bad tasting water as one reason that state legislators should locate Colorado's "Normal School" for teacher training on the Western Slope. By the early 1880s, town leaders could no longer ignore the problem, and proposed drilling a new well beneath the downtown area of Greeley to tap into artesian water. This came at a high cost as this source of groundwater could only be found at depths of 800 to 1,200 feet.

It was fortunate that this unique groundwater formation existed beneath Greeley. For millennia, snowmelt from the mountains had percolated underground into a deep geologic formation. This uncommon geological and hydrological system created a confined aquifer which contained groundwater under pressure. Technology of the 1880s enabled well drillers to tap into this pressurized water source, and allowed groundwater to rise above the land surface without the use of a pump. It now became a flowing artesian spring with a rich concentration of natural minerals. Artesian water is generally excellent drinking water.

In August 1883, the Swan Brothers of Denver were hired to drill the first such community well in Greeley. The drillers reached artesian groundwater beneath Lincoln Park at a depth of 1,200 feet. It cost the City $8,000 (around $200,000 in 2020) to tap, and when the drilling was completed in April 1884, a special edition of the *Greeley Tribune* was published to announce this significant achievement. Citizens and visitors lauded the artesian water and claimed that its natural minerals contained medicinal properties. Ralph Meeker (Nathan's eldest son) wrote approvingly in the *Greeley Tribune* that "Conductors and brakemen on the railway trains use it exclusively, carrying it away in milk cans."[14] Four months later, an August 27, 1884, *Greeley Tribune* editorial declared "OUR FOUNTAIN OF HEALTH," and praised not only the pure water that gushed from the artesian well, but also noted the burning gas it produced:

> "The artesian well is a surprising success, and its medical properties
> are attracting serious attention. An invalid from Colorado Springs
> received so much benefit from drinking the water, last week, that
> he went home cured, and said that he could get a hundred people
> to come here for their health. The Greeleyites are at the fountain
> with cups, buckets, milk cans and jugs at all hours of the day, and
> the more they use the water the more they praise it. Eli Hall says
> that he has not had a good night's sleep for ten years, until he began

OPENING OF THE ARTESIAN WELL.

Figure 3.1 In 1884, a *Greeley Tribune* extra edition commemorated the first 1,200 foot-deep, $8,000 artesian well drilled in the south part of Lincoln Park. Its supply of free-flowing groundwater diminished after seven other wells were drilled in other downtown locations. In 1901, the well became contaminated when the pump casing failed. City of Greeley Museums, Permanent Collection, Courtesy of the *Greeley Tribune,* AI-0008.

drinking the medicinal waters last week. Since then, his rest has been unbroken. . ."

The editorial further explained to readers of the *Tribune*:

"A singular thing about the well is, that every 20 minutes a powerful stream gushes forth for a minute or two and then stops. During the interval of about two minutes, escaping gas burns with a steady blue flame, and when the water begins to run again the flame follows down the stream and then expires."

Undoubtedly, the new well had also tapped into a pool of methane gas which gave off a blue color as it burned.

After 1884, seven more artesian wells were privately constructed around Greeley to replace the contaminated shallow groundwater sources. Boyd noted that, unfortunately, "as the number [of artesian wells] increased the flow [yield] in each slackened." In 1886, assuming that subsurface water was unlimited and free, the owner of the Oasis Hotel, Samuel D. Hunter, installed a steam pump on his property to draw more water from the eighth artesian well located in his hotel basement. This increase in pumping, unfortunately, had a negative effect on the artesian pressure of the area, and other deep well users soon experienced a diminution of water pressure, forcing them to install their own pumps or windmills.

By contrast, towns situated closer to the mountains generally had less access to groundwater, like Fort Collins. In the early 1880s, it decided to build a water treatment plant to divert water directly from the Cache la Poudre River. The citizenry accepted the higher rates of this type of water service as a benefit of urban growth.

A few years earlier, on March 6, 1880, fire consumed the local Greeley House hotel and two adjacent buildings. Sparks from the fire ignited other blazes about town, which volunteers from Greeley's fire department were able to quickly douse. The disaster was a "wake up" call for Greeley because most of the early commercial buildings on Main Street were made of wooden frame. After this fire, the majority of new commercial structures were constructed of brick. Water for fire suppression was included in the design of the new hotel, named the "Oasis" because of its location in the "Great American Desert." A *Greeley Tribune* article noted, "On each of the upper floors a large water closet, and above these the [water] reservoir is connected with a standpipe, so water can be thrown into every part in case of a fire." This requirement was another example of innovation in the new community.

The confluence of water and wastewater infrastructure became a vital part of Greeley's municipal government. B.D. Sanborn aggressively advertised and sold lots in the Cranford housing addition, touting, as Meeker once had, the superb views of the Rocky Mountains. In addition, it would have a "system of sewerage" and graded and graveled streets throughout the new subdivision. Quality and quantity of water, always important for Greeley's residents, would be incorporated into new residential and manufacturing areas. Public health and safety services, such as the sprinkling of streets to control dust, irrigation of parks, and maintenance of the community cemetery (Linn Grove) were new municipal initiatives.

In 1883, the prairie turned from green to brown as drought returned, as bad as the one in 1874, with the years 1886-1887 particularly dry. Conditions had not improved by the spring of 1888, leading prominent Greeley citizens Benjamin Eaton, John Sanborn, George and H.T. West, J. Max Clark and others to call upon Mayor Charles A. White and the city council to address "the urgent need of a better supply of water for domestic, sanitary, and fire purposes." Asking their town government to "take the matter under consideration without delay," the community leaders insisted on "building a complete system of water works at the earliest possible moment."[15]

The political pressure exerted on the elected officials led Mayor White and several councilors to visit communities in Colorado, Kansas, and Nebraska to inspect their "modern" water works systems. Greeley's "free" water would now have a price, and the vote on a subsequent $65,000 bond issue ($1.6 million in 2020) for a new water filtration system met stiff opposition from residents. In November 1888, however, the arguments against taxation and rate increases did not dissuade voters, who approved the measure by a margin of 54 votes out of a total of 344 cast. Those opposed to the referendum appealed to the city council to deny issuance of the water bonds, but to no avail. Greeley residents, then as now concerned about fiscal integrity, proved willing to invest in other major urban improvements; among them electric lights in 1886 and telephones by 1893. Improvements to the Greeley water system were not eyed with suspicion, but rather with fiscal responsibility as the test.

DESIROUS OF A first class water works plant, the town hired as its project engineer Charles P. Allen, Chief Engineer for the Denver Union Water Company. A native of New York, Allen had served as a consultant for water system development in Leadville, Fort Collins, Pueblo, and Denver. Allen was an accomplished inventor, and in 1886 filed for a U.S. patent for his design of a 48-inch wood-stave pipeline to deliver water to Denver; the first city in America to install this method for water mains. Greeley would later adopt this technology at the turn of the century.

With $65,000 in bond funds available, the City of Greeley acquired a 20-acre site located north of the downtown area and adjacent to Island Grove Park. A

Figure 3.2 Charles P. Allen, Chief Engineer for the Denver Union Water Company, received a patent on March 22, 1887, for his invention of a wooden stave pipe system. He was project engineer for the construction of Greeley's 1888-1889 water works plant, and in 1902 consulted with town officials regarding options to improve its water system at a reasonable cost. In 1907, a new gravity flow 38-mile-long wooden stave transmission line delivered clean mountain water from the Bellvue treatment plant to Greeley. Courtesy of Denver Water.

shallow well was drilled into the gravel alluvial aquifer of the Cache la Poudre River, providing groundwater from less than 10 feet below the land surface. A steam pump delivered up to one million gallons of untreated groundwater per day to the new water works plant, which had a bed of coarse gravel and slow sand filters. Well water slowly percolated downward through the filters, under the force of gravity, to shed its impurities. The clean, high quality potable water was then delivered by underground pipes to homes and businesses around Greeley.

David Boyd was curious about the quality of the drinking water provided by this innovative system. The University of Michigan graduate first compared data from his alma mater, which received treated water from the Ann Arbor municipal system. Next, he took a sample of water from the courthouse in Denver, and then from Greeley's new water works. Boyd also wanted to know if artesian wells produced higher quality drinking water than Greeley's filtering process of shallow groundwater. David O'Brine, a chemist with the experimental station at the Colorado Agricultural College in Fort Collins, analyzed Boyd's various water samples. He found that Greeley's filtered shallow groundwater compared quite favorably to the Denver, Ann Arbor, and local artesian well water. "In fact," wrote Boyd later, "[Greeley's filtered] water is good drinking water, clear as crystal and pleasant to the taste."[16]

The concept of using the slow sand filtering process was not new, as the technology had been developed in Paisley, Scotland, in 1804. In 1872, the technology was first adopted in the U.S. by the City of Poughkeepsie, New York, and became a model throughout the country. In 1888, Greeley adopted this proven technology to reduce contaminants that could cause typhoid and cholera epidemics. The completion of the Greeley Water Works plant was a significant milestone in the history of Greeley and its water department.

Greeley's first water works plant, built of brick with stone trim, measured 32 feet by 36 feet and included an apartment for the water works engineer and family. A water tower stood in front of the building and held treated water for the downtown area. A second storage tank, which measured 30 feet in diameter and 30 feet tall, stored 138,000 gallons of water on a hill south of 20th Street between 10th and 11th Avenues, known as "Inspiration Point" or "Inspiration Hill."

On August 31, 1958, the *Greeley Sunday Journal* carried reminiscences of the old Greeley Water Works system. Longtime residents spoke of the water tower at Inspiration Hill as "a favorite rendezvous for the young and the amorous then as now." In its shadow, said several interviewees, "flowers grew in abundance," while "all the little girls of that day picked flowers there for May baskets, as well as along the banks of the Number Three irrigating ditch."

More prosaic, if no less amusing, was the story told by the Greeley fire chief who estimated the level of community fire protection by looking through a "spy glass" at the water tower atop Inspiration Hill. "If water could be seen splashing over the top of the tower," the chief stated "[we] could figure on sufficient water to quench the blaze."[17]

THE CITIZENS OF Greeley began the last decade of the 19th century with a presumed long-term solution to the issues of water quality and quantity. None could have predicted, however, the swirl of competing forces in the community and nationwide that brought "hard times" to Greeley. Growth

Figure 3.3 In 1889, Greeley's first water works plant was constructed at 14ᵗʰ Avenue and A Street. Two steam pumps forced water from infusion chambers (dug at the site) into water mains under the streets, and to a 138,000-gallon water tower on Inspiration Hill. Daytime pump capacity was 45,000 gallons per hour. At midnight, pumps were shut down and then restarted at 5:00 a.m. As demand regularly outpaced supply, Greeley faced a water shortage crisis by 1900. City of Greeley Museums, Permanent Collection, AI-0014.

slowed as economic depression gripped the country in 1892, followed by the Panic of 1893. The U.S. Congress had hoped that its repeal of the 1890 Sherman Silver Purchase Act would alleviate problems created by the economic downturn. Instead, this action caused silver prices to plummet; a disastrous consequence in Colorado where silver mining loomed large.

Due to the poor economy, many liens and foreclosures were filed against businesses for delinquent mortgage and tax payments. The local newspapers printed lists of consolidations, dissolutions, and relocations of businesses as merchants attempted to downsize, remain solvent, and weather the difficult economic times. Greeley's pioneer merchants, many approaching retirement age, started selling their original residential and commercial properties.

Concerns about the fiscal stability of the Greeley Water Works led the *Greeley Tribune* to call upon the system to generate a profit. "The water works have, so far," wrote the editor, "failed to pay their way, to say nothing about a provision for the ultimate payment of the bonds." The newspaper calculated that revenues from the sale of treated water generated slightly more than one-third of the costs of operations and interest payments for the plant. "We may, in short, expect constant expenditure," the *Tribune* editor charged, "and each recurring year will undoubtedly bring its own burden not materially lessened by the expenditure of the year previous." City council members would need to heed the warnings and advice of the local newspaper, or risk being voted out of office at a future municipal election.

Regardless of revenues, demands on the water works plant increased with the arrival of warmer weather. "Several mornings last summer," the *Tribune* wrote in late May 1893, "there was hardly sufficient water in Greeley's street pipes for domestic purposes," including fire protection. "Why this was so," said the editor, "was a source of anxiety to our municipal authorities." The latter investigated the issue and determined that "a great many consumers were using the water on their lawns and garden patches all through the still hours of the night."

M.P. Henderson, Superintendent of the Greeley Water Works, wrote the *Tribune* to remind readers of the May 1893 "Ordinance No. 65," which defined outdoor watering restrictions. Homeowners could apply city water to their lawns and gardens from 6:00 a.m. to 10:00 a.m., and then again from 4:00 p.m. to 7:00 p.m. daily. "*Under no circumstances*," the ordinance declared in italics, "will water be permitted to be used through a hose without a nozzle or sprinkler attached thereto."[18] This ordinance was among the first mandatory municipal water conservation requirements in Colorado and the West.

Anxious city officials then hired two "watchmen" (Frank Brennan in the daytime and William Lee at night) to patrol the streets and issue citations for water use violations. Ordinance No. 65 called for fines between $5-$300 ($150-$8,500 in 2020), plus "any damages arising from any violations thereof." The City also hired young men dubbed "water dogs" to report late-night drawdowns from the irrigation ditches. Among the youth who guarded against water theft was Delphus ("Delph") Carpenter.[19] (Later, after his graduation from Greeley High School and the University of Denver Law School in 1899, Carpenter gained national fame for his work on river compact legislation as an attorney, state senator, and principal drafter of the Colorado River Compact of 1922.)

In 1893, the extensive development of irrigation in the region led to strengthening of the close partnership forged between farmers and the community in 1870. One month before Greeley's City Council approved an ordinance, which allowed the

Colorado Telephone Company to install lines throughout the city, several local irrigation companies formed the private nonprofit Poudre Valley Telephone Company. This cooperative installed 45 miles of phone lines, and a gauge at the measuring weir at the mouth of Cache la Poudre Canyon, to record and transmit water flow data, day or night, via "wire" to the Colorado Agricultural College at Fort Collins. The May 25, 1893, *Greeley Tribune* described the purpose of and benefits to the company:

> "The Poudre Valley Telephone Company was organized and incorporated about two weeks ago with a capital stock of $5,000, and within the past few days work has been commenced on the lines. The company will operate lines from Greeley to Eaton and from Greeley to New Windsor, Fort Collins and North Poudre Canyon. The object of the company is to assist the irrigating system of the Poudre valley, and not for personal profit. It is owned by several ditch companies of the valley and a few business men of Greeley, Eaton and New Windsor.
>
> "The company will control forty-five miles of lines and expect to be in working order about July 1, [1893], and no doubt it will be of incalculable value to the irrigators under the various ditches that control it. There is a self-registering gauge at the mouth of Poudre canyon, and this is to be connected by wire with the Colorado Agricultural College at Fort Collins, where a dial will automatically register the amount of water flowing over the weir at any time during the day or night.
>
> "This knowledge will be of the greatest importance, as it will daily inform any inquirer what amount of water is running and what the irrigator may expect to obtain for agricultural purposes, so that there need not at any time be more laterals open than the supply will warrant. With the telephone line in operation and the weir at the mouth of the canyon automatically noted every day, this section of the arid region will be enjoying all the scientific appliances now known in that direction, and the only place, we believe, in the Union that will be so benefited."

New technology was embraced throughout the region, but fiscal responsibility remained a hallmark of the maturing City of Greeley. As the decade of the

1890s closed, the local newspaper's opinion of the impressive Greeley Water Works (as an expensive indulgence) compelled city officials to restore ratepayer confidence. This effort began with a water quality study. In the summer of 1898, the City hired Professor A.E. Beardsley of the Colorado Normal School in Greeley to "determine whether the [water provided by the new filtration plant] is free from contaminations liable to injure the public health." In his laboratory on the Teacher College campus, within sight of the water works tower on Inspiration Hill, Beardsley examined water samples taken from taps in the building, a fire hydrant on campus, and from a water line near the Greeley Water Works storage tank. "The water was found to be clear and sparkling," he told the mayor and city council members.[20]

In May 1899, another strategy to keep the citizenry informed of the progress of their water works emerged when Superintendent Henderson invited a "*Tribune* representative" to observe "what was being done toward increasing the water supply." In particular, Henderson asked the *Greeley Tribune* to share with its readers the digging of a "gallery" (a slow-filtering channel) 150 feet in length and 21 feet deep. By lining the gallery with tile instead of wood, and despite the higher cost of the latter technique, the system would last longer and convey the filtered water more quickly to neighborhoods in the city. The *Tribune* reporter wrote approvingly that the water "sparkled clear as crystal and as long as it trickled into the gallery it looked as if it came from springs, instead from the underflow." The reporter also accepted an invitation from Lincoln Olney, engineer for the Greeley Water Works plant, to tour that facility. "Many changes have been made lately," wrote the local journalist, "and all for an advantage."

Newspapers were widely read in this era, and the voice of the community, the *Greeley Tribune*, was highly influential on the perceptions and attitudes of citizens regarding their water supply system. Greeley's decision makers and water superintendent Henderson kept close touch with both the *Tribune* and the city's residents to seek approval for water supply investments and expenditures of public funds. Led by the Greeley City Council (the water policy decision making authority), the City continued to employ highly-skilled staff and consultants to provide recommendations to the council, and to handle the day-to-day water operations. Always looking over the city council's shoulders were the citizens, watching the budget and keeping a close eye on expenses.

IN MANY WAYS, the citizens of Greeley reflected the qualities of the Progressive Era before they became recognized as national standards. Historian Gerald D. Nash identified the champions of modernization not as "frontiersmen of the nineteenth century," but as "wealthy and intelligent newcomers." The original Union Colonists approximated Nash's standard. They possessed such intangibles as "above average enterprise, talent, intellect, and culture." Nash also claimed that the Progressives "brought cunning, shrewdness, and calculation to the West." Calling them "go-getters who built their expansionist plans wherever they happened to settle," the new leadership "gave western society much of its forward thrust" in an age of transformation and change.[21] Nash's description offered a portrait of leadership that residents of Greeley had come to know.

While not part of the post-1900 Progressive movement, J. Max Clark possessed many of these best qualities. His 1902 memoir, *Colonial Days*, illustrated how the fledgling Union Colony had nearly collapsed.[22] Clark recalled that solving the water problem of the new settlement proved most difficult, as both of the Colony's ditches ". . . were in a crude, unfinished state . . . and had proved entirely inadequate to the demands made upon them with the little cultivation under them, even at that early day."[23] Clark often reflected "in after days . . . of the many troubles which followed in the manipulation of water by novices in the art."[24] Said the longtime Greeley resident: "What wonder, then, that many of our experiences with ditches and water and the water supply, have taken a deep hold on us, have sunken deeply in our hearts and have at last resulted in a set of convictions which, like our instincts, rise above reason and are neither subject to review or revision."[25]

In the early days of irrigation expansion in northeastern Colorado, faculty at the Colorado Agricultural College supplied their engineering expertise to irrigators in the region. This in turn helped shape the foundation of Greeley's post-1900 economy: large-scale food production and the development of sound water management policies and practices. In 1883, Elwood Mead (who grew up on a farm in Indiana) joined the faculty at Fort Collins to teach classes in physics and irrigation engineering. Mead's 1887 *Report of Experiments in Irrigation and Meteorology* documented his research to determine the most efficient and economic applications of irrigation water for a variety of crops.[26] Water management became a lifelong commitment for Mead. From his work in the Cache la Poudre Valley, he would become the Wyoming State Engineer. Later as director of the U.S. Bureau of Reclamation (1923-1934), Mead oversaw construction of the Colorado River's Hoover Dam and the early stages of design of the Colorado-Big Thompson Project. His work at the Colorado Agricultural College, and as Colorado's Assistant State Engineer, helped Weld County and northern Colorado become one of the top agricultural regions in the entire United States.[27]

Water management technology along the Cache la Poudre River was gaining national attention due to the credibility and the number of those who knew it first-hand, and wrote about it. In 1897, David Boyd, the Union Colony's first ditch rider, authored a telling report published by the U.S. Geological Survey, *Irrigation Near Greeley, Colorado*.[28] Relating hard lessons learned, Boyd described the flaws in construction and operation of the Greeley Number 3 Ditch, with corrections to improve it. These empirical observations produced better designs for larger, upstream irrigation ditches. He also suggested methods of reservoir construction; ideas that would be implemented later in the region.

In 1901, Edwin S. Nettleton published *The Reservoir System of the Cache La Poudre Valley*[29] which documented 30 years of the Cache la Poudre River irrigation experience. Nettleton's discussion of exchanging water between reservoirs and ditches, up and down the Poudre River, proved especially compelling. This practice of exchange alleviated strict enforcement of the water rights priority system by ensuring water to senior rights when and where it was needed. It also allowed junior rights to divert river water when these otherwise would have been shut down.

Like others of the first generation Union Colony, Nettleton achieved national recognition with his focus on the ingenuity of the Cache la Poudre River irrigators. He emphasized the crucial role that reservoirs played in augmenting the availability of water delivered to farms, towns and businesses in all seasons of the year. Wrote Nettleton: "Although the necessity for storage reservoirs and their utility and benefits are generally recognized, but few people outside of northern Colorado are aware of what has been accomplished in that locality by the utilization of small things or of the ingenuity displayed in making the most of them."[30]

Greeley was growing, in large part due to the expansion of agricultural lands in the area. The early work of Boyd, Nettleton, and their peers proved instrumental in developing the intricate water delivery and management schemes of the region, and in sharing their knowledge. The testimony of those who came to see what Greeley was ushering to fruition inspired other communities in Colorado and around the world. University of Wisconsin economist Richard Ely was enamored by Greeley's famed agricultural production. Known nationally for his studies of labor, capitalism, and community development in the age of the "Industrial Revolution," Ely came to Greeley in 1901 to see for himself whether Nathan Meeker's experiment offered something of interest to a rapidly urbanizing nation. The Wisconsin professor discovered that "perhaps the whole American continent affords no better place for this kind of sociological study than Greeley, Colorado." Ely had observed how, "within the short period of thirty years, we may see an economic development which has elsewhere frequently required a century."[31]

Where Ely had found extremes of wealth and poverty coexisting in the nation's large urban centers, he attributed Greeley's middle class status to farming; an occupation that "has shaped American thought and formed American ideals." In 1870, the Union Colony's locating committee had traveled up and down the Cache la Poudre, Big Thompson, and South Platte Rivers, as had so many Native peoples, explorers, and gold seekers before them, and "saw the vegetation along the borders of the streams." Ely surmised that "they had the belief that the apparently barren soil would be found fruitful if it could be covered with water."[32]

Ely then examined "the chief source of wealth in Greeley up to the present time—the potato, or as they frequently say in Colorado, the spud." The professor admitted that "Potato is king" does not sound so poetic as "Cotton is king," or even "Corn is king." Ely claimed that no Iowa corn field could match Greeley, where potatoes "stretch away for long distances towards the horizon, in long, straight rows, covered with the richest green and dotted with the beautiful potato blossoms."[33] Farms generated as much as $10,000 per year ($300,000 in 2020) on their potato crops alone.

"Everyone in Greeley," remarked the professor, "whatever profession or calling he follows, has an interest in potatoes." Ely also noted the local saying that "a Greeley banker would not stand well if he did not own a potato farm." Thus, he found it odd that the 1890s harvest festival known as "Potato Day" had "ceased to be celebrated

Figure 3.4 In 1891, farmer and implement dealer, William "Billy" H. Farr, and his partner, banker Charles N. Jackson, established the Farr Produce Company at 709-7th Street in Greeley. During the 1890's and the early 1900's, Greeley and Weld County were the top potato production areas in the country. The wagon load of potatoes pictured here had been brought to town to be shipped out by railroad, and weighed 18,100 pounds. City of Greeley Museums, Permanent Collection, 1139.0001.15.1.

in Greeley." Even more strange was the explanation given for this lapse of historical tradition. "It was feared," wrote Ely, that "the celebration of the potato day would attract great attention to the potato and lead to competition which would decrease the value of their product."[34] (More recently in 1987, Potato Day was revived by the Friends of the Greeley Museums, and is held annually in September to celebrate the close partnership between irrigated agriculture and the City of Greeley.)

BY THE LATE 1800s, the town of Greeley had come to identify itself as the "Garden Spot of Colorado," and also as the "city of homes" for its fine residences. In so doing, the legacy of Nathan Meeker and his quest for a community of families and middle class values seemed realized. Now a new generation of citizens occupied the former Union Colony; a cohort of peers whose knowledge of the past mattered less than their vision of the future.

Given the fading memories of their accomplishments, prominent Greeleyites such as Arvilla Meeker and J. Max Clark wished to remind their neighbors of their story, written in water. Mrs. Meeker, who had come reluctantly from New York City to Greeley with her husband, Nathan, and their family, spoke in 1897 to a "Colony Pioneers' Meeting." "Nothing but a wild prairie and cacti" had greeted the first settlers of the town, she recalled. This sentiment was echoed in Anna Marie V. Green's book, *Sixteen Years on the Great American Desert, or the Trials and Triumph of a Frontier Life.* The Greens were also original Union Colonists, arriving on May 21, 1870. Her book chronicled experiences with irrigation and the family's trials and tribulations with farming, locusts, and high interest rates. Anna Marie Green tells about her crying baby, Frank (who later would become Mayor of Greeley), upset by the swirling sands of the "Great American Desert," all the while trying to salvage the family's tent which was "almost daily blown to the ground."[35]

"Well we all remember," said Arvilla Meeker, "what we passed through;" the latter including the death of her husband at White River in northwest Colorado, and her own captivity and that of her daughter, Josephine, by the Utes.[36] "Now we see the fruit of our labor," Arvilla informed the attendees of the pioneer society. This she described as "homes surrounded with beautiful trees, sweet flowers nodding to the breeze," while "the attractiveness of wealth and plenty meet the eye on all sides." The story of Greeley Water begins with these early years of the Union Colony, and often focuses on the efforts of men in the fledgling community. However, the struggles, dedication and hard work of their spouses and other women settlers of the community cannot be overlooked or underestimated.

The end of the 19th century found the community of Greeley, Colorado, a prosperous one, owing much of its success to the water development efforts of its first generation. Clean water seemed plentiful, but more was needed as thoughtful leaders looked to the next phase of industrial growth and population expansion. That new source of water would be found in the upper reaches of the Cache la Poudre River.

CHAPTER FOUR

1900-1910

The Sugar Factory and Bellvue Treatment Plant

AT THE BEGINNING of the 20th century, Greeley faced a sobering moment of truth. While its population had tripled from the first decade of the 1870s, the community had only grown to 3,000 residents. This contrasted sharply with the rapid increases experienced statewide, particularly in Denver, which boasted 135,000 residents; a stunning expansion since its gold-rush days. While Greeley's new water works plant now delivered clean and safe water, the residents were concerned about their future prospects for growth.

William Daven (W.D.) Farr, grandson of Greeley pioneers, recalled in a 2003 interview: "After about 1890 . . . 1895, I can't tell you exactly, those pioneers that had come [to Greeley], they badly needed to have something that they could sell and get money for." The Union Colonists "had been self-[sustaining]." The first settlers, said Farr, "could raise and have enough to eat, and so forth, but couldn't make any [financial] progress."[1]

Thus, it fell to a new generation of civic leaders, at the beginning of the 20th century, to embrace the national trends of urbanization and industrialization known as "Progressivism." They would use the region's natural resources—in particular, water—to expand commerce and grow the population of Greeley.

POTATOES MAY HAVE been Weld County's signature crop, but sugar beets would soon demand the keen attention of both irrigators and the Greeley water department. Most citizens in the community of 3,000 still obtained their domestic water from artesian wells or from the Greeley Water Works built in 1889. Outdoor lawn and garden watering used a combination of untreated water from the Greeley Number 3 Ditch, supplemented by treated (and more expensive) water from the city's system.

Increased rail traffic through town also affected the amount of water needed, and transportation also fostered economic expansion. On March 19, 1901, the city council asked "that some means be employed to ascertain the number of locomotives watered at the railway standpipes daily."[2] Greeley's location, midway between Denver and Cheyenne on the Union Pacific Railroad, allowed trains to carry crops and livestock from Weld County throughout Colorado and the nation.

Greeley was now poised to become a larger, more regional city with agriculture as its signature characteristic. Therefore, a fortuitous event occurred on May 5, 1901, when a group calling itself the "Greeley board of trade" announced that the Greeley Sugar Company had raised $600,000 ($18 million in 2020 dollars) in pledges to build a four-story sugar beet processing plant. It would be located on 60 acres along the Union Pacific rail line on the east side of Greeley.

The *Greeley Tribune* printed a special edition announcing that "negotiations for a beet sugar factory had been completed," and that investors planned to open the new processing facility in time for the 1902 fall beet harvest. "The site for the factory had been secured," wrote the *Tribune*, "including water and right of way for side track." The factory would have a production capacity of 600-800 tons of sugar beets per day. Weld County farmers had been granted their wish—a market for their new cash crop—sugar beets, nicknamed "white gold."

Greeley's factory would be the third such plant opened in Colorado since 1899. Grand Junction was the first and Loveland the second community to welcome a sugar factory to their community. The *Fort Collins Weekly Courier* editorialized about their neighbor and competitor along the Cache la Poudre River: "All honor to Greeley's enterprising citizens."[3] W.D. Farr's observation (that the early Union Colonists needed to produce something they could sell, to make progress) had come true. This marked the beginning of food processing in the Greeley area. As the sugar factory building arose east of town, city leaders knew that water would become an essential feature for the success of the industrial plant and the community.

Establishment of the "Greeley Sugar Company" had surprised many, despite efforts since the days of Benjamin Eaton and Nathan Meeker to add sugar beets

Figure 4.1 In 1901, local businessmen and outside investors established the Greeley Sugar Company, and financed the construction of a beet sugar factory, which opened on October 30, 1902. It processed 600-800 tons of beets per day, and became the Great Western Sugar Company in 1905. The plant closed a century later in 2003 and was razed in 2007. City of Greeley Museums, Permanent Collection, 1983.48.0013.33.

to their agricultural portfolio. In 1871, Meeker had editorialized in the *Greeley Tribune* that "if [sugar] beet culture could be adapted to the Greeley area, real estate values would rise, the unoccupied farmlands would be settled, and the net wealth of the district would be enhanced." Meeker and David Boyd campaigned with federal officials and Union Colonists alike to try sugar beet cultivation, and the Colorado Agricultural College experimented with growing the crop. However, it would be left to the hard times of the late 1890s (when potato crops failed and Congress passed the Dingley Tariff Act in 1897 to place import tariffs on refined sugar) that sugar beet factories began to emerge in Colorado towns.[4]

News of the Greeley sugar facility meant more than jobs and celebrations of civic pride. On November 14, 1901, the *Greeley Tribune* editorialized that "until this year, Greeley has never had anything that resembled a boom." After the heady days of Union Colony settlement, said the editor, "the belief became fixed in the minds of the majority of residents that Greeley never would, in their time at least, become more than a city of 4,000 or 5,000 inhabitants." To many citizens,

"the prospect of getting a beet sugar factory has enlivened all branches of trade."
More people would move to town, leading the *Tribune* editor to prophesy, "It is
fair to suppose that the old timers' belief may be dispelled," and a community
of "8,000 to 10,000 inhabitants" (a tripling of the current population) would
materialize shortly.[5]

The successful promoter of the Greeley factory site was C.A. Granger, a
veteran of sugar plant construction in Utah and Michigan. Granger heralded the
"superior soil qualities" and "work ethic" he saw in Weld County and Greeley, its
county seat. Adding to the appeal of Granger's accolades was the *Greeley Tribune's*
endorsement that the irrigated acreage of the county was "not second to any
lands in the whole world." These were strong reasons for investors to sponsor
Granger's factory, but in exchange, the Greeley Sugar Company said it would need
"a [groundwater] well capable of producing 1.5 million gallons of water per day."

This alerted city officials immediately. Should the company also wish to
purchase city water, the volume would equal the entire daily output of filtered
well water produced by the Greeley Water Works plant. If the sugar company
drilled a well itself, pumping would surely impact not only the city's wells but
also those of its neighbors. The impact would be particularly acute during the
months of October through February when sugar beets were processed.[6]

The solution to Granger's water needs included three options: 1) delivery of
city water through a six-inch diameter water line, 2) utilizing the company's own
surface water supplies from the nearby Cache la Poudre River, and 3) drilling a
35-foot deep well on the sugar factory property. Upon completion of the factory
construction, proud city officials organized "Sugar Beet Day." On October 30,
1902, several thousand visitors joined Greeley residents to welcome the factory
to Greeley, and also the new facility in the nearby community of Eaton.

WITHIN A YEAR, the citizens of Greeley came to realize that their good
fortune had its limits, as they now supported a sugar factory and the new
residents who came to live and work there. Dan Tyler, author of *W.D. Farr:
Cowboy in the Boardroom*, noted that in 1902 two groundwater wells provided
all of Greeley's water, and required almost constant pumping to meet

increasing water demands. This was necessary since artesian well pressure had severely declined, and then the casing in the original Lincoln Park well collapsed in 1901.[7] These circumstances caused low water pressure problems for homes on the higher lands of the community and also for the upper floors of some downtown buildings.

Throughout the history of the Greeley Water Department, it is uncanny how the right person shows up at a key time to provide visionary leadership. Earlier in the 1870s, Benjamin Eaton volunteered to help the fledgling Union Colonists dig their first two irrigation ditches. Later, he was instrumental in organizing numerous irrigation projects in Weld and Larimer Counties, purchased scores of farms, and became the governor of Colorado in 1885, nicknamed the "farmer governor." Not universally admired for his entrepreneurial efforts in the new territory, Eaton was, however, held in high esteem as witnessed in 1904 when 500 people attended his funeral in Greeley, and the cortege to Linn Grove Cemetery extended for two miles. He was one of many key people in the early history of Greeley's water activities, in particular, related to initial irrigation efforts of the city and the region.

In 1901, Henry C. Watson became mayor and championed the development of a new Greeley water system. He was, like Benjamin Eaton, the right person, at the right place, at the right time. Watson was a trained wood worker, born and schooled in Lisbon, Ohio. He became a carriage trimmer and learned to shape, cut and fashion wood for horse carriages. When the Civil War broke out in 1861, Watson enlisted in the 19th Pennsylvania Infantry and later in the 6th Pennsylvania Cavalry of the Army of the Potomac, and served three years. After the war, on May 1, 1870, Watson arrived in Greeley with the first party of Union Colony settlers.[8]

Watson's association with water began immediately. He found work with an engineering corps to survey the Union Colony Canal Number 3 (a.k.a. "Greeley Number 3 Ditch"). Everyone soon realized, however, that design flaws limited the carrying capacity of the channel, and barely 200 acres were irrigated that first year. The ditch had to be enlarged/rebuilt three times during the early 1870s to correct grading issues and other problems. No doubt the future mayor of Greeley made a mental note of this engineering failure.[9]

Watson (the former carriage trimmer and wood worker) next ventured up the Cache la Poudre River to join a partnership to produce 100,000 feet of lumber for

Figure 4.2 Henry Corwin Watson (1840-
1921), Greeley's mayor from 1901-1905,
championed the development of a new
municipal water system. A Union Colonist,
he was among the first to plant potatoes in
Greeley, established the Greeley Mercantile
Company in 1886, and became the "father of
the potato marketing business." His diverse
skills and knowledge proved invaluable
as he recognized that an adequate water
supply would be essential for Greeley's
growth and success. City of Greeley
Museums, Permanent Collection, AI-5899.

track ties for the Denver Pacific Railway. Logs were floated downriver during the spring runoff to James Obenchain's sawmill at the mouth of the Poudre Canyon. Unfortunately, the partnership capsized and Watson lost his investment of $1,500 ($30,000 in 2020 dollars) in this short-lived venture. He left the area to look for other work, and in the summer of 1871 reappeared to survey and plat the town of Colorado Springs. From there, Watson made his way to Omaha, Nebraska, to work again as a carriage trimmer to replenish his finances by working with wood.

Watson returned to Greeley the following year and engaged in successful farming, business, and entrepreneurial ventures. In 1886, he organized the Greeley Mercantile Company at 7th Avenue and 7th Street, and also a warehouse in Lucerne. The business handled hay, grain, potatoes, and other produce, and he became the exclusive western agent for the horse-drawn Dowden potato digger machine, advertised as "built for four horses but strong enough for six." Henry Watson became known as the "father of the potato marketing business" in the area and he may have planted the first potato crop in Greeley.[10]

The Civil War veteran entered his first term as mayor of Greeley on April 16, 1901 (a little more than a year before the new sugar factory opened), and tackled the water demand crisis with vigor. In an August 20, 1907, article in the *Greeley Sun* entitled "Greeley's Water Works System," the reporter noted that Watson's first move was to organize an engineering corps to investigate the feasibility of securing water from the Big Thompson River near Loveland. Mayor Watson also appointed a "Water Committee," consisting of W.H. "Billy" Farr (W.D. Farr's grandfather), H.D. Parker and Chris Rugh, to investigate all aspects of obtaining mountain water. This included the legal process of purchasing and changing water rights, the design of diversion points, and determining the costs of a pipeline, storage reservoir, and repairs to the original Greeley Water Works.[11] These were far-sighted ideas that would shape the future of Greeley's water supply system.

For more technical advice, Mayor Watson invited back to town Charles P. Allen, who designed the 1889 system. The Denver Water Company's chief engineer explained what it would take to increase its existing capacity to two million gallons per day. Watson also sought a second opinion from Wynkoop Kierstad, a hydraulic engineer from Missouri and formerly superintendent of a Kansas City water works company.[12] The highly-regarded Kierstad (who had designed water works systems for about 100 communities across the country) learned that Mayor Watson and Ray Walters, a consulting engineer, "had gone carefully over the ground" in the Big Thompson Canyon, "even to carrying the chain" for measurement of distance. This allowed the mayor to know "every turn in the road" for a potential water pipeline to Greeley.

Kierstad's survey of the Big Thompson Canyon prompted him to recommend that "water from the mountains would be the best and, in the end, the cheapest and most satisfactory" source. Kierstad did not support increasing the supply through the present groundwater system, saying at best it was only stopping a leak.[13] He based this opinion upon the limited groundwater supplies in the area, and because of the water quality problems found with the existing well, drilled into the alluvial gravel bed of the Cache la Poudre River.

With Kierstad's counsel and his own observations, Mayor Watson informed the *Greeley Tribune* that it would cost the City about $175,000 (over $5 million in 2020) to build a conduit of "fir pipes, bound with steel" to the Big Thompson River west of Loveland. A wooden-stave conduit would cost about a third less than steel pipe, and seemed like a good option to the wood-savvy mayor. The porous material of the wood pipeline, however, created a variety of future maintenance problems.[14]

On September 16, 1902, (the first year of operation of the new Greeley Sugar

Factory) William H. Farr, H.D. Parker, and Chris Rugh delivered to the city council a report on their water supply findings. They agreed that "the increased use of water [for the sugar factory] makes it imperative that additional water be soon procured for our city." Farr and his colleagues determined that it would cost $20,000-$25,000 ($600,000-$750,000 in 2020 dollars) for "additional galleries to the [existing] well, some new machinery, and a new pipeline into the city." The committee warned councilors: "We doubt the wisdom of this expenditure unless no other water supply can be procured."

The committee believed that the City needed to purchase more surface water, not invest in more groundwater wells. A study of available river water rights, upstream of Greeley along the Big Thompson River, revealed that for $7,000 ($200,000 in 2020) the City might acquire seven cubic feet per second of Appropriation Number 1 on the Big Thompson River from William R. Adams, who utilized the Hillsboro Ditch for irrigation. Farr, Rugh, and Parker "believed this amount of water will be sufficient for the needs of the city for a long time to come."

A well-attended meeting of citizens endorsed the proposed plan, and a purchase option was secured on seven cubic feet per second (cfs) of river water from Adams. Proceedings were initiated in court to secure a transfer of the water right to the City. Complications soon arose, however, and the matter was placed in the hands of the court's referee. Given the weakness of its case, Greeley decided to not purchase the Adams water.[15]

On September 25, 1902, to "assist" the city council in its deliberations, the *Greeley Tribune* printed an extensive article entitled, "MUST HAVE WATER." The editor reminded readers that, between four and six o'clock each afternoon, treated water in the standpipe at Inspiration Hill "would be emptied by rate payers on their lawns, shrubbery and streets." Often, it would be midnight before the standpipe refilled. More water was needed now, and city officials explained to the *Tribune* that "purer and softer water" could be obtained from the mountains to help supplement existing groundwater supplies.

Greeley's interest in securing high mountain water caught the attention of an electrical investment company in Fort Collins. On December 8, 1902, a small group met with Greeley Mayor Henry Watson and the City's water committee "between trains" to discuss the potential of piping water from the Cache la Poudre River Canyon to Greeley.[16] The meeting was later reported on the front page of the *Greeley Tribune*.[17] Over the next few years a potential partnership with the City of Fort Collins was also explored. A decision had to be made: Should a new water pipeline be constructed from the Big Thompson River west of Loveland, or from the Cache la Poudre River northwest of Fort Collins? In either case, Greeley officials looked to the nearby Rocky Mountains and its cache of water for their future water supply. It would be a view that would dominate the outlook of Greeley water managers for the next 100 years.

EVENTS ACCELERATED. IN October 1903, the Colorado and Southern (C&S) Railway petitioned the City for water for its locomotives. The City required that the C&S Railway, and also the Union Pacific Railroad, install water meters at their rail yards to calculate water usage. For its part, the City charged each company 20 cents per 1,000 gallons. The water business had grown more complex, as collecting this money and other fees had become problematic for the water department. In response, the city council provided the water office with an assistant whose primary task was "looking after the water business." In 1904, the City's largest account was with the State Normal School, today the University of Northern Colorado, which was billed $1,000 annually (about $28,000 in 2020 dollars) and obtained water from the tank atop Normal Hill.[18]

More water was needed, and soon. As city officials sought potential sellers of mountain water, council members learned in August 1904 that Mrs. Nettie C. Poore claimed to have "certain lakes and reservoirs" she wished to sell along the Cache la Poudre River. Mayor Watson and Councilors Chris Rugh and C.C. Thompson traveled up the Poudre Canyon to inspect her "Mitchell Lakes." They came away "very favorably impressed with the proposition," according to council minutes, and "would recommend that the matter be referred to a committee to further investigate." By early October, however, the council had to report that "Mrs. Poore did not have the water appropriations as represented." The committee then pursued an offer from W.R. Dedricks, who said he owned "mountain water 1/3 feet from the old Routt Ditch," a proposition that also proved fruitless.

The following month in November, the council noted in passing that its water committee had determined that an unidentified source of water "near Belleview" (likely "Bellvue" upstream of Fort Collins) was "not feasible." In December, two gentlemen named Edwards and Kissock approached Greeley officials with an offer to sell "25 cubic inches" of water from what they described as "Priority No. 1 Cache la Poudre River." Nothing came of the Edwards-Kissock inquiry, so in early February 1905 the water committee sought to locate a source of high mountain water that Greeley could afford.[19]

These unsuccessful offers of water rights provide insight into the art and science of obtaining water rights for a city. Quite often, developers and other water entrepreneurs suggest an intriguing package of water rights. Closer inspection reveals problems, discrepancies, and sometimes outright fraudulent claims that were "overlooked" or "covered over" by the prospective seller. Today, population growth along Colorado's Front Range in the 21st century has escalated the value of already-developed agricultural water rights that might be sold and transferred for other uses. Consequently, cities and other public water suppliers are intensely scrupulous about proposed "water deals" to ensure that they will survive the scrutiny of Colorado's water court process.

The water debate of the early 1900s in Greeley focused on the question of which river basin to utilize—the Cache la Poudre or the Big Thompson? Both had good quality water, and there were advantages of having water sources in two neighboring river basins. Both required pipelines to transport water from the respective river canyons. This selection process was not easy and brings to mind the challenges faced by Nathan Meeker and his land committee, when they first visited the Colorado Territory in 1870, to select the Union Colony location 35 years earlier.

The water debate continued, and into this deliberation breach stepped Burton D. Sanborn, longtime champion of northern Colorado irrigation projects. Sanborn, identified in the *Greeley Tribune* as "the best authority on reservoir matters in this section, and probably in the entire state," had undertaken what the *Tribune* called "a plan of exchange, with reservoirs on the Thompson [River] similar to the Fossil Creek exchange [on the Poudre River]." Sanborn had watched with interest Greeley's unsuccessful efforts to purchase the Big Thompson River water rights of William Adams. "Because of adverse court decisions in this matter," said the *Tribune*, "the original plan was dropped and the Poudre river looked to as the only source of a supply."[20]

Sanborn continued to pitch Big Thompson water rights which he owned. Like many others in the community, Sanborn was born back East (in Vermont) and was a child when he came with his parents, original members of the Union Colony, to Greeley. Sanborn's parents are credited with being among the first to pitch a tent in the new settlement. He later served as secretary of the Colony and organized the North Poudre Irrigation Company, Fossil Creek Reservoir near Fort Collins, and Boyd Lake near Loveland. Aware of the challenges that a new bond issue posed to Greeley's ratepayers, Sanborn reminded his peers that "not alone will the shorter distance to the canon of the Thompson make the cost of constructing the pipe line approximately $100,000 less than to build to the Poudre canon."

Another factor for Greeley's consideration, Sanborn told the *Tribune*, was that "the water of the Thompson [River] is said to be fully as good as the quality as that of the Poudre." Boyd Lake, the off-channel reservoir developed by Sanborn and located near the Big Thompson River, "could be made to hold a supply sufficient for the city for twenty years, without refilling." Sanborn disclosed that it "is not the intention of giving this storage water direct to the city." He meant "simply to take the nice soft water that comes out of the [Big Thompson] canon and pipe it to Greeley, giving an equal amount of reservoir water to the ditches below."[21] It was a sound plan, if shadowed by his own self-interest. Sanborn stood to reap a tidy profit if Greeley bought into his Boyd Lake system.

Negotiations continued, but then stalled. On February 23, 1905, Mayor Watson published an open letter in the *Tribune*, telling the citizenry: "During the past two years the city council has been endeavoring to procure additional water and mountain water from the Thompson river." For a variety of reasons, those efforts had failed, said the Mayor, and "we are now compelled to look to the Cache la Poudre river for a supply of mountain water if we can obtain it."[22] Despite the efforts of Burton Sanborn, Greeley was not willing or ready to pursue a new water system on the Big Thompson River. That would have to wait several decades until the late 1950s, when "Billy" Farr's grandson, W.D. Farr, would lead the effort to bring Big Thompson and Boyd Lake water to Greeley.

Greeley's Mayor Watson hoped to convince voters of the inevitability of a new high mountain system and its high cost. The alternative was to convey more well water to town via the existing groundwater pumping facility, said Watson, but "the supply cannot be increased without the expenditure of a large sum of money for new galleries, an addition of a new boiler, necessitating an addition to the pump house, and the laying of a new supply pipe from the well or at least the center of town." This option, the least expensive, would cost ratepayers $30,000 (about $875,000 in 2020 dollars), but "at the present rate of growth these additional appliances will not be sufficient for more than five years."

More likely, said the mayor, Greeley would have to follow the lead of Fort Collins. Through a $123,000 pipeline ($3.5 million in 2020), that city "has obtained a very satisfactory supply of clear soft water" from the Cache la Poudre River. Watson also noted that "the term of office of the present council is soon to expire." It would be more prudent, he wrote, "not to undertake any new work upon the old plant or incur any expense in relation to a new system." Instead, on February 28, 1905, the council adopted an ordinance for the "qualified electors of said city, who are taxpayers under the law, the question of the construction of new and additional water works." The City estimated that such a project on the Cache la Poudre River would cost $250,000 ($7.3 million in 2020 dollars), funded from bonds sold at a five percent premium, "payable in not to exceed fifteen years."[23]

Now a new opportunity presented itself. On June 7, 1905, the *Fort Collins Weekly Courier* editorialized that "a worse fate might befall Fort Collins than to let Greeley in on our splendid water works system." Said the editor: "The pipe from the mouth of the [Poudre] canon to the head works is said to be big enough to furnish water for several towns the size of Fort Collins." The latter "would not be deprived of an adequate supply if Greeley should be allowed to tap the line." In other words, the two cities stood to gain much if they shared the existing water pipeline and water works developed by the City of Fort Collins on the Cache la Poudre's North Fork.

An added benefit for Fort Collins, said the *Courier*, was that "Greeley would then have to help pay the expense of keeping up the line and of putting in a large pipe should it be needed in the future." A Greeley-Fort Collins water partnership might also mean that "the two cities could combine their resources and construct a scientific filter at the head of the works." From this alliance, said the *Courier,* "both would have a supply of absolutely pure water." Greeley then would realize "why Fort Collins people bless the day that the change was made from the old to the new [water] system." Fort Collins would share with its neighbor "a water system and a water supply, which for quality and quantity, is not surpassed by any city of the same size in the entire Rocky Mountain country."[24]

The idea of regionalism and cooperation was intriguing for the two municipal water systems. Despite the generosity of the City of Fort Collins, the citizens of Greeley preferred to develop their own water system on the Cache la Poudre River. The offer was ultimately declined, and one month later, surveyors for Greeley returned from the Poudre Canyon with samples of water taken from several locations. They gave these to Professor J.C. Abbott of the State Normal School for testing, which he concluded were of good quality.[25]

On November 28, 1905, it was with much satisfaction that the Greeley City Council adopted Ordinance Number 141. It called for an election the following month, on December 26th, at which eligible voters would be asked to bond themselves for up to $350,000 ($10 million today, or about $2,000 per person in 2020 dollars) for "the purpose of supplying to said city and its citizens sufficient water from the Cache la Poudre river by means of a suitable and proper gravity system." This new facility would replace the old sand infiltration system located at 14th Avenue and A Street. While voter turnout was quite modest for a city of 5,000 people, the Christmas spirit prevailed as the measure received 370 votes in favor, and only 13 opposed.

The new facility would be called the Bellvue Water Treatment Plant and would become the centerpiece of Greeley's potable water program for the next century and beyond. Council members met within days of the 1905 election to authorize solicitation of bids for construction and to investigate the sale of bonds. Attorneys for the City of Greeley approached landowners along the proposed pipeline route in Larimer and Weld Counties, with the first such right-of-way agreement reached between the Greeley Water Department and the Larimer County Commissioners.[26] In February 1906, with guarantees of money in hand, the Greeley City Council opened bids for construction of the new project at Bellvue. The Jackson-Bade Company of Portland, Oregon, outbid the Denver firm of Gaffey and Keefe, with the former estimating a cost of $323,689.82 for their work.

The *Greeley Tribune* reminded its readers of the scale and scope of their new water facility, including "the storage reservoir on the Insinger place just south-west of the city" (the present-day site at the northwest corner of 23rd Avenue and Reservoir Road). The pipeline, which began at the Bellvue plant located near the mouth of the Poudre Canyon, could carry up to five million gallons of filtered water per day. The *Tribune* considered this "sufficient water for a city of 15,000 inhabitants, thus providing an ample supply for many, many years to come."[27]

Next, the City needed a reliable water right and a location for the new water treatment plant along the Cache la Poudre River. Greeley had already purchased a farm that included Whedbee Ditch water which had an August 1, 1862, water right. It was the Number 6 ½ priority water right (a peculiar number for a water right which will be explained later) on the Cache la Poudre River. On September 30, 1907, the Larimer County District Court ratified Greeley's purchase of the Whedbee Ditch No. 1 (named for one of the first settlers of Pleasant Valley) some eight miles northwest of downtown Fort Collins. The City now had a secure water right and an excellent irrigated farm site for its new water treatment plant. The 1905 bond election was a defining moment in the history of Greeley Water, setting the stage for future water development into the next century and beyond.

FOR ITS FIRST 35 years, Greeley had depended on groundwater wells and streamflow from the Cache la Poudre River for its drinking water. In 1906, with a high quality water source available from the Whedbee Ditch and with voter approval, the Greeley City Council approved the next steps to pipe waters of the Cache la Poudre to Greeley. Denver engineering consultant George Anderson advised the city council to "construct a 20-inch pipe line from the mouth of the [Poudre] canon, a distance of about 38 miles, to connect with the present water mains in the city." The Denver consultant further reported that "a reservoir or sedimentation basin and filter basin be constructed near the head of the pipe line, and also a storage basin near Greeley;" all of this to cost an estimated $319,856 ($9.1 million in 2020).

Anderson identified an intake point for the new treatment plant near the mouth of the Poudre Canyon, and drew plans for a pipe to carry water about 3,000 feet south to a 50 acre site (formerly the farm with the Whedbee Ditch water) where the sedimentation basin would be located. The latter could hold up to 26.5 million gallons of water, which Anderson considered "a supply for eighteen days at the present consumption."[28]

The City had also acquired 145 acres of land along the Cache la Poudre, a tract called the "Collmer and Jones" property, which included 4.5 cubic feet per second of water from the Pleasant Valley Canal. The Water Supply and Storage Company likewise sold Greeley six acres of land north of the river to construct the diversion dam and intake structure for the water treatment plant.

The new pipeline would be constructed of wood due to the high cost of cast iron. Denver had found success with this less expensive method of water delivery, and marketers of wood staves (narrow planks) shipped from the West Coast claimed it would last a generation, and at a much cheaper cost. Equally promising, said the *Greeley Tribune*, was the fact that "the right of way for the pipe line has been assured for practically the entire distance, and much below the estimated cost of Mr. Anderson, the project engineer." Still outstanding, the local paper noted, was "about 3,000 more feet of pipeline right of way to secure in Larimer county, and about two miles in Weld county, deals for which are underway."

In April 1906, the city council informed the citizenry that the nearby town of Windsor had adopted an ordinance "to lay the water pipes of the water works of the City of Greeley along certain streets of the Town of Windsor." Also offering access across its property for the pipeline was the Water Supply and Storage Company, the largest irrigation provider along the route. Smaller rights-of-way came in May 1906. In July, the Great Western Sugar Company granted an easement through its property in Windsor.

George J. Spear, owner of a farm west of Greeley, initially expressed opposition to the route. However, when the City authorized its attorney to pursue condemnation proceedings against Mr. Spear, he appeared before the council in March 1907 to change his stance. Spear told councilors that "he considered the right of way across the property to be of no damage to the property, and the only thing he had ever asked for was the overflow water."[29]

Not all property owners along the 38-mile route of the Greeley pipeline supported the project. In August 1906, a group of residents from the town of Laporte, located northwest of Fort Collins, filed suit in Larimer County District Court. Led by Dr. C.F. Wilkins and a dozen landowners, according to the *Fort Collins Weekly Courier*, they sought "an injunction restraining the City of Greeley from occupying the public highway in constructing a pipe line for that city's new water works system."

Greeley City Attorney Charles D. Todd "strongly combatted" this effort, reported the *Courier*, in which the plaintiffs "claimed title to one-half of the highway in front of their property." They also "demanded compensation for

Placing the Last Length of Pipe in Greeley's (Colo.) New Mountain Water System, August 24, 1907. This Pipe Line is 38 Miles Long, and Cost $350,000.

Published by Greeley Tribune.

Figure 4.3 On August 24, 1907, workers installed the last length of wooden stave pipe to complete the 38-mile pipeline from the Bellvue Water Treatment Plant to Greeley. The new mountain water system cost $350,000 ($9.5 million in 2020 dollars) and provided residents with high quality potable water, stored in City Reservoir No. 1 at 23rd Avenue and Reservoir Road. City of Greeley Museums, Permanent Collection, 1994.43.0096.

a right-of-way along the road passing through their property." Attorney Todd "pleaded the right to occupy the public highway for a public purpose." Greeley's legal representative further informed Judge Bennett of "the action of the county commissioners of Larimer county, granting the right to Greeley to lay its pipe line along and across all public highways in this county intersected by or lying parallel with the proposed pipe line."

The judge agreed with the City of Greeley, ruling that "the public highways are dedicated to the uses of the public and that the laying of a pipe line . . . was no infringement of the rights of owners of abutting property." The *Courier* noted that Bennett's decision had implications not only for Greeley, but also for communities in Larimer County. "If the petition of the applicants had been granted," the Fort Collins paper believed, "Greeley would have been put to great additional expense in constructing its water system by reason of having to purchase or condemn a right of way through highly improved and very valuable property."[30]

Interestingly, protests against the Greeley pipeline in this area of Laporte occurred again a century later. In 2011, the City requested the right to install a new 60-inch diameter water pipeline to carry treated water from the Bellvue plant to Greeley. Similar to 1906, Laporte residents filed a legal action to stop the pipeline installation. Their challenge proved unsuccessful, allowing completion of the new pipeline in 2017.

Returning to 1906, water users in Greeley anxiously awaited word on the progress of their new 20-inch wood-stave pipeline. In July, the *Tribune* took its readers inside the temporary "pipe factory," built north of downtown near the old water works plant. "From now on until the job is finished," reported the *Tribune*, "the plant will be busy night and day, with double shifts of men." The Jackson-Bade firm had subcontracted with the Seattle-based "Pacific Coast Pipe Company" to cut nearly 1.8 million feet of Oregon timber, which they shipped to Greeley by rail for assembly into the 46,000 sections that formed the 38-mile wooden conduit.

Work crews installed enough pipe each day to cover about one-half mile, starting at the nine acre site near Bellvue, where the sedimentation and filter basins were installed. This facility, the *Tribune* noted, could store up to 31 million gallons of water, guaranteeing that Greeley could have a 12-day supply, "even if there is not a drop of water run into basin from the river during that time." As an added benefit, wrote the *Tribune* reporter, "by this provision it will not be necessary to

Figure 4.4 Greeley's 1907 Bellvue Water Treatment Plant, located in Larimer County's Pleasant Valley, processed "mountain water" from the Cache la Poudre River in slow sand filtration beds, seen here. A distinctive anticline, the Bellvue Dome (a.k.a., "Bellvue Fold" and "Goat Hill") appears in the background. The river flows directly below the vertical cliff on the west side of the dome. City of Greeley Museums, Permanent Collection, Al-0959.

use the water from the river when it is muddy;" something that occurred sporadically with the older system that relied upon the flow of the Cache la Poudre at Greeley. The facility's size and double chambers also reduced operating costs by allowing the water treatment plant crews to clean the sand filters of one basin as they stored water in the other.[31]

Greeley's new water pipeline generated great interest from adjacent communities. Windsor could not afford the expense of its own water supply system, so its town leaders asked Greeley if they could tap into the pipeline that traversed their city. Greeley's City Council agreed, and at a rate of 25 percent more than was paid by Greeley residents, said the *Tribune*, "Windsor will get a fine supply of water with a very slight investment, except for rental [costs]." The arrangement benefitted Greeley, as the sale to its neighbor "may add materially to the gross income from the water works." Should Greeley find that it "cannot continue to furnish water to [Windsor]," it would give the town three months' notice "to allow Windsor to put its old pumping plant in operation again."[32] This lease was important because the *Greeley Tribune* stated a few years earlier (and many members of the community believed) that the new water facility needed to pay for itself.

On September 7, 1907, water flowed from the Bellvue plant for the first time, and was delivered to the Greeley municipal water system 38 miles away. City water mains and other distribution pipes were tested to purge the old lines of alkali and sediment, and to make way for the treated mountain water of the upper Cache la Poudre River. "There is no doubt about the softness of the water," wrote the *Tribune* editor, "as can easily be proved by the use of soap in the water," which lathered better because it contained fewer dissolved minerals. It had been a difficult process, but the new water source was transformational for the future of the city. The only issue that might arise, wrote the *Greeley Tribune* prophetically, was that "there are still a few leaks in joints in the pipeline but these are being tightened and are nothing serious."

The 1902 headline "MUST HAVE WATER" of the *Greeley Tribune* could now be replaced with the 1907 claim of "WE HAVE WATER!" To prove the merits of the new (and expensive) system to the city's ratepayers, the *Tribune* organized a train excursion to Bellvue. Some 200 passengers joined Mayor Frank J. Green (the crying baby upset by the swirling sands of the "Great American Desert" in 1870). The mayor and city council received "the first really clear idea that any of them had received of what the $350,000 [around $10 million in 2020] of the city's money was being spent for."

The train-excursion visitors agreed with the editor that "the whole thing has an air of solidity and permanence easily recognized by those familiar with storage reservoirs." Readers of the *Tribune* learned that "the facilities . . . are adequate for many years to come," and could look forward to a supply "as clear and sparkling as the water of any mountain stream."[33] In November 1907, George G. Anderson, the hydraulic engineer and construction manager from Denver, provided his final report for the project (which is preserved in the archives of the City of Greeley Museums).

Greeley's water leaders were imaginative forward thinkers, but also learned from the experiences of others. Lessons from the water system of New York City likely influenced the city's actions. David Soll, a historian of the New York City water system, wrote: "By the 1850s, two patterns that would define New York

City's approach to water supply for the next century had emerged: the city would seek pure water from far beyond its borders, and it would engage in a perpetual struggle to secure enough water to meet the demands of the metropolis." In 1837, New York City had ventured northward along the Hudson River to build the "Croton Aqueduct," a system with a large storage reservoir and a 41-mile pipeline to deliver clean and unpolluted water to a series of holding ponds and pumping stations within the city limits. Many of the Union Colonists had obtained water from this elaborate system when they lived in New York.

Seven decades later in 1907, Greeley's citizens constructed a 38-mile pipeline from the Cache la Poudre River to a series of holding ponds within its city limits. Greeley had also ventured toward the north (and west) to meet the growing demands of industry and its population growth for the next century. The Union Colonists carried the influences of New York City to Greeley, Colorado, and evoke interesting comparisons between their water systems.

SKILLED WATER LAWYERS have contributed significantly to Greeley's water legacy, and Delph Carpenter today remains the most widely known of a group that included Harry N. Haynes, Charles Tew, and William R. Kelly. However, their contributions occurred after Greeley contemporary, attorney Charles Todd, had secured the Whedbee Ditch water right which was the key source of water for the Bellvue Water Treatment Plant. Todd later obtained a change of location and use decree, from the Larimer County District Court, for "municipal, fire, irrigation and other purposes" for year-round use.

At the time, however, it was somewhat of a gamble for the Greeley City Council to proceed with construction at Bellvue before the Whedbee Ditch change of use decree was obtained. Todd fully believed he could deliver the decree, needed by the City, because his legal research convinced him that state laws would allow for the type of change of water right which he envisioned. As such, and relying on attorney Todd's recommendation, the city council proceeded to build the new water system, even before the court entered its decree.

Todd, the Greeley City Attorney who later served as mayor of Greeley (1917-1923), confidently navigated the complicated legal process. First, it was necessary to legally change the point of diversion of the Whedbee Ditch water right, from the intake of the irrigation ditch headgate on the Cache la Poudre River, to a new point of diversion some 3,000 feet upstream. In addition, the 7.5 cfs of Whedbee Ditch water, previously used for irrigation (during the April 15 to November 15 irrigation season), would need to be legally changed in the district court to a year-round domestic and sanitary use. In other words, much had to be approved by the court before Greeley could legally divert and use this water. Much was at risk. The Greeley City Council had already purchased the water right, and was constructing the infrastructure to divert, treat, and deliver the water, before it had made it through the legal process.

Attorney Charles Todd assured the city council that it could legally be done. He had closely studied Colorado's laws, which authorized and required the district court to consider whether a water right used for irrigation could be changed to municipal use. In 1891, Colorado's General Assembly had confirmed the authority of municipalities to "purchase water and water rights" and hold or sell *"the lands to which said water right is connected"* whether the land and water rights were within or outside municipal boundaries.[34] This provided a sound basis for Todd's legal opinion.

Todd's legal strategy also relied on an 1891 Colorado Supreme Court ruling that approved the City of Colorado Springs' purchase and change of location and use of an irrigation water right from lands the water right had historically irrigated, "so long as the rights of others, as in this case, are not injuriously affected thereby."[35] Also, in 1899, the state legislature passed a law that allowed cities to condemn *"so much private property as shall be necessary for the operation and construction"* of water works in accordance with applicable laws.[36]

Todd had analyzed another 1899 statute, whereby courts had authority to allow changes in points of water diversion as long as "such change will not injuriously affect the [water] rights of others."[37] In addition, in 1903 the Colorado Legislature had passed a law that allowed a water right to be changed in court for uses other than irrigation. Water use by a city is year-round, compared to an irrigated crop that only needs water generally from April to November.

The new law also allowed district courts to decree all water rights derived from *"any natural stream, water-course or any other source, acquired by appropriation and used for any beneficial purpose."*[38] This included *"power or manufacturing purposes, domestic use, storage purposes, or any other beneficial use of said waters."*[39] This law opened the legal doorway for water rights owners to claim the original dates for their appropriations, even if they had missed a prior opportunity for adjudication back in 1881. Thus, Greeley's petition for a changed water right for the Whedbee Ditch could be filed and decreed with its original appropriation date, provided no injury would occur to other downstream water rights.[40] Todd and the Greeley City Council were on solid legal ground with these laws in place.

Following a hearing where no other party asserted injury, Larimer County District Court Judge James R. Garrigues awarded Greeley a year-round decree for 7.5 cfs of water with an adjudication date of August 1, 1862, for their Whedbee Ditch water right. In October 1907 and with much relief, the city council joyously recorded in its minutes *"for all to see"* a Number 6 ½ priority awarded to the Whedbee Ditch water right for year-round use. The court slotted this priority right between the Number 6 priority of the Boyd and Freeman Ditch and the Number 7 priority of the Whitney Ditch—hence, the 6 ½ priority of the Whedbee Ditch on the Cache la Poudre River. Charles Todd had won a momentous decision for Greeley, and the sigh of relief of the Greeley City Council was probably heard all the way to the new sugar factory across town.

ON DECEMBER 17, 1907, the city council welcomed consulting engineer George Anderson's final report certifying the Bellvue pipeline's completion. That month the City also accepted the closing statement from Jackson and Bade on the Bellvue treatment plant construction project. The city council approved the operational procedures of the new water system, calling it the "Greeley Water Works." The water superintendent reported that "all reservoirs, sedimentation basins, filters, intake, pipe line, and all appliances connected therewith" were completed. The latter included "all water mains, taps, service pipes in streets, [and] fire hydrants." Greeley now had a full-fledged modern water system.

Lessons were learned from the operation of shallow groundwater wells along the Cache la Poudre River, and the importance of good water quality could not be over-emphasized. Given their commitment to the purest water the City could find, the city council declared in December 1907 that "it shall be unlawful for any person or corporation in any manner to pollute or contaminate the waters of the Cache la Poudre river or its tributaries for a distance of five miles above the intake of said water works." In that five-mile corridor, said the council resolution, no one could "have, keep or maintain at, along or near the banks of the Cache la Poudre river . . . any building, privy, pen, yard or corral for stock." The ordinance also gave the water superintendent authority to manage the city's sewer system, and to call upon plumbers to secure permits before installing fixtures, with a penalty not to exceed $25 (and the loss of one's operating license).[41]

That same month, the larger significance of Greeley's new water system became clear. A national construction trade journal, *The Engineering Record*, published an article in December 1907 entitled, "A Gravity Water System at Greeley, Colo." Authored by Denver consulting engineer George G. Anderson, *The Engineering Record* story examined the legal, scientific, financial, and engineering details of the water system on the Cache la Poudre River. Among its highlights were "the abundance and clarity of the streamflow". . . and the low bacteria counts during most of the year.

Then, as now, the journal reached a wide audience of public works professionals. Anderson reminded his national audience that "the value of a supply of this character to a community in the semi-arid region . . . is scarcely appreciated in sections of the country where water is plentiful, and quality of the supply is the chief consideration."[42] The engineering article underscored the wisdom of the City of Greeley to establish such an innovative water treatment plant at the mouth of the Poudre Canyon.

Greeley's water system benefited from the national importance of its place along the Front Range of the Rocky Mountains. In 1905, President Theodore Roosevelt issued a proclamation to protect the Laramie, Poudre, Thompson, and St. Vrain Rivers and the North Fork of the Colorado River within the Medicine Bow Forest Reserve.[43] President Herbert Hoover later issued an Executive Order on March 28, 1932, renaming the Colorado portions of this forest reservation, the "Roosevelt National Forest"[44] in honor of Theodore Roosevelt who created and protected these pristine areas of the state. When the City of Greeley obtained its 1907 water decree for diversion at the mouth of the Poudre Canyon, it had the benefit of federal watershed protection and a state water rights regime operating within the national forest and downstream. Today, Greeley's water supply includes water flowing from each of these sources.

IN MAY 1908, the *Fort Collins Courier* noted that several Greeley officials had come to town to thank them for their assistance with the rights-of-way for the new water pipeline. "In spite of the good-natured rivalry between Greeley and Fort Collins in the matter of hustle and growth," observed the hometown *Courier,* "the Fort Collins people are the right sort." The Greeley entourage echoed the sentiments of their city council "that the Fort Collins people had been very decent . . . all through the construction of the new Greeley water system." In particular, wrote the *Courier,* these local civic leaders "had often gone out of their way to help out the Greeley officials." Such cordiality extended a year later to plans of the Fort Collins Country Club to expand their facilities between Lindenmeier and Terry Lakes. "Water will be secured," said the *Courier,* "either by tapping the Greeley main [water line], which runs nearby, or by boring wells." The *Courier* noted that "good well water has been found on adjacent places," but the country club managers believed it "likely that, if permission can be secured from Greeley, water will be had from that source."[45]

As mentioned earlier, the new water pipeline drew attention from a variety of communities along its route, including Windsor and Timnath. In 1908, leaders from the Town of Timnath attended a Greeley City Council meeting to request water from the Bellvue pipeline. Timnath had the support of ". . . 25 to 30 probable users, had a fund subscribed and would like to make terms similar to those of the Town of Windsor." In exchange, Timnath would build 3,000 feet of connecting pipe to the Greeley water pipeline and would install several fire hydrants in town. That November, a group of eight Timnath residents returned to the council to ask for a one-year contract, with Greeley to charge them 20 cents per 1,000 gallons, an offer the Greeley City Council deemed satisfactory to recoup a portion of project costs.[46]

THE SEARCH FOR water for Greeley residents played out in an unusual way at the end of 1908. The German-Russians of Greeley, who perhaps symbolized the best qualities of the Progressive generation, needed water for their homes. The *Greeley Tribune* noted that the east Greeley newcomers had been working in the beet fields during the summer and fall. Once they moved into town for the winter, however, they needed a better source of indoor water and so started to drill wells.

Water Superintendent Jesse Nolin informed the German-Russian community "that these [wells] would not go [be legal] under the city ordinances." When they asked what could be done, Nolin advised them "to petition for city water." The city council approved their request, but the water works staff would not be able to start construction of water pipelines to their homes until financial conditions improved. This was not the answer they wanted to hear, so next the residents of the area of 10th Street in east Greeley invited Water Superintendent Nolin to come to their neighborhood to discuss their petition for piped water to their homes. Once there, said the *Tribune*, the superintendent "found the entire population willing to get on the job." They "asked for the privilege of working out some of the assessments that would accrue with the laying of the main." Superintendent Nolin saw this as a way for the city to expand its water system, while the users would eliminate service fees through their own labor.[47] It would be a win-win situation.

Since the onset of winter would affect the completion date of the 10th Street project (located east of 3rd Avenue), the German-Russian community mobilized to expedite its completion. "Women laying water mains in the streets of Greeley," reported the *Tribune* that December, "is one of the unique sights witnessed within the past two days on the east side." The *Tribune* remarked approvingly that "the job was finished in record time," as "women, as well as the men, grabbed picks and shovels and worked day and night at digging the big trench." Just as they would do in the sugar beet fields, said the *Tribune*, "the kids carried water and tea while their parents worked with feverish energy." Neither did "the coming of darkness . . . deter the enthusiasts who swung their picks and shovels far into the night."

Once the trench for the water main was excavated, said the *Tribune*, "the willing workers started on the [smaller] trenches necessary to make connections with their homes." More often than not, "the women alone handled the heavy tools." City officials informed the *Tribune* that "the east side has made a new record in getting water into the homes." The residents "did the work in a satisfactory manner to the city," all the while earning "a portion of their additional taxes by the process." The *Tribune* took note: "So far as known the women are the first in any city in Colorado to dig trenches for city water mains."[48]

THE EARLY 20ᵀᴴ century were years of maturation for the next generation of Union Colony descendants and immigrants as witnessed by the variety of completed water projects—large and small. The community of Greeley, Colorado, was in an enviable condition—water rights were now secure and water treatment was ongoing to protect the health of citizens. Thoughtful leaders were contemplating the next phase of development for both industrial growth and population expansion. All looked bright for the prospering city. As Greeley and its water leaders continued to look west to the Rocky Mountains for their cache of water, however, a looming world war would usher in the second decade of the 20th century.

CHAPTER FIVE

1910-1930

The Greeley Water System Matures

ON APRIL 4, 1910, attorney Charles F. Tew stood before the Greeley Commercial Club to promote a new phase of economic development for Greeley and the Cache la Poudre Valley. Tew praised his peers for their farsightedness and encouraged them to invest in the recently formed Greeley-Poudre Irrigation District. He described this as a planned network of irrigation canals, reservoirs, ditches and farms that would extend from the Cache la Poudre River northwest of Greeley to Nunn and the Crow Creek Valley to the east, a distance of over 40 miles. The new district was the vision of the "Empire Builder," Daniel A. Camfield, who wished to irrigate 110,000 acres of dryland in Weld County that would rival the Greeley area's renowned irrigated fields.

Tew had partnered with Camfield, owner of the Camfield Hotel and president of City National Bank in Greeley, to promote this farsighted land and water development venture. The opportunity was created by the Enlarged Homestead Act of 1909, which encouraged new homesteaders to settle in Colorado, with promises of farms and better lives. Tew declared that delivery of Laramie River water would make Greeley the center of the greatest irrigated "empire" in the West.[1] New towns and railroad branch lines were platted in Weld County during this era, all in support of agricultural expansion made possible by new sources of water. Tew and Camfield also hoped to benefit from this new opportunity.

ON CHRISTMAS DAY, 1909, three months before Tew's address to the Greeley Commercial Club, construction work had begun on a two-mile-long tunnel

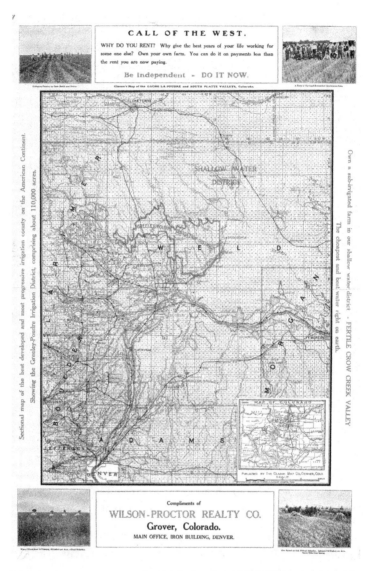

Figure 5.1 Irrigation entrepreneur Daniel A. Camfield (1841-1914) hoped that his 1909 Greeley-Poudre Irrigation District, outlined at the center of this map, would transform 110,000 acres of dryland prairie located north and east of Greeley into a prosperous irrigated region. Above average rainfall and promotional promises by realtors proved fruitless, however, when the project lost a landmark court battle over the appropriation of Laramie River water. Drought returned in the 1930s, sealing the project's fate. Image courtesy of Gregory J. Hobbs, Jr., private collection.

to transport water from the Laramie River Basin to the Cache la Poudre River.[2] The attorney for the project was Delph Carpenter of Greeley, who by then had spent the first year of his term as a state senator from Weld County. As this was a part-time position, Carpenter maintained his Greeley law practice and added the Greeley-Poudre Irrigation District to his client portfolio, which he had helped form in October 1909. Carpenter served both Colorado and this new irrigation project in what became a decade-long battle with the State of Wyoming over the amount of water that Colorado could appropriate from the Laramie River. Out of the ashes of a 1922 U.S. Supreme Court decision, which favored the claims of Wyoming, would emerge the concept of interstate water agreements.

In his first Colorado General Assembly session, Carpenter sponsored Senate Resolution No. 16, which called for a special committee to investigate the administration of Colorado's rivers and streams.[3] Interstate water sharing and management would become Carpenter's forté and singular devotion, and Colorado's foremost contribution to western states and U.S. water law, though not as he originally anticipated. Carpenter learned, through bitter experience with lawsuits in the U.S. Supreme Court, the practical necessity of creating equitable water treaties with neighboring states.

Initially, he had championed Colorado's sovereign ownership of all waters originating within its borders. As the headwaters state, Carpenter argued, Colorado should have the paramount right to divert whatever amount of water it needed from a river, and the state's prior appropriation water law would determine how those water rights would be established. Throughout his one legislative term (1909 to 1912), Carpenter questioned how Colorado could meet its future water needs. While the Laramie River appeared to offer a good water source for Weld County, if he could win the legal battle with Wyoming, Carpenter also believed that the Colorado River would be the state's best long-term water supply. He also expected there would be ample amounts of water, for both the Western and the Eastern Slopes of Colorado, from the state's namesake river.

In 1911, Carpenter wrote an editorial for the *Denver Republican* telling readers that "there is nothing in the law of Colorado—the only law by which the matter can be determined—which prohibits diversion [of water] for beneficial use from the Western to the Eastern slope."[4] Carpenter dismissed as "absurd" the

Figure 5.2 Delphus "Delph" Carpenter (1877-1951). Born and raised in Greeley, Delph was an 1899 graduate of the University of Denver Law School. His one term (1909-1912) as the first native-born person elected to the Colorado State Senate, launched his stellar career as a nationally known water attorney. Heralded as the "Father of the Colorado River Compact" and the "Water Oracle of Greeley," his forte was the development of interstate compacts to provide equitable distribution of water from river basins throughout the American West. City of Greeley Museums, Hazel E. Johnson Collection, 1991.42.0550A.

idea that irrigation would be interfered with near Grand Junction if Colorado River water was diverted to the Front Range through a tunnel. Carpenter told readers of the *Denver Republican*: "On the Western slope there is more water than it is practicable to use." By comparison, "on the Eastern slope the area of land to be irrigated is greater than the available supply of Eastern slope water." The Front Range of Colorado simply needed more water. Even today, more than 85 percent of Colorado's water arises on the Western Slope of the Continental Divide, while more than 85 percent of the people live on the Eastern Slope. The inherent opportunities to use Colorado River water created perennial conflicts that reverberated from its headwaters in Rocky Mountain National Park all the way down river into Mexico.

In July 1911, as destiny would dictate, completion of the two-mile-long Laramie River tunnel sparked both a celebration and a crisis. Gathered at the tunnel's outlet into the Cache la Poudre River, construction workers and honored guests were not exuberant. Just two months earlier, Wyoming had filed a "Bill of Complaint in Equity" before the U.S. Supreme Court to block diversions through the tunnel. Wyoming named as defendants the State of Colorado, the Greeley-Poudre Irrigation District, and the Laramie Poudre Reservoirs and Irrigation Company.[5] Wyoming claimed that it had a downstream prior appropriation water right superior to that of the Greeley-Poudre District.[6] Carpenter sought to protect the interests of his clients and others in Colorado from these legal claims the best he could, and if necessary, find another way to safeguard Colorado's water interests.

THROUGHOUT 1912, WHILE Carpenter engaged in legal proceedings against Wyoming and also campaigned unsuccessfully for a second legislative term, Greeley's local officials watched as urban water consumption increased. This trend placed greater demands on a system designed for a smaller population, but which now provided water to surrounding communities to generate revenues. The Great Western Sugar Company's Windsor plant, for example, needed more water. At peak demand that summer, unfortunately, Greeley's Bellvue pipeline ruptured near the B.H. Eaton Irrigation Ditch, south of Windsor. This forced Greeley residents to use poor quality groundwater wells, and to boil Greeley Number 3 Ditch water, for domestic use until the line was repaired.[7] Adequate water supplies were essential for Greeley residents, farmers and sugar factories, all of which contributed to the prosperity of the city and northern Colorado. As such, the Bellvue pipeline was being called upon to deliver more and more water.

In August 1913, the *Fort Collins Weekly Courier* published a story with the headline: "$30,000,000 (nearly $800 million in 2020) Sugar Beet Crop in Colorado This Year; Industry Has Made Farmers Richest in the World." Calling Great Western Sugar Company "a builder of greater Colorado," the Fort Collins paper declared: "No other industry among all the vast resources of Colorado has had the phenomenal growth, the extraordinary expansion, as has the sugar beet industry." Great Western and its peers had purchased the Greeley Sugar Company, and made Colorado the producer of "more beet sugar than any two other states combined."[8] Imagine the exuberance of local irrigators (and the pressure brought to bear on Delph Carpenter) to secure water from the Laramie River for irrigation of new lands proposed in northern Colorado.

Much as the economy had flourished in the days of the 1859 Gold Rush, and during the silver boom of the 1880s, Colorado's sugar beet production rewarded the worker as well as the grower and company investor. "The highest wages for this class of work in the world," said the *Weekly Courier*, "is paid in the Colorado beet fields." This, the Fort Collins paper believed, "virtually equals in value the gold that is taken annually from the Colorado mines."[9] All that was needed now was more water to expand sugar beet acreage.

IN 1908, JESSE Nolan became Greeley's first superintendent of the mountain water system, and was succeeded in 1912 by Robert Hall. In the spring of 1913, city employee Milton Seaman became superintendent of Greeley's water and sewer systems. His initiative and insights were invaluable in the development of the Greeley Water Department, and Seaman would become an icon of the City's water management efforts. Born and raised in Pennsylvania, Seaman came to Colorado in 1884 and worked as a teamster (drove horse-drawn supply wagons). His tenure with the City of Greeley began in 1898 when he was hired as street superintendent. Later, as superintendent of water and sewer operations for 27 years until his death in 1940, Seaman would earn praise as an innovator who helped make Greeley a modern city.[10]

In 1915, Seaman traveled back East to visit members of his family. Keen on sharpening his knowledge of the best practices in urban water utilities, he also visited the water departments of Kansas City, Chicago, St. Louis, Indianapolis, Pittsburgh, Washington, D.C., Baltimore, and Philadelphia. Upon his return, Seaman told a *Greeley Tribune* reporter: "Greeley people are exceptionally fortunate in the quality of their water and the character of their climate." He observed that Greeley's sand-filtering system was excellent, better than any he had seen in the East.[11]

Figure 5.3 Milton Seaman (1861-1940) was superintendent of the Greeley Water Department from 1913 until his death. Here he inspects a badly deteriorated portion of the wooden stave transmission pipeline that brought water from the Bellvue treatment plant to the City's reservoirs at 23rd Avenue and Reservoir Road. Funding, inspecting, and repairing leaks in deteriorating sections of pipe were almost daily concerns for Seaman and his staff. City of Greeley Museums, Hazel E. Johnson Collection, 1991.42.1204J.

Like Delph Carpenter, Milton Seaman would become a Greeley water legend. In 1940, the city's dam and reservoir on the North Fork of the Cache la Poudre River would be named for him; a fitting tribute from his peers for his commitment to public service. Seaman would establish an enduring tone for water management excellence.

With the *Wyoming v. Colorado* case in litigation, Seaman tackled repairs to the chronically leaking Bellvue water pipeline. Art Bolenbaugh, superintendent of the Greeley Water Department from 1948 until his retirement in 1958, began his career in 1913 as a construction foreman in the department, and served under

Milton Seaman. Bolenbaugh's first task was to replace 4-inch cast iron pipes in downtown Greeley with new 6-inch to 12-inch water mains. He also patrolled the 38 miles of the wooden Bellvue pipeline, inspecting it for leaks. To do this, Bolenbaugh rode a passenger train from Greeley to Fort Collins, then hiked to the head of the line at Bellvue. Beginning there, Bolenbaugh fixed leaks (sometimes 30 per day) as he walked along the pipeline. At Timnath, he caught the evening train back to Greeley. The next morning, Bolenbaugh would ride the train to Windsor, once again inspecting the pipeline and fixing leaks from Windsor to the city water reservoirs in Greeley.[12]

THE CITY'S WATER supply was a boom to the regional agricultural economy as European war clouds contributed to high sugar prices and other wartime crop production in Colorado. Gerald Nash wrote that the value of farms in the American West nearly doubled during the decade. Colorado wheat farmers, in particular, saw their prices triple in the years 1913-1919, along with increased prices for cattle and sugar beets. Municipal water was necessary to process these commodities and also to serve the growing workforce of the community.

Greeley's local economy remained strong until the winter of 1918-1919. Termination of wartime government contracts caught most western farmers by surprise, and an economic downturn followed. Historians Richard W. Etulain and Michael P. Malone reported that the total number of American farmers had peaked in the midst of the First World War. "The rural West," said Etulain and Malone, "had never known such prosperity before." Then "from 1919 through 1921, U.S. farm prices fell by 40 percent, and the boom descended into a deep agricultural depression."[13]

Two other pressing matters affected Greeley's water planning as World War I drew to a close. First, it became apparent that the City could no longer operate its sewer system by the old method of extending lines when household and commercial users offered to pay for the service. And second, in order to accommodate future growth, the City would need to either purchase or construct high mountain reservoirs in the Cache la Poudre River Basin. Some of these reservoirs might store Laramie River water which was currently flowing into Wyoming. However, the litigation with Wyoming in the U.S. Supreme Court created much uncertainty.

In June 1919, the *Greeley Tribune* reported that "the air at the Commercial Club meeting Monday night fairly vibrated with new ideas to boost Greeley." Vernon McKelvey, Secretary of the Colorado State Teachers College, told his audience that "the United States reclamation service should be induced to build a huge storage reservoir somewhere in the foot hills of Colorado to put the water supply of all the big irrigation ditches on a more certain basis." The *Tribune* reminded its readers that the paper had advocated a similar plan in 1914 "to be used as the balance wheel between wet and dry seasons . . . at that time the country was not suffering from drouth [sic] and the proposal did not attract much attention."[14] The call for high mountain reservoirs now received much needed consideration.

THE HOT SUMMER of 1919 once more prompted city officials to expand the holding basins for treated water on the west side of town. Superintendent Seaman told the city council that Greeley consumed four million gallons of water daily, which "equals the maximum capacity of the [Bellvue] pipe line." His visits to larger urban centers had influenced his opinions, and Seaman warned the city's councilors: "if Greeley stops growing now the present system will [still] be inadequate." Were the city to expand "as she has always done," said the superintendent, "it will mean a second pipe line [to the Bellvue treatment plant]." Seaman cited immense strain upon the four-inch pipelines that carried water throughout town. The pipes "were ample when they were installed 30 years ago." By 1919, however, "they are serving the largest possible city for their size."[15]

Seaman's visionary thinking paralleled the actions of the early Union Colonists; in building the Greeley Number 3 Ditch, purchasing the Whedbee Ditch water rights, and constructing the Bellvue Water Treatment Plant a decade earlier. Operation of the sugar factory now extended and prolonged the water demand season. *Tribune* readers learned on August 29, 1919, that a group of four local businessmen had drafted plans for a 46,000 acre-foot storage reservoir to be located immediately downstream of the Bellvue Waterworks and near the mouth of the Cache la Poudre River Canyon. Harry (Billy) Farr, William Kelly, Donald F. McCreery, and W.O. Roberts called for building the "Bellvue Reservoir." It would fill from stormwater runoff and snowmelt in the Cache la Poudre Basin, and be able to store water from the Greeley Number 2, the Larimer and Weld Canal, and the Water Supply and Storage Company systems.

L.L. Stimson, chief engineer for Weld County, claimed that the proposed reservoir would be among the largest in Colorado. In 1910, Louis G. Carpenter (no relation to Delph Carpenter), a former State Engineer and head of the Department of Civil and Irrigation Engineering at Colorado Agricultural College in Fort Collins, estimated the average annual Cache la Poudre flow to be 120,000 acre-feet. Only half of that would be needed to fill the proposed Bellvue Reservoir. Mayor Charles Todd told the *Tribune*, "the Bellvue plan is a direct result of the past season's drought." With this facility available, the additional water "will more than double the present reservoir capacity" of all northern Colorado.[16] Despite enthusiastic support and promotion for the project, that reservoir was never built. However, the search and promotion of high mountain storage on the Cache la Poudre River continued.

"To Delph Carpenter: The Father of Interstate River Treaties—we offer a salute. Whenever water users have settled their differences over river flows without expensive and protracted litigation, they owe a debt of gratitude to the man whose efforts, more than those of any other individual, have pointed the way."

—Governor Ralph L. Carr
Address to the National Reclamation Association
Denver, Colorado, October 29, 1943

The failure to acquire additional reservoir storage at Bellvue paled in comparison to the devastating legal defeat Carpenter would face in 1922 in the U.S. Supreme Court. But this loss, like that of his one term Senate seat in the Colorado

Legislature, spurred him on to even greater achievements. That same year, his commitment to negotiating the seven-state Colorado River Compact prevailed, and the South Platte River Compact followed soon after. Both compacts contribute directly to the stability of Greeley's water supplies. Far beyond the city's borders, Carpenter's legacy would rest in the annals of United States legal history.

Carpenter's upbringing deserves notice. His parents, Leroy and Martha Bennett Carpenter, discovered they were suitable marriage partners via a lengthy exchange of personal letters sent between Greeley and Iowa, where Martha lived. These letters, carefully preserved today in the Colorado State University Water Resources Archive, underscore the personal values they practiced and taught to their children. Delph Carpenter's parents valued education, religion, family, friends, community and hard work.

Water, too, was in their thoughts and dreams even before marriage. In their courtship letters, they good-naturedly bantered about who would carry whom across the Union Colony irrigation ditches. Their union would produce a remarkable son who would share his parents' interest in water. Delph grew up along the Union Colony ditches, and "ran water" to irrigate his family's farm. As a high school student, he worked for the Greeley water department monitoring residents who failed to comply with lawn watering restrictions. Carpenter later became the state's leading water expert—the "Greeley Oracle of Water" some would call him.

Carpenter, an 1896 graduate of Greeley High School, received his law degree from the University of Denver in 1899 and returned to Greeley to establish his law practice. On June 5, 1901, he married Ann (Dot) Hogarty, likewise a first generation descendent of Union Colonists, his classmate at Greeley High, and an 1898 graduate of the Colorado State Normal School majoring in music and teaching. They purchased a farm and ranch on Crow Creek east of Greeley that was irrigated by an extension of the Union Colony Ditch No. 2 (now called the New Cache la Poudre Irrigating Company). Daughter Michaela was born in 1902; Donald, the future Weld County and Water Court Division No.1 Judge, in 1907; Sarah in 1909, and Martha Patricia in 1914.[17]

Carpenter was Colorado's first native-born state senator, but lost his re-election bid in the fall of 1912. However, he was universally trusted for his dedication to Colorado and its water law. Soon after his re-election defeat, Colorado's Governor appointed him as the interstate stream commissioner for the state. In quick succession, Carpenter defended Colorado at the U.S. Supreme Court in lawsuits involving the State of Wyoming, for its claim of Laramie River water; Nebraska's claim for South Platte River water; and Nebraska's claims on the Republican River. This incomparable exposure to interstate and federal water conflicts placed Carpenter squarely in the eye of an intense water law and policy firestorm.

First and foremost, Carpenter believed that the State of Colorado owned, controlled and could use all water arising within its boundaries. The State of Wyoming lawsuit over the Laramie-Poudre Tunnel diversion project, however, began to unravel this legal concept and created uncertainty for Colorado and the City of Greeley's future water supply planning. Wyoming pulled the first big string out of the legal ball when it took on Carpenter's client, the Greeley-Poudre Irrigation District. Carpenter faced incredible pressure to win this landmark case to deliver Laramie River water into the Cache la Poudre River and Weld County.

On January 8, 1913, Carpenter entered his appearance in the U.S. Supreme Court as counsel to the Greeley-Poudre Irrigation District, and filed an answer he prepared on behalf of the State of Colorado, the Greeley-Poudre District and the Laramie Poudre Reservoirs and Irrigation Company.[18] Carpenter contended that Colorado possessed "inherent sovereign power to divert from the section of the Laramie River within Colorado the entire run-off of said section for use within the State of Colorado." All waters within Colorado "are owned by it," are subject to "the right of appropriations thereof under her laws." Use of this water is "to no extent affected by, or subject to, the laws of any other sovereignty than the state of Colorado."[19] He also asserted an August 25, 1902, appropriation right date in Colorado for the Laramie River Greeley-Poudre District diversions in the amount of 70,000 acre-feet of water, senior to the bulk of Wyoming's Laramie River uses.[20] The U.S. Supreme Court heard oral arguments three times in this case, indicating either their careful consideration of the facts and legal issues, a deadlock, or bewilderment about what to do.

Meanwhile, Carpenter was doing double-duty—defending the interests of the State of Colorado against Wyoming in Washington, D.C., while attempting to craft Colorado River Basin interstate water allocation compacts among six other western states (Wyoming, Utah, New Mexico, Nevada, Arizona, and California). Carpenter, the scholar and statesperson, now believed that the ultimate expression of a state's sovereignty (within the context of our federal Union) resided in joining with one or more other states to share, with Congressional assent, the waters of an interstate river system. He had been considering the possibility of compact negotiations for a decade.

In 1912, while still a member of Colorado's legislature, Carpenter wrote Senator Carl Hayden of Arizona and suggested invocation of the U.S. Constitution's Compact Clause to resolve interstate water disputes.[21] In a 1925 report, Michael Hinderlider (State Engineer of Colorado from 1923-1954) and R.I. Meeker (then Colorado's Deputy State Engineer) credited Carpenter for the interstate treaty idea as early as 1911 when, as counsel for the Greeley-Poudre District, he began work on the Wyoming case.[22]

Carpenter's foremost concern on the Colorado River was the looming threat of massive prior appropriation water use in the Imperial Valley of California. Substantial water rights had been appropriated in California to divert water from the Colorado River, some dating back to 1901, to the thirsty agricultural lands of southern California. What alarmed him most was the seniority of those water rights as compared to Colorado's future uses and rights. California was developing extensive infrastructure to divert Colorado River water. In 1911, the Imperial Water District issued bonds to construct the All-American Canal to transport water across the length and breadth of the southern part of the state. In addition, plans were being developed to build a massive flood control reservoir, on the mainstem of the Colorado River, upstream of the border with Mexico. Just as extensive water development on the Cache la Poudre River in the 1870s threatened the livelihood of Greeley, so too did the planned massive diversions of Colorado River water to California threaten the state of Colorado.

In 1920, the League of the Southwest convened a series of meetings promoting the Boulder Canyon Dam and the All-American Canal. Created in 1919, this powerful alliance lobbied hard for lower Colorado River Basin water development projects. The League was the brainchild of San Diego promoter Arnold Kruckman, who invited business and political leaders to join his efforts. Delph Carpenter perceived a gigantic powerplay developing from these alliances in California.

This civic promotion of water development in California echoed the speech of Charles Tew to the Greeley Commercial Club ten years earlier in 1910. Tew was a brilliant orator and litigator, and his speech focused on a different watershed, but the message was the same—divert a new source of irrigation water to an agriculturally productive area, and commerce would thrive. All that was needed was water. Arnold Kruckman in California and Charles Tew in Colorado were both setting the stage for great legal battles, over interstate waters, that were predicted by Delph Carpenter: "A suit between the States is but a substitute for war," Carpenter proclaimed. It should be "the last resort."[23]

This debate had the makings of a Hollywood-type movie, and Tew's wife, Elfie, did just that. In 1913, Elfie Tew created what was probably the first movie filmed in Greeley: "A Water War in Spudville," with a local producer, scenario writers, cast and crew, and advertised as "soon to be shown in a local moving picture theater." A *Greeley Tribune* reporter wrote, "There is something doing every second [in the movie]; there is love and combat running through the play with a happy wedding at the end of a strenuous day."[24] Movies sometimes mirror real life, and Delph Carpenter was likewise crafting and directing a first-time legal framework to create the marriage of interstate waters—with another happy ending at the end of many strenuous days . . . and years.

In May 1920, Congress authorized the U.S. Secretary of Interior to prepare a plan for Imperial Valley irrigation development, on public and private lands, in California. This was a grave warning for Colorado water interests. The League of the Southwest had been successful with its promotional efforts, and was prepared to use the Doctrine of Prior Appropriation (first in time, first in right) on the Colorado River to create downstream water rights superior (senior) to Colorado's junior upstream claims.[25]

One month later, at the League's June 1920 meeting in Denver, former Colorado State Engineer John Field called for the "telescope to be reversed" and upper river "problems and conditions studied close up." He singled out the transmountain Grand River Ditch in northern Colorado as an example of water that was needed for the fast growing Front Range. Colorado State Engineer A.J. McCune also rang the alarm bell. In an earlier League of the Southwest meeting, McCune had witnessed the Los Angeles Chamber of Commerce urging a halt to all development in the upper basin (Colorado, New Mexico, Utah and Wyoming) pending construction of the proposed Boulder Canyon Dam, today's Hoover Dam. This was a serious proposal largely opposed by upstream interests.

Carpenter absorbed this controversial information while he continued to challenge Wyoming in court over Laramie River water. His responsibilities to Colorado were dual—litigator and peace maker. In 1921, in a remarkable address to the Colorado Bar Association, Carpenter announced Colorado's commitment to forge as many interstate water allocation compacts as possible. The states should exhaust "interstate diplomacy," as a prerequisite for the U.S. Supreme Court granting "leave of one State to engage a sister state in the near equivalent of warfare."[26] It was vital to keep all of the strings tightly bound within the legal ball of interstate water law.

Again, the Colorado General Assembly rallied to Carpenter's leadership. On April 2, 1921, two months before the U.S. Supreme Court ruled in favor of Wyoming (the writing was already on the wall due to the prolonged time the court was taking to reach its decision), the Colorado Legislature passed a number of bills authorizing Colorado's river commissioner to help form and participate in compact commissions: Colorado and Kansas for the Arkansas River;[27] Colorado and Nebraska for the South Platte River;[28] Colorado and New Mexico for the La Plata River;[29] Colorado and Wyoming for the Laramie River;[30] and Colorado, Arizona, California, Nevada, New Mexico, Utah and Wyoming for the Colorado River with a duly authorized representative of the United States.[31]

In June 1921 (one month after Congress had authorized funds for the planning of the Imperial Valley irrigation system in California), Carpenter appeared before the U.S. House of Representatives Judiciary Committee to urge the creation of a Colorado River Compact Commission, comprised of appointees from the seven Colorado River Basin states, plus a federal representative. He also submitted an extensive written brief, regarding the Compact Clause and its historical invocation, to settle boundary disputes among eastern states. He advocated applying that clause to the apportionment of Colorado River water "to determine the respective rights of the states prior to any further large construction or extensive utilization of these waters."[32] Carpenter contrasted the two ways interstate river waters could be apportioned between states—by interstate compacts under Article I, section 10, paragraph 3 of the U.S. Constitution, or by a lawsuit between states before the U.S. Supreme Court.

Carpenter's arguments were heeded, and the Colorado River Compact Commission was formed in 1921 to examine available water supply, ultimate water demand, and the acres of land capable of being irrigated in each of the seven basin states, as well as in northern Mexico. A chart prepared by Ralph I. Meeker, Colorado's Deputy State Engineer, projected an "Origin Water Supply" of

Figure 5.4 Colorado is known as the "Headwaters State" and four major river basins—South Platte, Arkansas, Rio Grande and the Colorado—originate in its Rocky Mountains. The rivers flow into adjacent states, creating the need for cooperation and interstate compacts to ensure equitable water supplies from state-to-state, season-to-season, and year-to-year. This map shows the four Upper Basin and three Lower Basin States governed by the provisions of the 1922 Colorado River Compact. Map courtesy of U.S. Geological Survey.

20,943,000 acre-feet of water and an "Ultimate Water Requirement" of 20,339,000 acre-feet annually. Of this, the seven basin states would annually require a total of 16,139,000 acre-feet and Mexico 4,200,000 acre-feet. By state, California would require 4,926,000 acre-feet; Arizona 3,140,000 acre-feet; Nevada 283,000 acre-feet. Colorado would require 4,000,000 acre-feet; Utah 1,700,000 acre-feet; Wyoming 1,110,000 acre-feet; and New Mexico 980,000 acre-feet. Thus, the three lower basin states would require 8,349,000 acre-feet and the four upper basin states would require 7,790,000 acre-feet annually.

During its first eight deliberations in Washington, D.C., the Commission considered a revised set of tables based on Reclamation Service data projecting annual

Colorado River consumptive use requirements for the seven basin states and Mexico. This totaled 17,643,500 acre-feet of annual beneficial consumptive use.[33] Deducting Gila River flows (originating in New Mexico and Arizona) of about one million acre feet of water, the commissioners relied on recorded streamflow data for the years 1899 to 1920 to project an annual average mean of 16,400,000 acre-feet of water at Lees Ferry, Arizona. Inclusion of the year 1902 at 9,100,000 acre-feet of water demonstrated the commissioners' knowledge of extreme drought conditions in the Colorado River Basin. However, they could not agree upon a state-by-state division of water based on irrigated acreage. The negotiations needed a thoughtful continuation and a well-considered change of venue.

Carpenter counseled patience. "I know that to some members of this Commission, (which included its Chair, Secretary of Commerce Herbert Hoover, appointed by President Warren Harding), this seems to have been a fruitless conference. However, I am free to say—to me, this has been a very profitable conference and we are nearer a common accord than I expected when I arrived in Washington. I think it would be the height of crime to the people who sent us here to adjourn permanently now." Future U.S. President Hoover, who became a great friend to Carpenter in later years, agreed and suggested the commissioners continue to meet "someplace in the southwest."[34]

It took a total of 28 meetings (20 of which occurred at Bishop's Lodge in Santa Fé, New Mexico) to forge the 1922 Colorado River Compact—the first interstate water allocation compact in the country. Since the commissioners could not agree upon a specific quantity of water for each state, they instead allocated 7,500,000 acre-feet of beneficial consumptive use water annually to each of the Upper Basin States (Colorado, New Mexico, Utah and Wyoming) and to the Lower Basin States (Arizona, California and Nevada) with a provision for 75 million acre-feet of water to the Lower Basin on a 10-year running average at Lees Ferry, Arizona.[35] Creation of the Colorado River Compact in 1922 was critical to Carpenter's contingency plans for his other work in Colorado.

On June 5, 1922, the U.S. Supreme Court announced its *Wyoming v. Colorado* decision at the same time that Colorado River negotiations were proceeding. The court divided the water supply of the Laramie River largely in Wyoming's favor, and Colorado received only 39,750 acre-feet while Wyoming came away with 272,000 acre-feet annually. The court used prior appropriation rationale and dated the

Figure 5.5 Members of the Colorado River Commission stand behind U.S. Secretary of Commerce Herbert Hoover at the signing of the Colorado River Compact on November 24, 1922, at the Palace of the Governors in Santa Fé, New Mexico. Delph Carpenter is fourth from the left. Courtesy of Colorado State University Water Resources Archive, Delph Carpenter Papers.

Laramie-Poudre Tunnel's priority to be October 1909—the date when the Laramie-Poudre Irrigation District became a legal entity under Colorado law. Carpenter had argued in court for 70,000 acre-feet of Laramie River water as a minimum for his Colorado client. It was a significant blow to the project in Colorado.

Carpenter's emotions understandably ebbed and flowed. Five months after the brutal defeat in *Wyoming v. Colorado,* he confidently attended the signing ceremony for the Colorado River Compact on November 24, 1922, at the Palace of the Governors in Santa Fé. The Compact laid the foundation of interstate water distribution in the West, and ultimately led to the construction of Hoover Dam in the lower Colorado River Basin, and Glen Canyon Dam and Lake Powell in the upper basin. As Carpenter had hoped, Congress authorized the Colorado-Big Thompson Project in 1937 to divert Colorado River water for northern Colorado farms, cities and businesses, including Greeley. This son of Union Colonists proved himself to be one of the greatest of all water visionaries and statespersons, and ensured a vital supply of Colorado River water to Greeley and the Front Range of Colorado.

TWO YEARS EARLIER, in June 1920, E.V. Wilcox, a reporter for *The Country Gentleman*, visited Greeley, Colorado, as part of his magazine's series on the American farm economy. Wilcox's Philadelphia-based employer was considered a leading national source of information on current trends in agriculture. He had come West that summer hoping to find the "distinguishing characteristic" of "every [farming] community," and then identify "an atmosphere that was different." Within days of his arrival, Wilcox told his national audience: "You cannot wander about Weld County [of which Greeley is the county seat] very long without noticing a plan in the whole organization and development of the county."

The reporter knew from experience that many local people would be eager to provide him with "facts enough for an encyclopedia" about crop and livestock production. However, Wilcox was looking for something more profound. "I wanted the idea that runs like a red thread through all these details and determines the development of Greeley."[36] He sought a wise and authoritative person, a visionary, who could lead him to the core of the community's values and direction.

The red thread that linked Greeley and the Weld County community in the early 20th century was Delph Carpenter. Wilcox drove 15 miles northeast of Greeley to Carpenter's Crow Creek ranch where the former state senator, water attorney, and river compact collaborator was "branding calves and horn-marking the mothers." Not until 10:00 p.m. that night did Carpenter finish his chores. As Wilcox related, we "had a late supper and talked matters over far into the night."

The next day, "The Water Oracle of Greeley," as Wilcox described Carpenter, "motored with me over a good part of the Greeley country and explained what Greeley stands for."[37] Water, said Carpenter, was at the core of Greeley's values and achievements. He praised his neighbors and his predecessors, emphasizing their achievements. Fifty years after Nathan Meeker and his Union Colonists had stepped off the train on the windswept plains of Colorado, much had changed, yet much endured. "Greeley," wrote Wilcox, "is an idea, a philosophy of community life, including agriculture, home building, schools, civilization and religion."[38]

Undergirding these admirable traits were lessons learned by past, present and future irrigators and water managers. The reporter caught the "oracle" at the very time he was strategizing how to make peace with other southwestern states along the Colorado River. Carpenter was still smarting from the ongoing Laramie-Poudre water war. "In most irrigation districts," said Carpenter, "the farmers spend about one-third of their time irrigating and two-thirds fighting about water rights in court and out of courts."[39] Carpenter counseled a better way: make agreements with your neighbors and perceived enemies; whenever possible, avoid lawsuits. Through the years, Greeley and its water department have pursued these objectives.

Wilcox concluded his observations of the maturing Union Colony: "Irrigation missionaries have gone out from Greeley to every arid state to help water the desert." Even more impressive, concluded *The Country Gentleman* reporter: "Thousands of students of irrigation have gone to Greeley to learn how they do it there."[40] Greeley was on the national and international stage of water management and water law, receiving national media recognition as a leader in these fields.

FOR GREELEY RESIDENTS of the 1920s, the city's water system occupied much of their attention, serving also as a source of civic pride. While the community had not expanded dramatically as in the early 20th century, the "Roaring Twenties" decade presented a host of water issues and opportunities. System maintenance, replacement of aging infrastructure, and the search for more water rights were paramount. Throughout the decade, Superintendent Milton Seaman and his staff worked to address those concerns. They set goals to meet the needs and expectations of its residents with a 10-year plan appropriately called "Greater Greeley." Signs posted at the six main entrances into the city proclaimed, "Health, Wealth, and Mountain Water."[41]

Harvey D. Parker, a member of the State Board of Agriculture (1915-1923), called upon his Greeley neighbors to develop "a complete sewer system, an improved water system, park improvements, swimming pool, country club, and other accomplishments." Of these tasks, said Parker, a "Greater Greeley" would include a modern storm drain and sanitary sewer network. Heeding Greeley's 10-year plan and Parker's call, the Greeley City Council solicited proposals in early 1920 for "an adequate system of storm sewers, sanitary sewers and street drainage, adequate for the future requirements of Greeley." Parker, as a Ward

One councilor in 1901 and 1902, was a proponent of securing more "mountain water" for Greeley.

Burns and McDonnell, a team of consulting engineers from Kansas City, Missouri, were hired to review the city's water system. In addition, as the Greater Greeley effort would cost money, Seaman encouraged the city council to increase water rates for all users. He was on solid political footing with citizens, as the council also agreed to increase water rates for the Great Western Sugar Company factories in Windsor and Greeley.[42]

Perhaps one reason for the general public's acceptance of water rate increases was the community's belief in the high quality of their water system. In April 1920, the *Greeley Tribune* had learned that "Greeley has the best and purest [drinking] water of any town or city in the United States." On a trip to the East Coast, Delph Carpenter had met with a famous chemist (he is not mentioned by name in the *Tribune* story, but was probably James Morton Caird, a chemist and bacteriologist) in Troy, New York, "to secure some data regarding water tests." Upon learning that Carpenter hailed from Greeley, the chemist showed him a vial that he kept on his laboratory shelf. "That water came from your town," said the New York scientist, "and let me tell you now it is the best and purest water of any of the more than 1,000 samples of water from all parts of the United States which I have on hand."[43]

Carpenter then asked the man how he got the water and "what he was doing with it?" The New York chemist explained that he had taken the train through Colorado several years earlier, finding himself for a few hours in downtown Greeley. His natural curiosity about urban water quality led the scientist to draw "a sample from one of the drinking fountains of the city." He had "no interest in Greeley," Carpenter told the *Tribune,* "and merely took the water to add to his collection of samples." Upon testing it, however, the chemist "admitted to Mr. Carpenter . . . that he was surprised at its purity." He told Carpenter: "It was a common claim of many towns and cities to declare that their water was the purest and best in the country." But "Greeley's claim was no idle boast." Said the New York chemist: "That purity of water is an asset which cannot be overestimated by your people."[44] This was sage advice from the well-traveled and distinguished chemist from Troy, New York.

In the summer of 1920, Greeley city officials discussed upgrades needed for the water system. Mayor Charles Todd met with the *Tribune* editor to discuss the next decade of work facing Milton Seaman and his staff. The mayor, the legal veteran of the Whedbee Ditch purchase and change of use case in 1907, called for the expenditure of $5 million ($64 million in 2020 dollars) on a variety of municipal projects. "The sewer system," said Todd, "was built for a city of 2,500," and now Greeley had "quadrupled." Todd observed that "inadequate drains have been used for sanitary sewers for some time." Mayor Todd concluded: "Somehow the public must be convinced of the necessity of permanent building in city work." Todd informed *Tribune* readers that "the taxpayers must be prepared for heavy expenditures on the pipeline and lateral mains within the next few years if the city is to continue to grow."[45]

Seaman and his water department also discovered that more repairs were needed on the pipeline from the Bellvue plant. The superintendent realized that "we can only deliver at the reservoirs three and three-quarter million gallons [of potable water] every 24 hours by shutting everything along the line." This represented a "loss each day," said the superintendent, "of two million gallons, or approximately 35 percent of the City's water supply."

This was unacceptable, but correcting this problem would require replacement of part of the pipeline. "It will save expenses in plugging leaks," the superintendent reported, "save cost of purchasing more water, and will give us at least one million gallons more water every 24 hours." When the pipeline was built, it was estimated to last 20 years (manufacturers had boasted that it would last a generation). Instead, said Seaman, "it is now but 14 years old and part of it only served 6 or 8 years." When he became superintendent in 1913, six years after the pipeline was installed, it delivered only 2.5 million gallons of filtered water per year. Since then, the City had to replace over seven miles of pipe, with more than a mile of that being "second hand wooden pipe and the remainder with steel or cast pipe."[46] Incremental fixes had not solved the ongoing problem of a leaky water pipeline.

IN JANUARY 1922, representatives from Greeley, the U.S. Forest Service, and Fort Collins met to discuss, as the *Fort Collins Courier* reported, the "prevention of water pollution, policing of campers, prevention of the circulation of illicit whisky, and fire prevention" in the Cache la Poudre Valley. "Pollution of the streams above the water supply intakes of Greeley and Fort Collins," wrote the *Courier's* reporter, "have created a grave problem." In order to create a "Greater Greeley," and to maintain its exceptional drinking water, it would be very important to protect the water quality of the watershed.

The group examined the rapidly increasing tourist traffic along the river that had led to "stealing of various kinds, particularly of automobile parts." An idea of particular interest to the partners was hiring a patrolman in the Poudre Canyon, funded by state and federal agencies, to protect the water supply from pollution. Restrictions were placed on dumping waste and garbage into the river, and clothing could not be washed in the stream. The county health office called for a schedule of patrols every 24 hours, with violators fined a minimum of $100 ($1,500 in 2020) for each offense.[47] Interestingly, Milt Seaman (as superintendent of the Greeley Water Department) became the custodian of all captured illicit liquor supplies as part of the ongoing effort to protect the water quality of the watershed. "This city has the largest municipal stock of good whiskey in northern Colorado," reported the *Greeley Tribune* somewhat proudly.[48]

In April 1923, Superintendent Seaman announced that the newly-installed 20-inch cast iron pipeline, which replaced a portion of the deteriorating wooden line from the Bellvue plant, now delivered water much more efficiently to the city and with less water loss. He proudly reported to the *Tribune* that "the pipe line leakage has been reduced to 350,000 gallons a day." The repaired water line could now carry 2.5 million gallons of treated water each day to city storage reservoirs; a leakage rate of 14 percent.

In June 1923, those improvements were tested when the Cache la Poudre River increased to 7,500 cubic feet per second, "going over the Greeley water works dam up the Poudre." (This was a flow rate over 10 times greater than most months of the year.) Seaman reported that "at the Fritz ranch, near La Porte, the flood uncovered and floated a section of the pipeline but did not break it." Seaman also noted that "old timers said that the flood was the greatest since 'The Red Flood' of 1904."[49] This was the largest flood in the history of Fort Collins when a wall of water 10-15 feet high burst from the Cache la Poudre Canyon on May 20th, and destroyed 15 bridges and 150 homes.[50]

Unfortunately, flood waters of the Poudre River did damage a portion of Greeley's new pipeline, and created major problems for the city crews who worked around the clock to restore water service. One issue they faced, reported Mayor Walter Scott Hayden, was that "the line, which is full of dirty water and sediment, must be flushed out when this is done." When the repaired pipeline finally carried water on June 21st, citizens noticed that it was "as black as ink and almost as thick as mud." Superintendent Seaman conceded that "efforts to flush out the mud into Terry Lake, north of Fort Collins, and into irrigation systems at Timnath were only partially successful." Seaman warned that "utmost economy must be practiced until the situation is relieved," since the reservoirs in town held only a two-day supply.[51] "The pipe line is expected to break new records for daily delivery next week," the superintendent predicted, "when it will be opened up for a [thorough] test of capacity." Seaman and his crew were relieved to report no new breaks, which "speeded up the renewal of flow from the mountains beyond the expectation of city officials."[52]

Enthusiasm for the quick repairs of the Bellvue pipeline faded quickly, however, as the city's health officer, T.J. Gibbeon, found "colon bacilli" in the water system. Dr. Florence Fezer, the city physician, warned that "it would take more than a week for the water to clear up." She recommended that citizens "boil water for domestic use until they were notified that it would not be necessary."[53] (Dr. Fezer was a native of Greeley and her father was the community's first pharmacist. She graduated from Colorado College and the University of Colorado Medical School, at the turn of the century, and was among the first female doctors in the region.)

In 1924, chronic problems of water supply and delivery began to subside, as Superintendent Seaman sent out his crews to repair and reinforce the entirety of the 38-mile pipeline. The superintendent claimed that "except where sappy wood was used due to carelessness of those selecting wood for the staves," the Bellvue line was "in good condition, now as ever." Seaman made this declaration even though the line was a hybrid of "three miles of concrete, six miles of iron pipe, 23 miles of collared wooden pipe, and six miles of wooden pipe."[54]

As the year 1925 began, Greeley had two critical water challenges: improving its sewer system and obtaining more water supplies. The *Tribune* reminded its readers of Mayor Todd's warning in 1919 that an infrastructure crisis awaited the growing city if it did not meet future needs for water and improved sewer lines. Apartment houses, college dormitories, and new college buildings had increased demand for sewer service, even as no new main line sanitary sewers had been constructed. Aware that many residents might not recall the history of its water and sewer facilities, the *Tribune* noted that "Greeley's sewer system was never conceived or born." Instead, the editor claimed, "like Topsy, it just grew."[55]

In May 1925, Charles Lory, president of the Colorado Agricultural College in Fort Collins, wrote an open letter to the *Tribune* regarding Greeley's second critical water challenge. The former son of farmers, and a Weld County ditch rider in earlier years, Lory urged that ". . . farmers of the Poudre valley and the cities of Fort Collins and Greeley get together in the financing of a large channel reservoir to carry over [store] the huge floods of wet years to be used in the seasons of acute water shortage."

Lory knew the significance of expanded reservoir storage, having grown up on a homestead farm west of Greeley. Lory and his father had constructed one mile of irrigation ditch, with a plow and a team of six horses, to irrigate their land. This was difficult work and led to his later job in 1893 as a ditch rider for the Hillsboro Irrigation Ditch, near Johnstown.[56] In 1898, Lory received a teaching certificate in mathematics from the State Normal School in Greeley, and later obtained graduate degrees from the University of Colorado in Boulder. As the longest serving president of Colorado Agricultural College (1909-1940), Lory championed irrigation throughout the state, including advocacy of the Colorado-Big Thompson Project in later years.

IN 1862, ROBERT Boyd constructed the Boyd and Freeman Ditch along the Cache la Poudre River west of Greeley. This early Weld County water right was senior in priority to all existing Fort Collins and Greeley water rights on the river. It was a valuable water right and would enhance the supplies of both cities if they could cooperate in its purchase. Greeley hired Charles Todd, the former mayor and now in private practice, to investigate the purchase of the Boyd and Freeman right. He was well-suited to repeat his efforts that resulted in the 1907 decree for the Whedbee Ditch.

Roy A. Portner, a Fort Collins developer of high mountain reservoirs in the upper Cache la Poudre Basin, had acquired the Boyd and Freeman water right, and intended to sell the entire 59.4 cfs of the original decree to the highest bidder.[57] As Todd reported to Greeley's City Council on June 28, 1926, a large part of this water "had never been used." Soon thereafter, fifteen Poudre River irrigation companies banded together to ask the court to void the water right entirely. Colorado water law provided then, as it still does now, that any part of a decreed water right not put to beneficial use within a reasonable time is presumed "abandoned."

The objecting ditch companies were aware that Greeley was in the market for the Boyd and Freeman water. To avoid prolonged and expensive litigation, said Todd, "they wished it all settled for the time being, at once."[58] Fortunately, they were amenable to Fort Collins and Greeley sharing among themselves a reason-able portion of the Boyd and Freeman water right, amounting to 12.0 cfs based on historical actual usage, if the remaining 47.4 cfs was declared abandoned. Greeley had looked into purchasing an interest in a different water right, as Todd reminded the council, "transferring some old [water] rights in the Pleasant Valley Ditch." That irrigation company, however, had not agreed to a sale of shares of its water and "will fight the same to the end."

The council then gave Todd the green light to negotiate with Fort Collins for a reasonable share of the Boyd and Freeman water. Todd wanted Greeley to own half of this water, but Fort Collins had spent $22,500 ($323,000 in 2020 dollars) to exercise its option with Portner, and insisted upon 8.0 cfs as its fair share. The cities eventually divided the water, with 7.0 cfs for Fort Collins and 5.0 cfs for Greeley. Each community agreed to pay a pro-rata share of the costs that the objecting ditch companies had incurred in preparing for the abandonment suit, and included water measurement, engineering and legal fees."[59]

The Larimer County District Court decree, dated June 19, 1926, Case No. 5326, contained significant provisions affirming and protecting these water rights. The court allowed Greeley to combine its Number 6 priority for 5.0 cfs of the Boyd and Freeman right together with its 6 ½ priority for the 7.5 cfs Whedbee Ditch water right. The court found that Greeley could transfer (move) a total of 12.5 cfs to a new point of diversion closer to the mouth of the Poudre Canyon. It also ruled this would cause no injury to any other water right on the river.

The court also ordered the remainder of the Boyd and Freeman Ditch water right to be abandoned upstream of the Greeley Number 3 Ditch diversion structure. This historic decree, particularly its abandonment finding, improved and protected Greeley's Number 3 Ditch priority as well as the city's upstream water decrees. For Greeley, the cost of acquiring five cubic feet per second of Boyd and Freeman water was $32,748 (around $475,000 in 2020). Todd estimated that the combined 12.5 cfs would be "sufficient for a number of years."[60]

The Boyd and Freeman Ditch water purchase came at a critical time for the City of Greeley. Now a major player on the Cache la Poudre River, the City needed to continue to protect its water rights and the quality of its streamflow. In February 1926, readers of the *Tribune* learned about a new potential threat to all water users on the river: the proposed extension of the boundaries for Rocky Mountain National Park. L.R. Temple, attorney for the Water Supply and Storage Company (WSSC), had written to a Loveland newspaper about his recent meetings with federal officials in Washington, D.C. "Should the park be extended," said Temple, "there can be no further [water] development of the headstreams of the Poudre, Grand, the Thompson or St. Vrain." Such actions, the WSSC lawyer warned, meant that "our water supply would be limited to approximately our present diversion."

Temple placed blame for his client's plight on the "Denver Tourist Bureau" for its "disregard of farming interests in northern Colorado." This organization, said Temple, thought only of "inducing tourist traffic," doing so "without reference to the rights of local people for irrigation and mining purposes."[61] An urban/agricultural rift had developed along the northern Front Range of Colorado in 1926, one that persisted for decades. In contrast, former mayor Charles Todd counseled the City of Greeley to focus its energies on "the future needs of the water system," and not concern itself with the proposed expansion of Rocky Mountain National Park. Cautioned Todd: "Above all other things the city must maintain a pure and adequate water supply. Compared to the importance of water supply," said the former Greeley mayor, "everything else [including the Park expansion plans] is a side show."[62]

IN MAY 1927, into this water development ring stepped the sideshow performances of traveling water entrepreneurs from Tulsa. The Greeley City Council listened politely to a remarkable offer from the firm of Minck and

Olaison, identified as construction engineers from Oklahoma. They wanted to purchase the entire Greeley municipal water system and operate it as a private enterprise. The engineers claimed to have the money on hand and "were prepared to make a cash offer," the council noted. The *Greeley Tribune*, not sure whether this was serious or not, reported on May 4th that "Greeley's water system is not for sale." While the offer may have flattered city officials, the council needed no "more than half a second" to deliberate the measure, and they "instructed the [city] clerk to refuse it."[63] Former Union Colony land owner, P.T. Barnum, the "Circus King," would probably have guffawed at the offer from Minck and Olaison from Tulsa.

Today, this 1927 offer to purchase the Greeley Water system in its entirety is intriguing because the "privatization" of municipal water systems is a growing trend across the U.S. and around the world. Water conglomerates such as the French companies Veolia (the world's largest provider of water services) and Suez are dominant in this endeavor. Other global companies have experienced mixed results after purchasing municipal water systems, and a few cities (such as Atlanta) have cancelled operational contracts due to unfilled commitments and expectations. Greeley's water leaders made the right decision in 1927 to continue to manage their own water system.

IN 1927, EVEN as irrigators and municipal water districts expressed concerns regarding potential development partnerships with "outside" groups, such as the Denver Water Department, the U.S. Bureau of Reclamation came to the area to conduct a geologic survey of the Cache la Poudre Canyon. Reclamation, as the Greeley Tribune described it, sought "to determine the possibilities of large-scale storage of water for irrigation on the upper stretches of the river." The goal was to locate two or more on-channel reservoir sites that could capture flood waters for use in drought years.[64] The irrigators and the cities of Greeley and Fort Collins were "elated," in the words of the *Tribune's* editor, "over the reclamation department's decision to make a [thorough] investigation of the river's possibilities."[65]

As the summer of 1928 approached, water users in northern Colorado anticipated the release of the Bureau of Reclamation report regarding potential water storage reservoirs. The publisher of the *Fort Collins Courier*, George C. McCormick, had sought as early as June 1923 to enlist Reclamation's assistance in this matter. "For many years efforts have been made, without success," wrote McCormick to Interior Secretary Hubert Work, "to secure the building of a large channel reservoir west of Fort Collins." Where the Greeley interests often declared their independence from federal involvement in irrigation, McCormick admitted that "the project seems too big for the local irrigation companies to put through."

McCormick's foresight and promotion, like his peers in Greeley and that of Colorado Agricultural College President Charles Lory, drew the attention of the U.S. Department of the Interior. The *Courier's* publisher identified for Secretary Hubert Work "several good sites, the largest and the one which would catch all the water from the North Fork [of the Cache la Poudre River]." Said McCormick: "Rist Canyon, etc., is five miles west of Fort Collins, where the river comes through the first hogback, between Laporte and Bellvue." Should the Bureau of Reclamation construct a dam at this site, it would "prevent disastrous floods in the Cache la Poudre valley extending from Laporte to the Platte east of Greeley."

Local promoters of the Greeley-Poudre Irrigation District had hoped their private design might also qualify for Reclamation support. Elwood Mead, well known in northern Colorado from his years at the agricultural college in Fort Collins, and in the Offices of the State Engineers for Wyoming and Colorado, was now Commissioner of the Bureau of Reclamation in Washington, D.C. He corresponded with parties involved in the Poudre River investigation. R.L. Huntley, Chief Engineer for the Union Pacific Railroad, also sought Mead's advice. Huntley's company owned large sections of the land to be irrigated by the proposed Greeley-Poudre Irrigation District, as well as the rail line between Cheyenne and Greeley.

The Union Pacific had put up some of the money to construct the Laramie-Poudre Tunnel, but the vast majority of those costs were secured by bonds issued locally by the Greeley-Poudre Irrigation District. The railroad's investment stood in jeopardy, said Huntley, because "the use of the tunnel . . . has been enjoined [by the State of Wyoming's lawsuit in the U.S. Supreme Court] and that litigation has been in progress for some time relative to this diversion of irrigation water."[66] Their concerns were heard, but the potential storage project was lost when Elwood Mead's agency declined to fund water storage on the Cache la Poudre River.

AS THE DECADE of the 1920s came to an end, despite its best efforts, the City of Greeley had not secured additional high mountain water supplies. Of more immediate concern to Milton Seaman was further deterioration of the Bellvue pipeline. It ruptured again in August 1928 near Fort Collins, requiring Greeley to order what the *Tribune* described as the "cessation of street and lawn sprinkling, automobile washing and all other uses of water that are not strictly necessary." Members of the Snyder family, who farmed about three miles southeast of Fort Collins along the pipeline route, reported that "several feet of the wooden stave pipe line had been blown out of the ground."

The *Tribune* also reported that "the break caught the town of Windsor without any water in its storage tank," which the City of Greeley had supplied through the now broken pipeline. To provide water for its residents, Windsor had to resort to pumping groundwater from its old wells. Compounding matters for both communities was the hot weather, which led water users to draw down their municipal reservoirs. Greeley did not escape these troubles either as ongoing maintenance had left the water storage reservoirs at very low levels.[67]

This latest crisis with municipal water service was on the mind of A.A. LaFollette, a former Greeley City Council member and state legislator, who spoke that month at an Exchange Club luncheon in Greeley. "Some measure must be advanced," said LaFollette, "to conserve the water supply of Greeley or to increase it." With the purchase of the Boyd and Freeman water rights two years earlier, LaFollette claimed that "there is enough water wasted in Greeley to furnish another city of a similar size." His solution was to install water meters in all households. This, LaFollette believed, could reduce "fully 40 percent of the present consumption."[68] It was a conversation that would go on for decades.

At the end of the 1920s, the city council accepted the recommendation, of the state sanitary engineer for the Colorado Board of Health, to build its own water testing laboratory. This was timely since a new threat emerged; timber companies were lobbying the state legislature to gain approval to float logs down the Cache la Poudre River to sawmills in Fort Collins and Greeley. This proposal was not well received in Greeley, and city council minutes of February 7, 1929, stated that the logging practice "would be a menace to the fish life in the stream." In addition, harvesting timber in the watershed would accelerate snowmelt runoff "that should be held back for irrigation and domestic uses late in the season." The logs themselves would "damage and destroy the [diversion] dams across the stream," while the turbidity would "make the water unfit for domestic purposes without added purification."

By contrast, William R. Kreutzer, Superintendent of the Colorado National Forest, spoke to a gathering of Fort Collins service clubs and argued that "millions of feet of lumber must be removed to keep the forests in good growing conditions." Market forces had made species, like Engleman spruce, increase exponentially in value; from $8 per thousand board feet to as much as $87. Kreutzer hoped that "all interested parties in both the Fort Collins and Greeley districts" could attend information sessions to solve "the problem of getting lumber to railheads at economical cost."[69] The issues of forest health and management were emerging in the region.

Adding to the City of Greeley's heightened interest in water quality in the Poudre Basin was its joint ownership, with the City of Fort Collins, of the L.O. Rockwell Ranch; a 1,040-acre property located some 40 miles northwest of Fort Collins. In 1928, the two cities had purchased it jointly to prevent the construction of summer cottages on the land. The Greeley City Council did so to guarantee "protection of the watersheds of the South Fork of the Cache la Poudre River, from which said cities have derived and will continue to derive their water supply or a portion thereof." Greeley and Fort Collins paid $14,250 for the property (around $215,000 in 2020 dollars). This was one of many examples of the collaborative efforts between the two communities to ensure a stable and safe water supply for their citizens.[70]

THE YEARS BETWEEN 1910 and 1930 changed Greeley and its water department in many ways. While not experiencing population growth on the scale of the century's first decade, Greeley nonetheless maintained its commitment to agricultural prosperity, and the expansion of support services to the farm families and communities of Weld County.

Delph Carpenter and Milton Seaman inherited the Union Colonists' vision to fulfill Nathan Meeker's promise to "make the desert bloom." Attorney Carpenter worked diligently to secure transbasin water supplies for the region, confronting unforeseen obstacles and turning them into landmark legal accomplishments. Water superintendent Seaman took pride in delivering the best quality water to the Greeley community, and invoked the latest technology expected and demanded by ratepayers. This would be an ongoing theme for Greeley Water— planning and innovation in construction, operations and maintenance crafted through trial and practice, negotiation and collaboration, trial and error.

Delph Carpenter excelled as a model in the art of negotiation and collaboration. As the 1920s had opened with *The Country Gentleman* interviewing Delph Carpenter about the history of his hometown, it would end with Carpenter in his new role as Colorado's Interstate Stream Commissioner. He was very concerned about pending legislation at the statehouse in Denver in January 1929 "which would unconditionally cede all the state rights in [Rocky Mountain National Park] to the United States."[71] Carpenter, whose legal expertise had guided the Colorado River Compact Commission in 1921-1922, called upon state lawmakers to reserve "the right to build all necessary ditches, tunnels, reservoirs and other works necessary to divert and store water" within the national park.

Carpenter and his peers wanted (and needed) to secure more mountain water supplies for Greeley and the Front Range. The *Greeley Tribune* reported that "Mr. Carpenter foresees the day when a long tunnel which will traverse the national park will divert water from the Grand Lake Country into the tributaries of the Poudre and the Thompson." Carpenter's reasoning, said the *Tribune*, was that "in arid country, development is rigidly limited by the water supply."[72] The vision of the future Colorado-Big Thompson Project would soon become clearer, and a new chapter in Greeley's water story was coming into focus.

CHAPTER SIX

Greeley Water in the 1930s

Dark Clouds

THE GREELEY WATER Department operated efficiently during the 1920s, but this all changed with the Stock Market Crash at the end of the decade. On October 29, 1929, "Black Tuesday" hit Wall Street investors. On a single day, 16 million shares of stock traded on the New York Stock Exchange (four times the normal trading activity). The market dropped 36 percent in value, and billions of investment dollars disappeared. Banks collapsed, jobs vanished, and the unemployment rate in the U.S. climbed to over 25 percent.

The citizens of Greeley and their water utility faced major economic challenges, as did the rest of the country. Many families had no financial safety nets, since federal bank deposit insurance did not exist, and the social security system would not be created until 1935. Local banks shuttered and jobs evaporated. Alone and in groups, riding the rails in boxcars, clutching train tops, or driving across the country in old vehicles, men, women and children traveled from town-to-town in search of work. Others stood in long bread lines. Charity among neighbors and strangers would be offered, even as it proved inadequate to meet the demands for assistance.

The Great Plains of the U.S. and Canada faced devastation during the most severe drought in U.S. and Canadian recorded history. Water-starved crops withered away, emaciated livestock died, and an old blight known to the Union Colonists of the 1870s (grasshoppers) chewed on everything—crops, clothes, even fence posts. With a crisis in the city's water department growing worse, Milton Seaman and his employees responded by working around the clock to plug pipeline leaks to save water. They also pleaded with city officials to improve residential water conservation measures, and provided leadership during a most difficult period.

Then in the late 1930s, Congress approved the Colorado-Big Thompson Project to resurrect a long-held dream to divert Colorado River water, through the Great Divide of the Rocky Mountains, to the farms and cities of northeastern Colorado.

SIX DECADES AFTER the Union Colonists first arrived, Greeley had become a community of 12,000 residents. While modest in size compared to Denver's 287,000 people, Greeley ranked fourth in population among Colorado's municipalities, claiming to be the largest urban area north of the capital city.[1] For the next decade, said Gerald Nash, the Great Depression "abruptly curtailed the westward surge of population [and] dashed many western hopes for further rapid economic growth."[2]

The "Great Crash" rolled like "deafening and frightening thunder that heralded an approaching storm," wrote Nash. Within four years, farmers' income fell by half; grain and cattle prices did the same. Great Western Sugar Company's president called the 1929-1930 harvest campaign "the worst year in beet history."[3] Unemployment in Colorado quadrupled by 1932. "More than one-third of the smaller banks in the [West]," said Nash, "were forced into bankruptcy." The dry cycle afflicting the Eastern Plains of Colorado from 1931-1941 had not been witnessed in anyone's lifetime. In contrast, the generation prior to 1930 had benefited from two decades of wetter than normal weather—a period of sustained population and economic growth throughout northern Colorado.

Most tragic, recalled W.D. Farr, were the Weld County dryland farmers who came to Greeley, surrendering ownership of their homesteads because they could no longer make their mortgage payments.[4] Articles in the *Greeley Tribune* chronicled "tough times" in the area. Charles Ovid Plumb, a prominent farmer and grandson of former Mayor Charles A. White, advocated the creation of a mortgage arbitration board in Greeley. He also called for a voluntary moratorium on Weld County foreclosures until refinancing help for farmers was established through federal agencies. There were 85 cases of foreclosures initiated or finished in Weld County from September through October 1933, with only one redemption.[5]

THE FALL OF 1929 witnessed massive environmental change which confronted Weld County farmers and Greeley residents alike. Sugar beets froze in the ground, and people awoke to broken water pipes in their homes and beneath unpaved city streets. Temperatures dropped well below their historic averages, with 20 days in a row of subzero temperatures. Several night-time lows plunged below minus 20°F, with a minus 28°F reading on January 21, 1930.[6] Loss of the sugar beet crop aggravated the distress of the Great Depression.

To protect their plumbing, Greeley residents left faucets running to keep water pipes from freezing, which caused a water shortage in city reservoirs. Superintendent Seaman asked the city council to convene a special meeting on January 28th to address this water emergency. Open taps and breaking pipes had cost the City over one million gallons of water.[7] By the end of January, reservoirs had dropped below 50 percent of capacity. Threats of fire throughout the city also increased, due to frozen hydrants. The City hired sixteen Colorado State Teachers College students to distribute 4,000 handbills to every household, informing residents of the water crisis. Students also asked permission to enter homes to see if residents were leaving their water taps running, and reported infractions to the water department.

Despite such extraordinary efforts, voluntary water use reductions were disappointing, and made the situation more serious. "It was estimated that so far at least 700 service pipes have frozen," the *Greeley Tribune* wrote. The Home Gas and Electric Company sent out six "thawing crews" to help ease the crisis. Superintendent Seaman reported "miles of frozen water mains in Greeley at this time." Said the superintendent, "Mains and service pipes are breaking in all parts of the city;" the Weld County Hospital had no water for over a week, even after the City reopened all but one fire hydrant.[8] Throughout February 1930, Seaman and his work crews struggled to restore service as residents persisted with their water use habits. The City also learned that local plumbers were cutting notches into faucet gaskets so that water could trickle through instead of freezing. The city council immediately ordered all plumbers to replace notched gaskets with new ones to conserve water. Seaman did report that only 350 feet of water mains had burst beneath the paved streets, as these were insulated from the cold.[9]

In March 1930, Bellvue pipeline repairs neared completion towards the end of a very difficult winter season. With its 27-inch capacity, new sections of concrete line promised better service. The water department decided to salvage five miles of the old wooden stave pipeline, laying a second line parallel to the new one near the storage reservoirs in Greeley. The City hoped these improvements would double the volume of water flowing into water mains.[10] Seaman's prediction about future low flows on the Cache la Poudre River also proved to be accurate. The *Tribune* reported in May 1930 that rainfall totals for the year stood at 30 percent of normal.

As the 1930s progressed, the water department encountered more challenges. In his 1930 annual report, Superintendent Milton Seaman reported a revenue increase; an event that would not occur again for another decade. By 1932, water revenues had decreased by 17 percent while bonded debt nearly doubled to $303,000 ($5.7 million in 2020). The water department's income had now fallen to its lowest level since 1920. Not until 1947 would it exceed 1930 revenue levels, and this would be caused by wage and price inflation during and immediately following World War II.[11]

RAINFALL RECORDS WERE kept at the Great Western Sugar Company's Greeley plant. During the month of April 1920, the city had received 4.43 inches of rain (almost a third of the total precipitation for an entire year); and nearly the same amount as in 1929. These were exceptionally wet months, and D.M. Scott, weatherman for Great Western, observed that "the first four months of 1929 had more rain than any similar period in a decade, though 1927 and 1920 ran close seconds." In April 1930, the factory measured only 0.47 inches of rain for the entire month, a 90 percent decline. Unknown to Scott, this was the start of the notorious "Dust Bowl" or "Dirty Thirties" that dried out and scorched the Great Plains for a decade. He did recognize the seriousness of this unexpected long-term drought for Greeley when he told the *Tribune*: "If this [1930] is to go on record as a normal year in the matter of rainfall, from 12 to 14 inches more of rain must fall [in the next eight months];" this in a region where 12 to 14 inches of precipitation in an entire year was considered "average."[12]

The second year of the Great Depression (1931) witnessed further declines in both precipitation and employment, creating extraordinary pressures on the water department and the City of Greeley. By year's end, state officials called upon the City to provide employment for laborers who had no other options, even as Greeley confronted the failure of residents to pay their monthly water bills. Drought, economic collapse, and infrastructure maintenance demands forced city officials in the spring of 1931 to restructure its public works offices. Milton Seaman, who had served as superintendent of the street department since 1898, relinquished some of his duties. He remained as supervisor of the water department, with James Proctor as assistant water superintendent. A.H. Bolenbaugh became the "Water Foreman," and Ted Stephenson was designated as his assistant foreman. Seaman's commitment to the daily operations of Greeley's public works had been exemplary; a city council member even called him the unofficial "City Manager." His age (71 years old), however, and the workloads facing each office had prompted the council to make these managerial changes.[13]

The summer of 1931 continued with more challenges for city staff. Water use remained high, and the city council discussed conservation methods as well as the controversial issue of water meters. "If residence properties were all on meters," said a city council member, the "cost of sprinkling and for domestic purposes would be increased about 50 percent." Instead, the council called upon the water department to employ two "inspectors" whose task was to "be diplomatic" as they encouraged residents not to waste water. The inspectors quickly learned that many citizens ignored the call for voluntary conservation. In July 1931, they reported "six to twelve violators of sprinkling violations found each day." In a change of policy amidst increasing frustration, Mayor W.E. Anderson ordered inspectors to "haul all violators of the [sprinkling] ordinance into Police Court."[14]

Greeley resident's wasteful use of water became a constant theme, compounded by losses due to leaks in pipelines and storage reservoirs. Just as the national economy had "bottomed out," so too had Greeley's 1907 City Reservoir No. 1. In March 1934, Milton Seaman discovered a crack in the floor of the 7.5 million gallon reservoir, which leaked 400,000 gallons of water per day. R.W. Gelder, the city engineer, estimated that repairs would cost $13,342 (about $210,000 in 2020 dollars), and would last for 25 years. The reservoir's flat floor was rebuilt with a diagonal trench to make cleaning easier as part of the repairs.[15]

Perhaps the best news that summer came from Mayor Anderson, who "impressed it on all members of the council that they should offer the glad hand to all oil men interested in the new oil field." The mayor had learned that "nine families had moved to Greeley and 20 to 40 single men are living here and more coming." Anderson had it on good authority that their "reason for moving here is [on] account of good mountain water and [the] fair treatment they had received."[16] The Greasewood Flats area 35 miles east of Greeley became Weld County's first "hot spot" for oil and gas exploration.

Even with the modest oil and gas development, the deepening financial crisis affected all of Greeley's city government. In the fall of 1931, Mayor Anderson reported on the Salvation Army's regional council meeting held in Denver. The relief organization anticipated an influx of unemployed homeless families. "[The City of] Sterling is preparing for winter," he told the council, "while Colorado Springs has fed 25,000." In his city of 35,000 people, the mayor "thought [it] better to try to make work for our own people than [to give] too much charity." City engineer R.W. Gelder suggested that "quarrying rock and facing down at [the] filter [plant] would be practically all labor." Alderman Christansen added that "the land south of Island Grove Park needed to be drained, which could furnish some labor."[17]

The city council encouraged the water department to collaborate with the Weld County Commissioners on projects that each could sponsor to hire unemployed laborers. Rebuilding fire hydrants at the County maintenance yard, and installation of a pipeline along 11th Avenue to the Weld County Hospital, could be completed with what the council called "unemployed labor" using water department personnel as supervisors.[18] The city council and the Weld County Commissioners preferred creating jobs, if possible. For example, a new pipeline from the city reservoirs, around the north side of Glenmere and through the "college hill section" to 7th Avenue, was completed in 1934 at a cost of $35,180.50. The City paid $30,000 for materials, and the Civil Works Administration (CWA) paid $5,180.50 for the labor.[19] The CWA was a temporary New Deal program that paid unemployed workers for manual labor public works jobs during the severe winter of 1933-1934.

Then the signs of a very dry winter appeared. Barren hillsides foreshadowed a bankrupt water supply. February brought word from Milton Seaman that "there was no snow in the mountains."[20] Because public works offered the best option for hiring unemployed laborers, the water department began to align its projects with the goal of improving the local economy by providing jobs. The novelty of this practice appeared in March 1932, when Water Superintendent Seaman told the city council that "common labor" was being hired by the "Associated Relief Agency" for replacing a water pipe line at Island Grove Park at the rate of "$1.00 per day," or about 12 cents per hour. Instead of paying in cash, the City gave each worker "groceries for that amount." Seaman reported to the council on July 12th that 71 "empty houses" had come to his attention, while 13 others had their water service terminated "for non-payment of tax." Seaman also warned, "if the hot dry weather continues, it will be necessary to conserve on water as the reserve is now being drawn upon."[21] A dire situation only seemed to be getting worse.

As the City struggled with revenues and requests for financial support, the council announced on December 13, 1932, that "an emergency exists and that stringent financial restrictions must be made in order to maintain the activities of the regular departments of the city government." This meant that on January 1, 1933, "all salaries and regular allowances now paid officials and regular employees of the City be reduced 10%."

In spite of financial challenges, the water department advised councilors that work on the Bellvue pipeline had advanced, with "32 easements signed by the city for access." Yet the provider of pipe, the Colorado Fuel and Iron Company of Pueblo, "wanted to close down the plant in a little while." The City needed CF&I to stay in business at least long enough to supply them with materials for its many work projects. This work included 70 laborers on the new Bellvue pipeline, which by year's end had advanced down river as far as the Windsor cemetery.[22]

LIKE THOSE BEFORE him, Superintendent Seaman was continually challenged by the overuse of water in Greeley. He liked to tell the story of his arrival in Greeley in 1884, where he first learned of its "free" water system.

Before the construction of Greeley's first water works plant in 1889, said Seaman, "the town had one public town pump, located on Main Street, somewhere below the post office building." He marveled that "no restrictions were placed on when or how much water you used."

For citizens wishing to have wells drilled in the local shallow aquifer, said Seaman, "I.H. Paine was the town plumber, and he would install your pump, furnish material and labor, and guarantee you abundance of hard water for $10.00;" (about $250 in 2020). Those days were a distant memory, as Seaman told the city council: "Water collections were coming in slower during the first two months than at any time since he had been with the Water Department." The superintendent further warned councilors that income "would be $10,000 less in 1933 than in 1932 mostly due to the shorter Sugar Company campaign [caused by the drought-reduced crop yield]."[23]

Efforts to increase revenues for the water department were met with strong resistance from residents protesting against higher water rates. In December 1932, the city council directed the water department to reduce its charges by 25 percent to the fire department, street department, and for irrigating parks. The City also cut costs by reducing its contribution for the work of the "Sanitary Inspector" in the Poudre Canyon (the effort started in 1907 to protect the water quality of the Cache la Poudre River upstream of the Bellvue Water Treatment Plant). The city engineer for Fort Collins had advised the Greeley City Council that he considered the $3,000 annual salary of the inspector ($56,000 in 2020 dollars) to be "too much." A 50 percent reduction in the inspector's compensation was negotiated, to which Greeley contributed $500.[24]

During 1933, Greeley water ratepayers were less concerned about employment issues than their inability to pay for the services they received. In April, the city council had ordered an investigation to "see if a reduction can be made when bills are sent out in July." A month later, city officials agreed to a 10 percent reduction in fees. The council believed this was a result of the "present emergency, and the present financial stringency." The council considered it a high priority "to protect the public health and maintain sanitary conditions . . . and to prevent contagion and disease." The reduced water fees did not extend, however, to the water department's largest customer, Great Western Sugar. Councilors agreed that "said rebate and/or credit shall not apply to or be considered, in any way, as affecting water sold to and/or water rents or charges against the Great Western Sugar Company;" this despite the fact that the company needed less water than its existing contract allowed.[25]

With revenues declining, city finances were stretched thin. So, it was an unwelcome surprise when the state sanitary engineer notified the City's physician in August "that something must be done regarding sewage disposal." For the past two decades, under Seaman's direction, the City had built a network of sewer lines to carry wastewater from Greeley neighborhoods to the east side of town. From there the raw, untreated sewage was released directly into the Cache la Poudre River, a common and low-cost practice followed by most communities nationwide. While Greeley water users had spared little expense to secure clean drinking water from the Cache la Poudre River upstream of Fort Collins, the mayor advised his colleagues "that Greeley's attitude should be that if all other towns took up the matter of sewage disposal then Greeley would also."[26]

In May 1934, Mayor Roy M. Briggs received a notice from the State Board of Health "ordering the City of Greeley to cease polluting the Poudre River." As Greeley faced daunting financial obligations and revenue shortfalls, the beleaguered mayor responded to the state board's demand for construction of a sewage treatment plant: "The City has no funds for any such construction." Mayor Briggs believed that "the taxpayers of Greeley are in no position to pay an additional mill levy in future years to provide funds for such construction." He openly criticized "Denver and other Colorado municipalities, as well as many manufacturing concerns," for "polluting the South Platte and Cache la Poudre rivers." Even if the City complied with the executive order, said Briggs, "the pollution of such streams would not be materially reduced."[27]

The mayor's concerns became apparent when he asked the City's physician, Dr. Schoen, to address the issue of water pollution in the Cache la Poudre River at Greeley. Schoen warned the council that a sewage disposal plant "must eventually be built by the city." He also advised the city council: "The State Board of Health has power to compel such action." Schoen, in agreement with the mayor, said "he saw no need for Greeley to build such a plant until all cities cease dumping sewage into the Poudre." Alderman Carrel supported Dr. Schoen, but warned his colleagues, "The Council should begin to plan now for a plant before very many years."[28] He was right.

THE PRACTICE OF discharging raw sewage into the Cache la Poudre River at Greeley persisted, but drought, now in its fourth year was of greater concern. In June 1934, the Governor's Office warned of threats to state water users from the "exceptionally dry winter," and urged Colorado's agricultural sector to prepare for "its most precarious situation in history." Even with abysmal Poudre River flows, and an outdoor irrigation ban by the City, Greeley residents continued to water their lawns as chronic summer heat continued into autumn. C.H. Wadsworth appeared before the city council on October 2nd to ask that "property owners be permitted to water lawns and shrubs at least two days this fall." Council members reminded him and other citizens in the audience "that the water situation was not improved." The City "now has no water in the river that is its own." The best that councilors could offer residents was a promise that "as soon as it was felt that enough water was stored ahead, the watering of lawns would be permitted."[29]

To obtain a closer look at these water supply issues, Superintendent Seaman escorted the mayor and several councilors on a tour of the upper Cache la Poudre River to its headwaters. At the November 6th council meeting, Alderman Moffat "thought every citizen who would make the trip and see the condition clear to Chambers Lake would see the necessity for conserving water." At the November 13th city council meeting, complaints were made regarding the "very offensive odor" emanating from the Greeley Number 3 Ditch, "since the sugar factory at Windsor had started up." Without a strong river flow, sewage did not dilute as in the past and foul odors persisted.[30] Drought and water quality issues could no longer be ignored.

With the onset of spring 1935, city officials continued to see chronic low flow conditions in the Cache la Poudre River. They also heard grim concerns regarding the need for more storage water. In March, the *Greeley Tribune* counseled that, "the City of Greeley [should] purchase a mountain lake as insurance against extreme water shortage on the Poudre river, such as exists at present . . ." Several sites had been recommended, among them "Mirror Lake, located adjacent to Rocky Mountain National Park."[31] As an advocate for economic prosperity, the *Tribune* touted the benefits of acquiring water for the city's future growth, which the Mirror Lake proposal seemed to address. "The question of how often the lake could be refilled," the *Tribune* conceded, "is a controversial one." Situated at an elevation of 11,000 feet, Mirror Lake "once filled . . . would keep the city free from water famine for three or four months in times of extreme shortage on the Poudre."

To give readers a sense of scale, the *Tribune* compared Mirror Lake to the city's existing storage reservoirs, with the former being about 12 times the size of the latter. Engineering studies of the lake estimated a cost of $5,000 (about $100,000 in 2020 dollars) to purchase the property, water rights, and to construct an outlet tunnel. Nearby, reported the *Tribune*, was "another suggested acquisition for the city;" Hourglass Reservoir on the Little South Fork of the Cache la Poudre River. Roy Portner of Fort Collins had built Hourglass as part of his Mountain and Plains Reservoir and Irrigation Company.[32] Tempting as it was to urge city officials to pursue the mountain reservoir purchases, the *Tribune* also noted the concerns of W.J. McAnelly, water commissioner for the Cache la Poudre River. McAnelly had been caretaker of the Rockwell Ranch in the late 1920s, and cautioned city officials that "the proposal of Greeley using Mirror lake as a reserve water supply had been put up to him by interested parties and that he thought very little of it." The City "would be lucky," said McAnelly, "to fill it once in 20 years." He reminded city officials: "You know the difficulties in filling the later reservoirs on the Poudre even in favorable years." The commissioner concluded that the enterprise "to develop the lake as a reserve supply for the city is impractical."[33] Similar discussions and debates, regarding high mountain reservoirs, would continue for decades.

IN 1935, A year after the City received notice from the State Board of Health to cease polluting the Cache la Poudre River, the Greeley City Council agreed to seek a $60,000 bond issue (around $1.1 million in 2020) to construct sanitary sewers and a "sewage disposal works."[34] The measure passed, and city officials next discussed with the federal Public Works Administration (PWA) "an outright grant of 30%" for the plant. The PWA administrator came to Greeley in May to discuss the sewage treatment plant proposal. New regulations favored Greeley's request, said George M. Bull, the Colorado engineering representative for the recently formed Public Works Administration. The federal government could provide a loan of 55 percent, with the remaining amount given as a grant. Bull also advised city councilors: "If a grant is asked for, the PWA wage scale will have to be used which is 60 cents an hour for common labor, 75 cents for semi-skilled, and $1.10 for skilled [workers]."[35]

The City invited consulting engineers to review the pollution control plans drafted by the sewer department staff. Council offered the PWA the sum of $42,075 as the City's share for sewage plant costs. The International Trust Company agreed to purchase up to $50,000 of the City bonds at 2.25 percent interest. By year's end, the water department announced it had offered a contract to J.S. Schwartz Construction Company to construct the network of "intercepting sewers" required for the new sewage treatment plant. The Colorado Springs based firm made the successful bid of $16,993 ($325,000 in 2020) for this work.[36] On March 3, 1936, the Greeley City Council approved a contract for the construction of the city's first sewage treatment plant. The low bid was $52,394.53 (approximately $960,000 in 2020 dollars). Raw sewage would no longer be discharged into the Cache la Poudre River, and federal water quality regulators welcomed this significant improvement in Greeley's water system. On September 8, 1936, with the Greeley Sewage Treatment Plant nearing completion, the facility's operator was appointed.[37]

THE 1930S BROUGHT many challenges to Greeley due to the collapsing economy and the devastating drought which gripped eastern Colorado and the Great Plains. Once again, leaders in the community converged to meet the challenge. On a Saturday morning, July 29, 1933, Greeley water attorney William R. Kelly encountered Fred Norcross, formerly chair of the Greeley Chamber of Commerce and a two-term state senator, as well as irrigation engineer L.L. Stimson, at the city post office.

Their discussion resurrected the dream of a tunnel beneath the Rocky Mountains to deliver Colorado River water to northeastern Colorado. Necessity was paramount, the times—and timing—were right, and modern tunnel-boring technology was available. Colorado's legislature had explored such a possibility

Figure 6.1 In March 1936, with financial assistance from the federal Public Works Administration (PWA), the City accepted a bid of $52,394.53 (about $1 million in 2020) to construct its first wastewater treatment plant near 1ˢᵗ Avenue & 10ᵗʰ Street. This May 15, 1936, photo shows workers constructing the circular anaerobic digester (foreground) and the circular primary settling tank (background). City of Greeley Museums, Permanent Collection, C1-1970.22.0022.

as early as 1889, when House Bill 161 authorized $20,000 (around $600,000 in 2020 dollars) to investigate diverting water from the Western Slope to South Boulder Creek on the Front Range. At that time, Edwin S. Nettleton, Colorado's second state water engineer and the first surveyor of Greeley's direct flow water ditches, believed this project infeasible.[38]

Forty years later, the ferocity of drought and the country's determination to escape the Great Depression created local, state and federal partnerships of enduring worth and significance. The proposed transmountain water diversion tunnel from Grand Lake to Estes Park became the catalyst for a major reorganization of Colorado law, policy and public governance. This initiative focused on the state's entitlement to Colorado River water under the 1922 Colorado River Compact—Delph Carpenter's "impossible" dream. U.S. Senator Alva B. Adams of Pueblo, chairman of the Senate Committee on Irrigation and Reclamation,

Figure 6.2 In 1902, Charles Hansen (1873-1953), a journalist in Grand Rapids, Michigan, arrived in Greeley and became publisher of the *Greeley Tribune–Republican* in 1913. His extraordinary advocacy efforts, for the Colorado-Big Thompson (C-BT) Project, resulted in Congressional approval of the project in 1937. On the 50th anniversary of the Reclamation Act, June 17, 1952, the U.S. Department of the Interior presented its coveted Conservation Service Award to Hansen in recognition of the many years he "devoted to the conservation, diversion, and fullest utilization of the surplus waters of the Colorado River." City of Greeley Museums, Permanent Collection, 1983.48.0090.

stood ready to navigate the tunnel project through Congress. He believed that President Franklin Roosevelt's "New Deal" called for just such a measure to save the towns and farms of northern Colorado. Greeley leadership was capable and willing to collaborate and chart a course for success.

On August 14, 1933, just two weeks after Kelly, Norcross and Stimson had their impromptu post office discussion, a meeting was organized with the Weld County Commissioners and George M. Bull of the recently formed Public Works Administration. Could the federal agency move this venture forward? "Those in the room saw the creation of a 'Grand Lake' project as a counter-attack against the Depression," wrote C-BT historian Robert Autobee. Weld County, with an area of 4,022 square miles (approximately the size of Connecticut), had become one of the world's largest irrigated regions (347,909 acres) and needed water now and for its future. Soon, the plan was the center of discussion in northern Colorado's dusty town halls, clubs and lodges, and private offices.[39]

Three days later, on August 17, 1933, the Greeley Chamber of Commerce appointed a group called the "Grand Lake Committee" to undertake surveys and solicit funds for the project. By 1935, the committee had evolved into the Northern Colorado Water Users Association. Contributions poured in from Weld and Larimer Counties, the Greeley Chamber of Commerce, and private citizens. The Association also sought support from large private companies, such as Great Western Sugar, the Union Pacific Railroad, and the Burlington Railroad. Among the most staunch advocate for the "Grand Lake Project" was Charles Hansen, the well-respected publisher of the *Greeley Tribune*, who became its chief spokesman and organizer.

First as a reporter and then publisher of the *Greeley Tribune*, from 1913 until his death in 1953, Hansen employed his vast knowledge and genial influence to explain, promote and support the water project to his readers. Like Nathan Meeker and others of the Union Colony era, Hansen knew that water would always be the lifeblood of Greeley and the region.

Said Robert Autobee: "Hansen organized high plains farmers, businessmen, and local politicians to familiarize the Bureau of Reclamation and federal government officials with the advantages of Northern Colorado." Autobee called Hansen an apostle of "quiet evangelism," coaxing all parties to cooperate. "He would talk in a low voice to anyone who would listen; then he would take you down in the basement of the *Tribune* office in Greeley and show you the worksheets, the preliminary drawings, the calculations. You would come away convinced that the C-BT project would somehow, some day, come into being."[40]

In October 1936, for the first time, city officials publicly discussed their involvement in the initiative that would change the face of northern Colorado into the next century. As historian Daniel Tyler wrote, the Greeley City Council drafted an ordinance endorsing the U.S. Bureau of Reclamation's role in initiating the project to bring 310,000 acre-feet of Colorado River water to the South Platte River Basin. Greeley's City Engineer, Theodore B. Moodey, provided documentation to the Northern Colorado Water Users Association of the city's need for additional water. Said Moodey: "The City of Greeley is at times short of water for domestic purposes on account of prior appropriations and low stages of water in the Cache la Poudre River." To mitigate those circumstances, "an additional supply of water would be of great benefit to the city for its present needs and future development."[41]

Moodey calculated Greeley's existing and future water needs, which revealed the ambitions and challenges facing his community. The year 1935 had seen the city use 4,640 acre-feet of water, and Moodey estimated that Greeley would need to increase its water supplies by 50 percent to meet peaking demands as high as 7,060 acre-feet. He anticipated serving 17,000 people along the Bellvue pipeline route—Greeley with 14,000 residents, and 1,500 more in Windsor and the surrounding area. Rural residences located along the pipeline comprised the remaining 1,500 customers.

Moodey projected that the Greeley water system would double in usage within a decade, needing 12,140 acre-feet to serve 20,000 people in Greeley, 3,000 acre-feet in Windsor, and 3,000 acre-feet more for "others along the pipeline." Two new customers, said Moodey, would be the town of Eaton, which would have a population of 4,000 by 1946, and the neighboring communities of Evans and La Salle (another 4,000 water users) ten years in the future.[42]

By February 1937, councilors had authorized petitions to the U.S. Congress to endorse the Colorado-Big Thompson Project. The city council's February 2nd proclamation declared that Greeley was "practically at the center of the 800,000 irrigated acres of Northern Colorado." The region is "vitally interested not only for its economic value to the surrounding farm lands," but also because "it offers the most feasible prospect of additional municipal water supply for Greeley and its adjoining towns." To that end, said the city council, the City "strongly approves and urges the speedy building of the proposed Colorado-Big Thompson irrigation project for its feasibility and comparative cheapness."[43]

While residents of Greeley continued to cope with the cycle of economic and environmental challenges of the 1930s, readers of the *Tribune* were intrigued by the high praise of Merle Thorpe, editor of *The Nation's Business*, directed toward the development of northern Colorado. Invited to Colorado to speak at an insurance sales meeting in Denver, Thorpe traveled north to Greeley in August 1937 to conduct research on the sugar beet industry. Having made the journey, in his words, "a half-dozen times in the past 30 years," Thorpe spent time with N.C. McCreery and other officials of the Great Western Sugar Company. "Northern Colorado," said the business editor, "is distinctive as an outstanding example of development achieved largely through voluntary collectivism, as opposed to political collectivism, which politicians are now trying to force upon people in all corners of the world."[44]

What he found in Greeley and Weld County, by comparison, pleased Thorpe immensely. "I don't know of any other place in the United States," the editor told the *Tribune*, "that has shown greater advancement during the past 30 years than this section." Thorpe defined this as "a development in tempo," or "something you find in a community [through] the sixth sense—the life-force that drives individuals to achievement [through] voluntary collectivism." Thorpe also noted northern Colorado's "need for the additional water to be supplied [through] the Colorado-Big Thompson project." The business journal editor had learned of this initiative, he said, through an interview of "considerable length with Charles Hansen, president of the Northern Colorado Water Users and publisher of the *Greeley Tribune*."[45]

HISTORY OFTEN REPEATS itself with inevitable comparisons. Charles Hansen's leadership, promotion, and endorsement helped secure the necessary public support for an innovative federal water project to serve Greeley and the surrounding region. Horace Greeley, Nathan Meeker and Charles Hansen understood the power of the written word, and the power of the press, to garner public support for noble causes. The list goes on: Boyd, Nettleton, Watson, Todd, Kelly, Seaman, and others. They were all catalysts, in the right place, at the right time, with the right message—and the people listened and responded.

In early October, the *Greeley Tribune* editorialized about the achievements of the C-BT planning process. "Northern Colorado united in a conservancy district," said the *Tribune* publisher on October 1st, and "with virtually no opposition took a step that reveals more than anything else a solidarity of purpose against the common enemy of any irrigated area—drought." In spring 1937, former city attorneys William R. Kelly and Thomas Nixon convinced the state legislature to permit establishment of taxing entities called "conservancy districts." The Colorado-Big Thompson Project, and the new Northern Colorado Water Conservancy District, would be the first collaboration of its kind between local irrigators, cities, and the federal government.

This very significant state legislation allowed advocates of the Colorado-Big

Thompson project to conduct a local election to create a new property tax of three-tenths of one mill throughout the Northern District lands. "Probably no tax assessed against the people of this region," said the *Tribune*, "has been more necessary for its salvation."[46] What made the success of the C-BT initiative notable, the *Tribune* also noted, was the equitable distribution of the financial burden for construction and maintenance of the project. "The expense has been assumed [through] the tax levy," said the *Tribune*, which declared: "It is right that should be so, for the urban and town dwellers themselves will benefit quite as much from a plentiful water supply as will the direct user irrigating his fields."

One of the directors of the newly created conservancy district board, Ed F. Munroe of Larimer County, spoke for many about the wisdom of the C-BT project. "We must have water," Munroe told the *Tribune*, "or move out." The Northern Colorado Water Users Association board was "as aware of the extent of the task that faces them as they are of the necessity of its being accomplished." Said Munroe of his North Poudre Irrigation Company: "It is a question in my mind if we can hang on until the water gets to us."[47]

In the waning days of 1937, the *Rocky Mountain News* of Denver recognized what northern Colorado water officials had accomplished by means of their conservancy district, and of their support for the largest Bureau of Reclamation project to date in the country. After explaining to its Denver readership how the C-BT system would make agriculture prosper again in Colorado, the *Rocky Mountain News* editorialized about the impact on urban areas of the South Platte Valley. "Five or six years from now," said the *News*, "Eastern Colorado will be able to support 10 percent more population." The paper, which had endorsed the Union Colony enterprise nearly seven decades earlier, predicted "the assurance of plenteous water for all of or more than 600,000 acres." From this would come "more farm population," and for northern Colorado "more sugar beets to be handled in the factories."[48]

About four decades later in 1974, the vision for the Colorado-Big Thompson project was memorialized in the work of Pulitzer Prize winning author James Michener and his bestselling book *Centennial*, which later became a widely watched television mini-series. Michener had taught at Greeley's Colorado State College of Education from 1936-1941. Through his interaction with city leaders and C-BT promoters like Charles Hansen, Michener became familiar with the

Colorado-Big Thompson Project, even voting in the 1938 special election that authorized the new Northern District tax on property in Greeley.

Michener's fictional character in *Centennial*, "Potato Brumbaugh," expressed his vision and passion for a tunnel to divert water from the Colorado River to the Big Thompson and South Platte Rivers and Greeley:

> "He [Brumbaugh] was staring at the mountains in a bold new way, seeing them for what they really were, a barrier thrusting itself into the heavens, impeding the natural circulation of clouds and knocking water from them before it could cross the crests and fall upon the eastern slope. It was the Rockies that had caused the Great American Desert; it was the Rockies that kept Potato Brumbaugh from getting as much [irrigation] water into the Platte [River] as he wanted."[49]

As actually occurred, Brumbaugh's solution was to drill a tunnel through the high mountain rock barrier. Charles Hansen, municipal leaders, farmers, northeastern Colorado residents, engineers, attorneys, legislators, contractors, and construction workers would bring the vision of Michener's fictional character into the world of non-fiction when the 13.1-mile-long Alva B. Adams Tunnel became operational in 1947.

A KEY COMPONENT of the Colorado-Big Thompson Project was the creation of a local water agency to partner with the U.S. Bureau of Reclamation for project administration. The 1937 Water Conservancy District Act was a signature accomplishment of Greeley attorneys William R. Kelly and Thomas Nixon. Sponsored by Weld County legislator Moses Smith (who was Speaker of the Colorado House of Representatives the previous year), the Water Conservancy Act enabled creation of the Northern Colorado Water Conservancy District based in Greeley, with headquarters later in Loveland and now in Berthoud. Greeley water leaders played a major role in its formation, and later, its Municipal Subdistrict which built and operates the Windy Gap Project.

William R. Kelly's decades of service to Greeley and northeastern Colorado warrants a closer look. Kelly moved to Greeley with his parents in 1890 and received his law degree from the University of Colorado in 1907. He gained practical experiences in irrigated agriculture growing up on his parents' farm north of Greeley near Lucerne. He, like Delph Carpenter, graduated from Greeley High School, and planned to attend Colorado School of Mines to become a mining engineer. However, an August hailstorm destroyed the Kelly family's crops and abruptly changed William's plans. If this Lucerne hailstorm had not happened, Greeley would have missed out on the future talents of a fine water attorney.

In 1909, after a brief stint in New Mexico following graduation from law school, Kelly established his Greeley law practice and served as a water referee for the Colorado courts from 1911-1925. He was also Greeley's city attorney from 1916-1921, and Weld County Attorney from 1921-1928. During his career, Kelly represented the Laramie-Poudre Irrigation District for many years, the New Cache la Poudre Irrigation Company (the original Greeley Number 2 Ditch), and the Cache la Poudre Reservoir Company for 40 years. He was also counsel to the Northern Colorado Water Conservancy District for 21 years.

The rich water history of the Union Colony filled Kelly with enthusiasm and legal rigor—so much that Colorado U.S. Senator Ed Johnson called him "Mr. Water Law." Kelly practiced water law in Greeley for 60 years and shined as a water historian.[50] He provided legal representation to the Colorado-Big Thompson Project, without pay, for five years during its formative years.

William Kelly and Thomas Nixon collaborated on writing the Water Conservancy Act in 1937, and later prevailed in the Colorado Supreme Court's *Rogers v. Letford* decision upholding its legality.[51] Kelly had a very good teacher— Delph Carpenter. Kelly had worked with Carpenter in the 1920s to salvage the assets of the Greeley-Poudre Project following Colorado's disastrous loss of Laramie River water in the 1922 *Wyoming v. Colorado* case. Kelly dealt with bond defaults and the foreclosure of tax liens on many farm properties, and realized that "the irrigation district form of financing a new development of lands proved unwise generally for Colorado."[52]

In 1934, Delph Carpenter wrote a letter to the Northern Colorado Water Users Association proclaiming it was "now or never with the Grand Lake and other projects in the upper basin of the Colorado River drainage." Construction of "colossal water projects on the lower Colorado River, with funds of the United States, make imperative immediate construction of the Grand Lake tunnel project."[53] Carpenter was referring to Lake Mead and Boulder Dam (renamed Hoover Dam in 1947) constructed between 1931 and 1936.

After the Weld County Commissioners brought the Greeley-Poudre Irrigation District into existence by court order on April 9, 1909, the district levied assessments on every acre of land within its boundaries with a 20-year bond repayment period. "Too short a time; a too-high interest rate," Kelly states in his retrospective. "Landowners could not pay, tax buyers would not buy, when the lands were annually, through 1929, being sold at tax sales."[54] This experience on project development and land taxation would be a strong reminder to Kelly as he developed the legal logistics for a different kind of water district for northeastern Colorado.

Plans for the Colorado-Big Thompson Project advanced in Greeley and in Washington, D.C. In the summer of 1935, the Colorado State Planning Commission created a Water Resources Advisory Committee, and its 17 members met for the first time in Denver on June 13-15. Glenwood Springs attorney Frank Delaney, of the Western Slope Protective Association, immediately brought forth a resolution declaring that, "to protect and insure the growth of Western Colorado, every plan for transmountain diversion projects shall incorporate and include as an integral part of the cost thereof to be borne by the proponents compensatory storage equal to the amount to be diverted."

This bold statement was the beginning of West Slope/East Slope compensatory storage negotiations. The committee next ranked and recommended several projects for federal Public Works Administration funding.[55] Resolution No. 17, introduced by Greeley's Charles Hansen, urged the U.S. Bureau of Reclamation to commence construction of the Grand Lake Transmountain Diversion Project, with the proviso that it would include protection for the Western Slope as provided in Resolution No. 1.[56]

On January 7, 1936, President Franklin Roosevelt informed the Colorado Congressional delegation that the Public Works Administration would not provide grants for irrigation or storage projects. Instead, the funding request would have to go through the Bureau of Reclamation under its laws which required project repayment.[57] This added a new wrinkle to the planning process but did not significantly impede progress.

As the economic recovery of the 1930s slowly progressed, Colorado Governor Ed Johnson convened two extraordinary sessions of the General Assembly in 1936. Among many measures that were enacted, the Assembly acknowledged the State's inability to construct "essential storage without the aid of the federal government."[58] The legislators declared that the laws of Colorado permitted the organization of water users to contract with the Bureau of Reclamation, the Public Works Administration and other federal agencies.[59] Without specifically mentioning the C-BT Project, the Colorado Legislature stated that a substantial need existed for supplementary water to assure "permanent security to those lands which for many years have been and now are being farmed in crops adapted to existing conditions."[60] The political table was getting set, and federal funding would soon be ready.

In late 1936, Kelly and Weld County attorney Thomas Nixon, on behalf of the Northern Colorado Water Users Association, continued negotiations with Frank Delaney and the Western Slope Protective Association over the terms of an agreement for construction of the C-BT project. Kelly proposed that the project would not interfere with the Shoshone Power Plant priority call for 1,250 cfs of Colorado River water in Glenwood Canyon.[61] Delaney responded that a larger compromise about the "future use of the waters of the Colorado River" was needed. He called a meeting of four Northern Colorado Water Users Association and four Western Slope representatives to formulate a plan.[62]

The 1936 general election brought Wayne Aspinall of Mesa County into the Colorado General Assembly as Speaker of the House, along with Judge Clifford Stone of Gunnison County, both from the West Slope. Aspinall and Stone were statespersons committed to achieving cooperation between disparate geographical regions of the state, and with federal agencies.[63] Their efforts helped to bring about the Colorado Legislature's unique 1937 session which produced a statewide water framework for the future. It created the Colorado River Water Conservation District,[64] Colorado's Water Conservancy Act,[65] and the Colorado Water Conservation Board.[66] These three legislative acts resulted from Colorado's realization that it lacked legal institutions with the authority, revenue, and staying power to develop Colorado's share of water under various interstate compacts.[67]

The sponsors of these three landmark legislative actions demonstrate how the political negotiations, over the C-BT project, precipitated a much larger statewide water development forum. Clifford Stone, future Director of the Colorado Water Conservation Board, and State Representative Wayne Aspinall of the Western Slope, co-sponsored the legislation to create the Colorado River Water Conservation District. Moses Smith of Weld County and Clifford Stone of Gunnison County co-sponsored the creation of the Colorado Water Conservation Board legislation. Moses Smith was lead sponsor for creation of the Water Conservancy Act legislation. A provision of the Water Conservancy Act restricted transmountain diversions to no more than an annual average of 320,000 acre-feet from the Colorado River Basin, for all conservancy districts combined, pending a division of water by compact among the upper basin states.[68]

On September 20, 1937, the Weld County District Court entered its findings and decree organizing the Northern Colorado Water Conservancy District "which includes generally the lands in the agricultural areas in the vicinity of the St. Vrain, Big Thompson, Cache la Poudre rivers, and of the Platte River from Platteville to the eastern line of Colorado." Together, the farm lands and the cities growing out of them, such as Greeley, Eaton, Boulder, Fort Collins, Longmont, Loveland, Fort Morgan, Brush, Sterling and Julesburg, were then producing a total assessed valuation of $140,000,000 (over $2.5 billion in 2020) for all property within district boundaries. In addition, an integral component of the project included "the construction of a reservoir on the Blue River on the western slope for the purpose of replacement of water diverted to the eastern slope and to compensate and stabilize the flow of the Colorado river."[69]

The Water Conservancy Act empowered the formation of such districts across the state as "quasi-municipal corporations" with authority to assess and collect taxes, special assessments, and established rates for water it provided.[70] U.S. Senate Document No. 80, dated June 15, 1937, spelled out the features and manner of operation for the C-BT Project.[71] Senator Alva B. Adams worked with Congress to obtain a hugely important exception, from the Reclamation Act requirements. This authorized the use of C-BT water for direct domestic, municipal, and commercial purposes within district boundaries, as well as for supplemental use on farms already being irrigated within the Northern District's seven northeastern Colorado counties. In addition, a provision of the Reclamation Law was changed to allow irrigation of agricultural units up to 160 acres, rather than only 40 acres.[72]

Figure 6.3 On July 5, 1938, Northern Colorado Water Conservancy District board president Charles Hansen signs the Repayment Contract with the United States, allowing construction of the C-BT project to begin. Seated (left to right) Thomas Nixon, Charles Hansen, J.M. Dille. Standing (left to right) Fred Norcross, Burgis G. Coy, Robert J. Wright, Robert C. Benson, William A Carlson, Ralph W. McMurray, Ray Lanyon, Ed F. Munroe, Moses E. Smith, William E. Letford, and Charles M. Rolfson. City of Greeley Museums, Permanent Collection, 1989.41.0001.

On May 21, 1938, the Northern Colorado Water Conservancy District Board of Directors passed a resolution placing the C-BT repayment contract with the United States up to a vote of the district's electorate, who had paid a property tax the prior year. The vote carried 7,510 "for" with 439 "against." On July 5, 1938, Charles Hansen, now president of the Northern Colorado Water Conservancy District Board, and John M. Dille, its Secretary, signed a certification for delivery of the contract for filing with the Weld County District Court. The C-BT contract was the first of its kind in the United States which authorized the development of a federal reclamation project for municipal and industrial water supply, in addition to irrigated agriculture. Delph Carpenter's work, in securing an apportionment of the Colorado River through compact negotiations for all of Colorado, paved the way for the future growth of Greeley and northern Colorado.

Ironically, Kelly's foremost trial and triumph as a lawyer came through conflict with none other than Charles Hansen—who had championed the C-BT Project in the first place. Professor Dan Tyler recounts this story in his book, *The Last Water Hole in the West*. In 1947, Denver had claimed water rights for the Dillon Dam and Roberts Tunnel projects on the Blue River, upstream from Green Mountain Reservoir, and were moving forward in the U.S. District Court for Colorado. The Denver Water Board, as opposed to the Northern Colorado Water Conservancy District Board, had not agreed to construct a compensatory storage reservoir for the Western Slope. Hansen felt a "moral duty" to keep faith with his Western Slope counterparts due to the hard-nosed bargaining that had led up to the signing of the C-BT contract and passage of the Water Conservancy Act.

He summoned Kelly to his office in mid-1948, directing him to draw up legal documents for subordinating the Northern District's West Slope water diversions to future Western Slope water needs. Kelly resisted vociferously. He argued that Green Mountain Reservoir (constructed as the first C-BT feature of 152,000 acre-feet of compensatory storage) satisfied the Northern District's contractual obligation. Subject to that obligation, Colorado's prior appropriation law should protect C-BT water diversions in the future. Otherwise, the Northern District would be replacing water for uncompensated Denver diversions. Charles Hansen did not agree at all with this interpretation; as one of the original negotiators he felt at the very least a moral obligation to his Western Slope counterparts.

Fired-up, Hansen obtained a resolution from the Northern District board in August of 1948 to override Kelly's objection. At this juncture, perceiving a threat to the C-BT's water rights, Weld County Judge Claude C. Coffin (who held the power of appointment for Northern District board members under the terms of the Water Conservancy Act) asked the board to reconsider its controversial resolution. Judge Coffin questioned whether an "assumed policy to make the Northern District's priorities subservient to future use on the Western Slope" might be "contrary to long settled rules of law pertaining to priorities of right to appropriated water." He asked the board to reconsider whether its resolution complied with Senate Document 80, through which Congress had authorized the C-BT Project.

In November 1948, following consultation by Charles Lory (former president of Colorado Agricultural College) with Judge Coffin, the Northern board adopted a resolution satisfactory to both Hansen and Kelly. Senate Document 80, whatever it provided for, would be given effect. The new resolution did not include any reference to the "right of the people of the West Slope . . . to the present or future use of water in the basin of the Colorado River."[73] This was a major compromise; however, the strain on the Hansen/Kelly relationship festered until Hansen's death in 1953.

RETURNING TO THE previous decade, on February 1, 1938, the Greeley City Council adopted a resolution to purchase 15,000 units of C-BT water. This amount coincided with Greeley's future growth projections, first calculated two years earlier. The City of Greeley, said the *Tribune*, believed this volume (a significant increase from the 1936 requested amount of 6,070 units) would be "sufficient to supply domestic water to 40,000 people." Greeley officials, the *Tribune* contended, were "convinced that new water supplies from the [C-BT] diversion project will cause population increases in Greeley and surrounding towns sufficient to utilize the water."

The City felt fortunate that it had bid for about five percent of the Colorado River water, as "it is likely that the [conservancy] board will be faced with the necessity of allotting less water to some farms than is being applied for." These allotments would affect 13,000 parcels of irrigated land in the Northern District. Another benefit to the citizens of Greeley, who had voted to tax themselves to obtain C-BT water, said the *Tribune*, was that "water rented in [the Poudre Basin] cost as high as $10 an acre-foot." By comparison, C-BT water "is being sold for $1.50 an acre-foot a year, or only 15 per cent as much as rented water cost desperate North Poudre district farmers."[74]

As the year 1938 advanced, the financial resources of the Greeley Water Department improved greatly. Evidence of this appeared in its annual report: "Greeley's two-million-dollar water system in 1937 delivered 103 million more gallons of water from the headworks than the same system did in 1936." This increase in usage coincided with pipeline improvements that reduced leakage from over 70 million gallons in 1936 to 58 million gallons in 1937. Pipeline efficiency had grown to 96.87 percent, a substantial improvement from earlier years. Per-capita water consumption for the population of 17,000 was 293 gallons.[75]

The 1930s closed on a more optimistic note than could have been imagined a decade earlier. The Bureau of Reclamation, an agency that had not allied with Greeley water interests in the 1920s, now asked the City to finalize its bid for units of the C-BT allocation. City councilors discussed whether they should seek contracts to obtain more than their original estimate of 15,000 units.

Three Northern Colorado Water Conservancy District officials appeared before the Greeley City Council to answer questions about future water demands in northern Colorado. Charles Hansen president; John M. Dille, manager; and Thomas Nixon, attorney, convinced councilors, in the words of the *Greeley Tribune*, that "the city would have no trouble in reselling that part of the water contracted for which is in excess of immediate demands." Alderman C.H. Young believed that Greeley could grow to 35,000 people with its C-BT allocation, and that "the city may want to furnish water as far south as LaSalle and north to Eaton."[76]

AT THE CLOSE of 1939, Greeley had regained momentum as northern Colorado's most-prosperous city. The call of "Must Have Water" in 1902 shaped much of Greeley's history and economic success, and would do so again in the harsh conditions of the 1930s. Community-minded leaders had joined with others throughout the state to petition Congress to authorize the Colorado-Big Thompson Project. The new system would deliver water just in time for another dry cycle: the 1950s. While it may not have been clear to Greeley's leadership as the decade ended, Greeley could hope for brighter days ahead as the 1940s came into view.

CHAPTER SEVEN

1940-1950
Water for War and Peace

Greeley Transformed

THE GREAT DEPRESSION and drought of the 1930s profoundly affected the nation's agricultural, commercial, and industrial sectors; a challenge that America faced with determination. President Franklin D. Roosevelt's New Deal initiatives created federal agencies to provide training programs, public works jobs, refinancing, loans, and relief measures for the people, leading the way to economic recovery. Americans moved forward, but the carefree attitudes and unbridled optimism of the 1920s had disappeared. Historian Gerald Nash found it "hardly surprising that the mood of many westerners about the future . . . was somber and cautious, a mood of limited expectations."[1] Greeley, like its peers nationwide, relied heavily upon New Deal programs, such as the Works Progress Administration (WPA), Public Works Administration (PWA), and the Civilian Conservation Corps (CCC) to help employ people to keep the local economy viable.

The advent of World War II delivered new opportunities and economic fortunes to Colorado and the nation. "No other single influence," said Nash, "brought such great and cataclysmic changes to the West." The U.S. government recruited and drafted millions of soldiers, sailors, air and medical personnel, and constructed defense installations and military bases across the country. Billions of dollars in federal expenditures, salaries, and contracts appeared almost overnight for the war effort, many of these in rural or remote areas, including Greeley and Weld County.

During the 1940s, northern Colorado returned to a 10-year wet cycle, boosting crop and livestock production to feed those on the home front and on the battlefields. The optimistic character of the American West also reasserted itself in the post WWII era. "Westerners now had visions of unlimited growth and expansion," said Nash. Greeley and its peers had "emerged from the war as a path breaking self-sufficient region with unbounded optimism for [the] future."[2] As it had for decades, water served as a prime source of economic health for the city.

The *Greeley Tribune* expressed the optimism of Greeley's agricultural community in a 1942 article, "'No More Drouths,' Boast Farmers in Greeley and Loveland." The article noted that several hundred farmers, served by the Greeley and Loveland Irrigation system in the 20,000 acre area to the west and southwest of Greeley, "have been lifted out of the dust and drouth bowl forever." In 1942, Lake Loveland and its Seven Lakes' reservoirs were full, with enough water to last three years, and Boyd Lake was full for the first time since 1928. Good soil, a prime location, and proximity to Greeley meant that farms under this "water rich" system were the most prized of northern Colorado, boasting high crop yields of beets, potatoes and beans. Large farming fortunes were made in the region during the wet years.

Population growth was inevitable in the region. Between 1940-1950, Greeley expanded from 16,000 to 20,300 residents; a growth rate of 21 percent. When compared to its northern Colorado neighbors in 1950, the city outranked Fort Collins (14,937 people); Longmont (8,099); Loveland (6,773); and even the college town of Boulder (20,000). Only Denver, with 415,000 residents, surpassed Greeley's population. Like other communities nationwide, Greeley's leaders hoped to make wartime prosperity more permanent.

During the decade of the 1940s, Greeley water revenues were an important indicator of economic health. Federal funds and a municipal bond sale provided money to construct Milton Seaman Dam and Reservoir on the North Fork of the Cache la Poudre River. These funds also allowed for improvements to the Bellvue pipeline, and the acquisition of the high mountain reservoirs to enhance the city's water portfolio.

A great sense of civic urgency also prevailed during the early 1940s. On March 29, 1941, a half-page notice/declaration in the *Greeley Tribune* was purchased by 22 prominent Greeley businessmen. They included Charles Hansen (publisher of the *Greeley Tribune* and president of the Northern Colorado Water Conservancy District) and W.D. Farr (future president of the Municipal Subdistrict of the Northern Colorado Water Conservancy District, and chair of the Greeley Water

Board). Its headline declared: "Keep Greeley's Water Supply Out Of Politics!" Reminding readers that "water is the very life blood of Greeley," the group claimed that "our needs for water come ahead of all city politics and ahead of any desires of any individual for election to office." The most important message of this declaration was, **"Look ahead and plan for others as others have planned for you."**

The authors of this notice included a section, "WHAT ARE THE FACTS." It then listed 13 points which included statistics about streamflows versus purchased water rights, such as "Since March 15, there has been no water in the [Cache la Poudre] river for Greeley." While "this has been the best year for steady flow on the river for the past six years," said the article, cold spring weather would leave the city dependent upon its "temporary storage . . ," calculated to be about "50 days of lowest consumption." It went without saying, the group noted, that "growth demands more water."[3]

The businessmen also addressed in their notice, "OUR IMMEDIATE NEEDS," and the threat that some person or group might call for reduction in city water rates and water supply acquisitions. Given current streamflow data from the state water commissioner, the Greeley water department, and the city council's water committee, they noted "it is idle and even dangerous to even consider cutting Greeley's present low rates." The group considered it "fortunate that so far no candidate [for Greeley City Council] has publicly promised voters support for immediate cuts in water rates." Instead, wrote the businessmen, "the income of Greeley's Water Department is not too high." To emphasize their point, the group stated in capital letters about the fee structure: "IT IS ACTUALLY TOO LOW!"[4]

IN JANUARY 1940, Greeley's Mayor E.M. Colpitts, president of the Colorado Municipal League and a former official of the Great Western Sugar Company, traveled to Fort Collins with Water Superintendent Milton Seaman to meet with that city's mayor. Greeley officials sought collaboration for a proposed new reservoir located on the North Fork of the Cache la Poudre River. Mayor Colpitts invited the Fort Collins City Council to "come to Greeley Friday night to talk the proposition over." The gathering was cordial, and Greeley officials later arranged a meeting with State Engineer Michael Hinderlider to explore the project's feasibility. The Greeley City Council also directed the city attorney to "investigate the legal phases of a storage reservoir and its construction."[5]

By March 12th, city water officials reported that both communities had authorized Edward Selander, a well-known contractor, to "make further investigations into a retaining reservoir in connection with the city water supply." A month later, Greeley City Council Chairman Charles Capron reported that "the Water Department has completed plans with the River Commissioner which makes it possible to continue with construction."[6] Fort Collins had decided not to participate in the new reservoir project, but entry into this dam site did cross through the property of the Fort Collins Water Treatment Plant.

The urgency of the new reservoir project was underscored on June 18, 1940, when the city council learned from Chairman Capron that Greeley's water use had exceeded 8.5 million gallons per day, "more than could be brought into the reservoirs." City officials warned that "acute water shortage in the city" required a reduction in outdoor sprinkling in favor of "giving any advantage possible to the farmers." Greeley anticipated yet another influx of residents during the 1940s, but also wanted to lease excess water supplies to area farmers, ranchers and other municipalities as it had in the past.

The City also hired Homer Sims, a former Greeley police officer, to "check against water waste," Sims later told the *Greeley Tribune*: "I never would believe so many people would waste water." He praised the council's decision to reduce sprinkling to mornings and evenings rather than implementing nine-hour watering periods on alternate days. Mayor Colpitts noted on June 19th that Greeley had not yet fully recovered from the dry winter, "when the Poudre dropped below 40 second feet [cubic feet per second]." These low flows created a "non-preferred necessity"—using raw water from irrigation ditches instead of treated water from the Bellvue plant.[7]

That summer, the State Board of Land Commissioners had approved the City's application to purchase 106 acres of state-owned land for the new reservoir site. Longtime Greeley water engineer, L.L. Stimson, a collaborator on several mountain reservoir projects with the City, offered his services as a consulting engineer for dam construction. Stimson reminded the council: "I made the surveys for the North Fork reservoir as engineer for the Laramie-Poudre Irrigation Company." He further offered to make his maps and charts available, at a cost of $500 (around

$10,000 in 2020 dollars), while cautioning that the irrigation company "will need to run main Poudre water through this reservoir site in order to get it to their [downstream] canals." William R. Kelly, the former Greeley city attorney who now represented the Laramie-Poudre Irrigation District, asked the city council to permit the district "to carry water across [through] the reservoir and to enlarge the reservoir for irrigation purposes as long as the enlargement would not injure the reservoir."[8] Greeley's plan for the proposed North Fork project was readily accepted by the Denver and Greeley offices of the WPA (Works Progress Administration). In addition, they agreed that a federal work camp would be established and maintained if enough men could be hired.

One month before construction began, longtime superintendent Milton Seaman passed away after a long illness. In a September 1940 tribute, the *Greeley Tribune* published a feature article about his life, calling Seaman "one of the best-known municipal administrators in the Rocky Mountain Region." In 1913, his destiny had led him to "take charge of Greeley's mountain system when it was comparatively young."[9] Greeley councilors echoed this praise with their September 24th Resolution: "Mr. Seaman has devoted the greater part of his life to faithful, conscientious and intelligent effort in the service of the City of Greeley and in the development of a wholesome and adequate water system." The super-intendent, who had spoken at so many council meetings over the years, "[had] as few others, advanced and protected the welfare and health of his community." The council announced that his son, Roy Seaman, would become the water department superintendent, "effective immediately."[10] They also voted to sign documents for construction of "Milton Seaman Dam" in his honor.[11]

The earthen-filled dam, 400 feet long at its crest and 400 feet thick at its base, was constructed between 1940 and 1945. Blasted through solid rock, its diversion tunnel extended 275 feet, with a width of 18 feet cresting into an 18-foot-high arch. The $330,510 project (nearly $6 million in 2020) provided work at its peak for about 200 men, affording additional water storage for the rapidly growing community of Greeley.[12]

In early August 1941, State Engineer Hinderlider visited the construction site, and reported back with excellent news: "All of the bedrock exposed so far in excavations for the base of the dam fill shows that such bedrock is of excellent quality and from the appearance of the granite formations on the cutoff trench."

Hinderlider complimented the selection of the reservoir site, reporting that "the granite formations beneath the entire length of the dam should be practically water tight or impervious to material amounts of seepage." He told the *Greeley Tribune* on August 6th: "From all present indications . . . this damsite seems to be one of the best sites I have ever found."[13]

On September 26th, the State Engineer confirmed the final dimensions for Seaman Dam. Its official location was "across the North Fork of the Cache la Poudre River in Sections 28 and 33, Township 9 North, Range 70 West of the 6th P.M. [Principal Meridian]." This would place the structure "about one mile above its confluence with the main stem of the Cache la Poudre." A major structural feature of the site was the "granitic formations forming the canyon." The City of Greeley would have "a reservoir to provide supplemental water [with] a capacity at spillway level at elevation 5480 of 6,000 acre-feet, and a surface area of 140 acres."[14]

Additional details for the dam appeared in the WPA's Construction Design Report. The central feature would be "a combination structure consisting of an impervious earth core, with adjacent semi-pervious shells of fine and coarse sand." These would be "supported on the upstream and downstream slopes with heavy blankets of loose rock." Its height "above the foundation will be about 112 feet, and the crest width will be 26 feet." Another critical feature of the dam would be its spillway, which Hinderlider said would provide "a gross freeboard of 12 feet between the crest of the dam and the highest point in the bottom of the spillway." The latter could handle up to 18,000 cubic feet per second of floodwaters, which the State Engineer estimated to be "a maximum depth of 4 feet above the crest."[15]

Construction of Seaman Dam was hampered by chronic labor shortages, as men were drafted for overseas military duty. In October 1941, after reviewing construction work plans, the WPA director of operations declared there was an insufficient number of workers at the camp to continue with the project. Said the director: "When we arrive at such a condition the only thing, in my opinion, is to close down the camp."[16]

This action would jeopardize a considerable investment and threaten the city's water storage plans. Federal expenditures had reached the 67 percent level—$146,167 (around $2 million in 2020 dollars) out of a total authorized budget of $221,748 (about $3 million in 2020).[17] The WPA district manager next summoned the State Engineer to his office, along with Greeley's new water superintendent and consulting engineer. Pronouncing his displeasure with the slow construction progress, the WPA manager implied that Greeley had designed the project improperly.[18] Not long after that meeting, the Greeley City Council learned on October 21st that the WPA had suspended work on Seaman Dam due to a lack of workers.[19]

This was a serious setback, but work continued on another important water project for the city. The following month, on November 26, 1941, less than two weeks before the Japanese attack on Pearl Harbor, the water department completed installation of 6,000 feet of new cast iron and/or steel-reinforced pipe to upgrade a portion of the chronically leaking Bellvue pipeline. In anticipation of future delays to procure hard-to-find pipe for the project, the City explored allocating some pipeline funds to the stalled reservoir construction effort. "If [national] defense priorities make it impossible to get deliveries on some of this pipe [for the Bellvue pipeline]," said the *Tribune,* "a part of the [bond] issue may be used on construction of the Milton Seaman Dam on the North Poudre."[20]

At the end of 1941, the Greeley City Council learned that its water bonds had sold "at the lowest rate of interest in the history of the city." Harris Trust and Savings Bank of Chicago agreed to manage sales of the $125,000 ($2 million in 2020) bond issue at a rate of 1.1 percent. "There were 14 bids from bond houses," said the *Greeley Tribune* on November 26th, "with offices from New York to San Francisco [interested in the bond sale]." The water department's previous record for a bond sale was in 1935, with a 2.4 percent interest rate offered for construction of the new sewage disposal plant.

The following spring on May 19, 1942, the WPA terminated all of its work camp operations. The War Production Board had denied Greeley's request for "a higher priority rating for headgates," due to the wartime steel shortage. Since the federal government administered all tests on its water projects, an unfinished dam like Seaman would have to wait until all existing federal water facilities could be assessed for their safety. Seeking other options, water superintendent Roy Seaman traveled to Denver to meet with the "head of the utilities division [from] Washington, D.C." The federal utilities director listened and advised Seaman to send requests directly to him, so that he could "give it his personal supervision."

The communications were successful, and two months later the Civilian Conservation Corps resumed work at Seaman Dam. Charles Capron, chairman

Figure 7.1 Work Projects Administration (WPA) and City funds were used to construct Milton Seaman Dam and Reservoir in 1940-1945. Labor and material shortages during WWII periodically hampered construction. A succession of employees included WPA and Civilian Conservation Corps (CCC) workers, and Mennonite conscientious objectors, who were housed in a 125-man camp near the North Fork of the Cache la Poudre River. Photo courtesy of Richard Stenzel.

of the city council's water committee, reported that "the State Engineer had inspected the dam [construction site] and was very well pleased." Hinderlider had also "just returned from Washington and felt that it would be possible to secure gates for the dam."[21] In addition, the City had negotiated successfully with the U.S. Department of Agriculture to allow the use of CCC workers on the project." By August 18, 1942, said the State Engineer, "the work on the Seaman Dam was progressing very nicely."[22]

Shifts of 30 men swung into action with a new labor source that included 100 Mennonites registered as conscientious objectors. Work crews were housed at the Poudre Civilian Conservation Corps Camp near the mouth of the Poudre Canyon.[23] Given the distance to the nearest city (Fort Collins), workers spent their leisure hours at the camp. At the end of each 60-hour work period, workers were transported back to their homes.

The camp had six barracks, each housing 25 men, plus a recreation center, bath house, infirmary, mess hall, machine shop, and administrative building. All structures had concrete floors and tar-papered wooden walls. A 20-foot deep groundwater well was drilled near the Cache la Poudre River to provide water for the camp. An automatic electric pump delivered well water to a 7,000 gallon concrete storage tank, 75 feet up the mountainside. The mess hall could serve up to 115 men at a time. A large pantry, holding a 40-day food supply, adjoined the modern kitchen. A large ice box stored meats, butter and dairy products. Made of logs and covered with dirt, an underground root cellar cooled fresh fruits and vegetables.[24]

With workers in comfortable housing and plentiful food available, winter work at Seaman Dam continued in tandem with replacement of a three-mile section of the pipeline with a 27-inch line near Fort Collins.[25] This work was necessary because the old line had been "eaten away by sulphates in the soil and worn out by age." Leaks were a big problem, and by 1943, over half the Bellvue pipeline would be replaced with 20-inch cast iron and steel-reinforced concrete pipe.[26]

JAPAN'S ATTACK ON the U.S. Naval Station at Pearl Harbor, Hawai'i, in December 1941, ushered in another age of wartime spending, restrictions, and challenges for the citizens of Greeley and their water department. Farmers in the communities surrounding Greeley increased crop and livestock production for the war effort, as they had done during World War I. Other communities also prepared for their increasing water needs. On December 16, 1941, the Mayor of Eaton wrote to Greeley Mayor Lacy Wilkinson "asking that if at any time, through the construction of Milton Seaman Dam, Greeley had surplus water" available from the Bellvue pipeline, they would like to explore a contract for its use. The Town of Windsor asked Greeley for an extension of their five-year contract for surplus water. The farming community of Timnath, despite its modest size of 147 residents, was next in line to request that Greeley expand its water services contract to five years; up from the one-year agreements Timnath had negotiated in the past. Given the uncertainties of WWII and future water supplies, city councilors declined Timnath's request.[27]

Farming and food production were vital to the war effort, and one federal initiative appealed to many in Greeley—the Victory Gardens project. It was

created to reduce urban consumption of farm products that were needed overseas and for the military. First started in World War I, families and communities
were encouraged to grow fruits and vegetables, in their yards or in vacant lots, for
domestic use and for sale to neighbors. At its peak, the Victory Gardens project
enlisted 18 million families nationwide, with Greeley and surrounding towns
actively participating. One local project was the Victory Garden located on future
vacant park land on the west side of Greeley.[28] Irrigation water was provided by
the City of Greeley Water Department, and the site would later become Luther
Park (located along 23rd Avenue between 9th and 11th Streets).[29]

ON FEBRUARY 15, 1943, the U.S. Army approached city officials "to
construct a hospital on a site to be selected north of the city limits." That
same evening, the city council stated "the City of Greeley is very anxious to
obtain such Government hospital and to extend the waterworks and sanitary
sewer system to such site, or any other site which may or might be selected."
The water department offered to build, at its own expense, a water line about
1,000 feet north of the Cache la Poudre River.[30] On April 29th councilors
reviewed a report from First Lieutenant Rudolph E. Eberle to the Surgeon
of the 4th District of the Army Air Forces Technical Training Command
(AAFTTC). Posted to the Army's Buckley Field in Denver, Eberle conducted
a thorough survey of all features of the Greeley water system, as part of a
feasibility study for the proposed military hospital in Greeley.

Eberle's report noted that Greeley's water department served approximately 20,000
customers, and its daily use patterns peaked in the summer months at around seven
million gallons. "The apparent excessive consumption during the summer months,"
noted the lieutenant, "is due to watering of lawns and gardens and irrigation in the
city." The city's water supply came from a watershed that Eberle called "mountain-
ous, heavily wooded, and very sparsely inhabited." These conditions reduced "to a
minimum the possibility of pollution of the water." The Army officer also observed
the ongoing construction of Seaman Dam. This facility, when completed, said Eberle,
would store approximately 1.6 billion gallons (4,910 acre-feet) of water for release
into the Cache la Poudre River during times of low flow.[31]

In addition to the abundance of water that Greeley offered to the Army, Eberle devoted space in his report to describe the water treatment and delivery facilities of the city.[32] Beginning at Bellvue, the city's water came via a 27-inch pipeline for 13 miles, where two cast-iron pipelines of 20 inches in diameter then carried the treated water to storage reservoirs on the southwestern edge of Greeley. These could each hold up to 7.5 million gallons. Eberle concluded that the city had a system that "appears to be constructed and operated in a satisfactory manner." Of particular concern was wartime security. "All reservoirs, basins, filters, and intakes are well protected," said Eberle, "by strong man-proof fences and are regularly guarded to prevent entry by unauthorized persons." The transmission pipelines were "patrolled regularly," while "precautions necessary to maintain an adequate and safe supply are being satisfactorily carried out."[33]

Discussions continued, but for a number of reasons the Army decided against locating a military hospital in Greeley. Eberle's water system report, however, did not go unnoticed. Only four months after the original hospital study announcement, the Greeley City Council received correspondence from the War Production Board "asking utilities to arrange for a maintenance program and explaining the new priority regulation." Water Superintendent Roy Seaman explained to the council: "They want us to make a survey, and file a letter with this Board, as to what our [water] demands may be as of January 1944." It appeared that the U.S. Army had another plan in the works for the Greeley community.

By summer's end, Greeley citizens discovered why the U.S. Army had devoted so much time studying their water system. On August 31, 1943, the city council responded to a proposal to sell water to the U.S. Army for a proposed German prisoner-of-war (POW) camp, to be located west of the city. As part of the war effort, the Allied forces needed secure facilities away from European battle lines to imprison more than 425,000 German soldiers and sailors captured in combat.

The U.S. Army Corps of Engineers would ultimately construct 700 facilities in 46 states for this purpose. Colorado would have 46 such camps, of which Greeley's "Camp 202" ranked among the largest. At its peak, the POW complex housed over 3,000 war prisoners on 300 acres, eight miles west of downtown Greeley. Primarily from Germany and Austria, the prisoners worked in the

Figure 7.2 Greeley Camp 202, under the command of the 9th Division of the U.S. Army (with headquarters at Omaha, Nebraska), was a World War II prisoner of war internment camp. Built in 1943 on 320 acres eight miles west of Greeley, it was supplied with water from the Bellvue pipeline and could accommodate 3,600 prisoners. City of Greeley Museums, Permanent Collection, 1976.83.0007.

irrigated sugar beet fields of northern Colorado as part of the "Emergency Farm Labor Program." The camp remained active until the summer of 1946, about a year after the fighting ended in the European and Pacific theatres.[34]

The Army agreed to pay prevailing rates for the use of an unlimited supply of water, and the City built and maintained the water delivery pipeline to the camp at its expense. Estimates of water usage ranged from a low of 750,000 gallons per month to as much as three million gallons or more.[35] The camp had a fire station, hospital, theater, library, classrooms, sewers and electricity, along with armed watchtowers, tall wire fences, spotlights and guard dogs. The initial prisoners were captured during the North Africa campaign led by General Erwin Rommel of desert warfare fame. A notable prisoner at Camp 202 in Greeley was Rommel's personal automobile mechanic.[36] One wonders about the course of history if Rommel himself had been captured along with his assistant.

PROVIDING WATER TO large volume customers during WWII seemed like good business to the Greeley City Council. Yet an arrangement with the neighboring communities of Garden City and Rosedale, just south of Greeley, generated criticism. On December 28, 1943, Dr. Oliver M. Dickerson wrote a lengthy *Tribune* article entitled, "Greeley Water for Garden City Menaces Local Development in Opinion of Dr. O.M. Dickerson." The professor, a former college president and instructor of government and history at the Colorado State College of Education, at Greeley, had spent time in the water department office reviewing the contract between the City and a "duly incorporated pipe line company—apparently organized for profit." In the 1930s, Dickerson had served on a committee offering suggestions to city officials for public works projects. He now observed a private enterprise seeking City sponsorship: "There is no limitation of the area in which the water may be distributed by the company." This could include the towns of Evans and La Salle, as well as Garden City and Rosedale.[37]

In 1943, Professor Dickerson's critique of city government, combined with the business community's concerns, significantly influenced Greeley water system operations. "The time has come," said Dickerson, "for frank explanations and very clear thinking." He reminded readers of the *Tribune*: "Water granted to others no longer remains available to Greeley." He then predicted a far-reaching reform that in 1958 would lead to establishment of the semi-autonomous Greeley Water Board. This "manner of negotiations," Dickerson claimed, "has made it obvious that Greeley can no longer leave the right to alienate its water rights in the hands of a Water Committee [of the Greeley City Council]."

Dickerson bluntly stated: "The present ordinance authorizing [these water sales] . . . should at once be repealed." In their place, the citizens of Greeley should draft a rule stating that "the water resources of Greeley are the sacred property of the people and that they cannot be disposed of, sold, or alienated except by ordinance approved at a regular election." The professor concluded: "It is possible that our water department has outgrown the capacity of a busy city council to handle properly and that we need a water commission to handle it." He called for hiring "an attorney of the highest caliber to serve the needs of the water department."[38]

In fall 1945, anticipating postwar growth, Greeley officials decided to expand the city's water supplies. It also accepted the Town of Evan's request for additional water, in spite of Dickerson's warning. One month later, the city council entertained a proposal from former city attorney, William R. Kelly, to purchase four high mountain reservoirs on the South Fork of the Cache la Poudre River. As legal counsel for Roy Portner and his Mountain and Plains Irrigation Company of Fort Collins, Kelly outlined the benefits to his hometown if the City purchased Big Beaver (also called Hourglass), Comanche, Twin Lake, and Timberline Reservoirs.[39]

On January 8, 1946, after consideration of Kelly's offer, city officials recommended issuing $367,000 (nearly $5 million in 2020 dollars) in water works bonds. Following negotiations with Roy Portner's company, the council learned that the City could acquire the four reservoirs for a total of $125,000 (about $1.6 million in 2020). This amount would include "all outstanding preferred water rights, rights to the use of said water rights, except the resort and fishing rights outstanding in the Consolidated Hour Glass Resort and Reservoir Company and its stockholders."[40]

This water acquisition proposal from Kelly and Portner sparked debate regarding the existing contract for 15,000 units of C-BT water, for which the City of Greeley had subscribed, which was the largest allotment of any Northern Colorado Water Conservancy District customer. On February 11, 1946, the *Greeley Tribune* reported on an exchange between city officials and Northern District board members. Several Greeley City Council members had appeared at the Northern District's monthly board meeting to request "cancellation of at least some of the contract between the district and the city entered into in 1939."

Council member Frank B. Davis told the Northern board that "the City now had an opportunity to buy from Roy Portner and other Fort Collins parties some small reservoirs on the Little South" branch of the Cache la Poudre River. Davis wanted to know whether Greeley could rent some of its excess C-BT water to surrounding agricultural users. Said Davis: "If the 15,000 acre-feet we have contracted for is more than enough for the city's needs, and it looks to me as [though] it would be, will we be able to sell [lease] the excess to irrigation users?"[41] John M. Dille, General Manager of the Northern District, told city leaders: "Your contract with the District provides for exactly that procedure."

Dille further informed Davis: "The District's big problem is going to involve stretching our 310,000 acre-feet far enough to fill the demands." He observed that the Northern District had allotted no water since 1939, "because it seemed best to wait until the war was over and we had a more definite idea on the time that the project could be completed." Speaking to Davis' point about reducing Greeley's commitment for C-BT water, Dille advised that the Northern District "will not cancel any part of its contract with the City of Greeley." He also reminded councilor Davis that C-BT water "will be of such clearness and fine quality that with a little chlorinization [it] could be taken directly into the Greeley pipeline, for consumption."[42]

The Northern District's promise to accommodate Greeley's concerns, regarding renting C-BT water to agricultural users, continued with a lengthy editorial in the *Tribune*. Its publisher, Charles Hansen, also gave column space in March 1946, to recent water department considerations—the plan to acquire what Hansen called the "high-range" reservoirs from Roy Portner. The *Tribune* cited a speech given by Councilor Frank Davis to the local League of Women Voters. In his remarks, Davis claimed that "these high-range reservoirs are the only source of water for the [recently constructed] Seaman Dam." Said Davis: "The Milton Seaman Dam is unique, for there was no [yet-decreed] water for it when it was built." He also noted that "high mountain reservoirs do not always furnish a reliable supply, and at the time it is needed for exchange." Davis warned his audience: "There has been little said about this recently, since it is understood that such flood water, even if retained temporarily, would belong to the [Cache la Poudre] river as a whole, subject to the [senior] priorities as stated."[43] This fact would be at the center of controversy regarding the high mountain reservoirs 40 years later.

DISMISSING COMPLAINTS THAT the C-BT would transport "hard" water with a high mineral content, to homes and businesses in Greeley, the *Tribune* noted that "the entire purpose of the Colorado-Big Thompson Project was to eliminate an economy of scarcity in the irrigation of northern Colorado's eastern slope." The best news, reported the *Tribune*, was that "the 13-mile tunnel through the mountain range above Estes Park was completed Thursday with the last cement being poured in its lining."[44]

The question thus became whether to retain all 15,000 units of C-BT water (which would not come on line for another decade), or add the Mountain and Plains Reservoirs to the City's water portfolio. On the evening of July 2, 1947, the city council heard from consultants hired to examine the Cache la Poudre River high mountain reservoirs proposal. Warning that the City did not have adequate supplies presently on hand, the firm of Crocker and Ryan recommended the purchase of "all of the facilities of the Mountain and Plains Irrigation Company." Rather than acquire only four of the reservoirs, as previously recommended, the consultants advised the City to acquire all seven storage structures. The *Greeley Tribune*, which in March 1946 had considered these facilities an unwise transaction, now deemed the proposal "a high degree of statesmanship and civic foresight." By agreeing to bond themselves in the amount of $190,000 ($2.5 million in 2020 dollars) to secure three more reservoirs, said the *Tribune*, the council was "assuring the city [of] an adequate supply of high quality water for many years to come."[45]

That same evening, after considerable discussion, the city council resolved the debate by doing both: keeping the C-BT units and adding the high mountain reservoirs. Councilors authorized a bond issue for all structures owned by Roy Portner and T.E. Schuerman of Fort Collins. The complete system included seven reservoirs and two mountain diversion ditches, with a combined capacity of 12,872 acre-feet. The list included Hourglass Reservoir, with its 1898 priority and 1,675 acre-feet of storage; Twin Lake, with an 1899 priority and 272 acre-feet; Comanche, with a 1923 priority and 2,593 acre-feet; Timberline, with 754 acre-feet and a 1901 priority; Peterson, with a 1921 priority and 2,134 acre-feet; Barnes Meadow, with a 1921 priority and 3,402 acre-feet; and Portner Reservoir, between Fort Collins and Loveland, with a 1921 priority and 968 acre-feet of storage. The diversion ditches were on Bob Creek, which emptied into the Roaring Fork (with 20 cubic feet per second of flow), and Columbine, at the headwaters of the North Fork of the Cache la Poudre River (which flowed at the rate of 10 cfs).[46]

EXPANSION OF THE city's water supply in the late 1940s gave the City of Greeley the capacity to serve surrounding farms, towns and businesses which

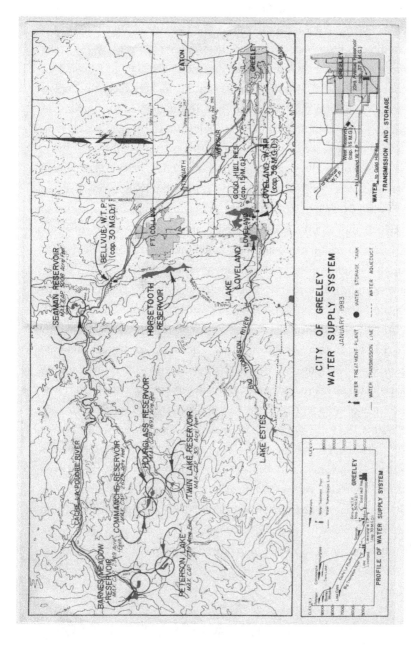

Figure 7.3 In 1947, Greeley purchased five mountain reservoirs from the Mountain and Plains Irrigation Company. They are located in the upper Cache la Poudre River Basin west of Fort Collins (in Larimer County) as seen on this map. These reservoirs are an integral part of Greeley's storage portfolio. City of Greeley Museums, Permanent Collection, AI-5860.

needed more water. In February 1948, the neighboring community of La Salle joined forces with its largest employer, the Union Pacific Railroad, to petition city councilors for a substantial increase in the railroad's water contract. Superintendent Roy Seaman gave council members a survey of the railroad's request, and of Greeley's ability to provide water. The water department could sell up to five million gallons per month, according to its engineering report, while the superintendent claimed that more could be found for such an important customer.

Roy Seaman advised the council that by comparison, Greeley had delivered up to 6.6 million gallons per month to the Army's now-defunct POW Camp. The *Greeley Tribune* reported that "Union Pacific officials are eager to get the council's decision as quickly as possible." The Omaha headquarters of the UPRR, said the *Tribune*, "must know soon whether to make plans for using Greeley water or building a treatment plant at La Salle." Yet another motive for the Union Pacific, said the *Tribune*, was its plan to decrease its consumption of water as it transitioned from steam engines to diesel fuel.[47] After much deliberation, Greeley accommodated the Union Pacific request.

Greeley's ongoing policy of providing water to irrigators greatly helped the agricultural economy of the region. In mid-to-late July 1948, farmers in the Cache la Poudre Valley petitioned city officials for the sale or lease of water stored in Seaman Reservoir. Water department staff noted that "there would be a considerable volume of water available in the City's recently acquired mountain lakes in excess of the requirements of the preferred rights holders." The department could report that "as the city's Seaman dam is full, Greeley has a safe reserve supply there and can spare the new lakes' water." Most of this water was in Hourglass, Comanche, and Twin Lake Reservoirs. The *Tribune* reported that "Weld County farmers in Greeley's trade area under ditches north of Greeley will be given first opportunity to purchase what water the city can spare."[48]

By mid-August 1948, the city council reported the lease of 60 million cubic feet (1,363 acre-feet) of water stored at Seaman Reservoir to the Cache la Poudre Irrigation Company. Water users along the former Union Colony Number 2 Ditch, said the *Greeley Tribune*, "were badly in need of extra water and asked that the city sell [the] company 50 million cubic feet." When added to the requests of other irrigators, city water officials could supply enough water to receive between

$9,000 and $10,000 ($100,000-$150,000 in 2020) in annual revenues.

City officials learned on July 28th that the water department had rented 3,500 acre-feet of water from the five high mountain reservoirs, which resulted in a profit of $20,056.87 (over $250,000 in 2020 dollars). The Larimer and Weld Irrigation Company had leased 125 million cubic feet (2,900 acre-feet) from this sale, while the Cache la Poudre Irrigation Company obtained 30.38 million cubic feet (700 acre-feet).[49]

GEORGE DAVIS, WHO identified himself at a public forum on Greeley's water future as a 10-year member of the city council (with four years on its water committee), wrote a column in the *Greeley Tribune* entitled, "Why the Water Restrictions?" Davis believed that his peers on the city council should be "contemplating the growth in the past and anticipating a conservative increase for the future."[50] Davis reminded *Tribune* readers of the impending supply of additional water from the Colorado-Big Thompson Project.

Davis recommended that "the possibility of a site for a rapid filter and connection with the Big Thompson River [near Loveland] might be gone into as a means of using part of the 15,000 acre-feet contracted for with the Northern Colorado Water Conservancy District." If Greeley constructed a dual line from the Big Thompson River to town, "insurance rates would be lowered and a survey no doubt would bring out other possibilities."[51] The idea of securing treated water from two separate river basins—the Cache la Poudre and the Big Thompson Rivers—had gained momentum.

With the summer of 1949 nearing its end, and the water department under increased pressure to resolve its water supply concerns, city leaders called a public meeting to air grievances and gauge sentiment to acquire additional water supplies. The *Denver Post* found this story compelling enough to send a reporter, who on August 17th wrote a column entitled, "A New Pipe Line from Loveland." The Denver journalist learned that "Greeley owns ample water but lacks conduits to deliver it to Greeley in quantities sufficient to permit unlimited use." This meant construction of a larger pipeline from the Bellvue water treatment plant on the Cache la Poudre River, or building a new water treatment plant along the

Big Thompson River, or both.[52]

The *Denver Post* reporter offered a suggestion. Since Greeley owned 15,000 units of C-BT supplies, "why not take the Colorado-Big Thompson water from the nearest point, which would be somewhere west of Loveland?" This strategy also avoided leaving Greeley's water in Horsetooth Reservoir, then under construction west of Fort Collins. The *Post* reporter believed that the advantages of this design included "a shorter pipeline to Greeley, when the cost per mile will be so high that even a few miles [less] will be appreciated." By not storing the fresh mountain water in a lower elevation reservoir, Greeley customers would acquire "water that is clear, that is, not turbid, at any time."

Speaking from experience in Colorado's largest urban area, the *Post* reporter remarked that "any city would pay heavily for the guarantees of a water supply from the two sources;" the existing Bellvue plant on the Cache la Poudre River and a new treatment plant on the Big Thompson River. The journalist concluded: "This ought to be given serious consideration before several million dollars are spent to duplicate the present pipe and enlarge filter facilities west of Fort Collins."[53]

A final concern of attendees at the August 1949 public meeting was lease of surplus water to surrounding communities and irrigation companies. Art Bolenbaugh, who had replaced Roy Seaman in 1949 as superintendent, estimated that the City provided water to 22,000 residents in town. In addition, several rural water companies on the edges of Greeley, as well as the towns of Timnath, Windsor, and Evans, had leased over 104 million gallons (2,400 acre-feet) of the City's water the previous year. These sales had generated a revenue stream of $13,722.35 (nearly $150,000 in 2020).

To this point a member of the audience asked, "How long must Greeley serve these users?" Bernard Houtchens, a former city attorney, replied "'forever' since the [Colorado] Public Utilities Commission would probably not allow the cancellation of these commitments." A.J. Ryan concurred, with his belief that "the city should sell all the water it can to surrounding towns." This strategy "not only helps develop them but brings the city with practically no expenses added revenue that can well be used for developments of the water system."[54]

Media coverage concerning Greeley's water future did not escape city officials. On August 31, 1949, Mayor Frank Berger announced that he had invited 25 "representative citizens" to serve on a committee "which will aid the city council in determining the city water program for the future." Berger spoke for his colleagues when he noted that "the council is reluctant to obligate the city for a large sum to pay for an expensive program unless that is the wish of a majority of the people." The Colorado State College of Education, at Greeley would send two individuals to the committee: Glen Turner, the college's comptroller, and Dr. Oliver Dickerson, the former professor of political science "who has taken an active interest in civic affairs," said the *Tribune*.[55]

Many divergent ideas were discussed at the August 17th meeting of concerned citizens, adding to them "another school of thought—that the present system is even more adequate for about nine months of the year." Whatever the outcome of their deliberations, said the *Greeley Tribune* as the 1940s came to an end, the City could not remain at a standstill. "So, in a nutshell," it concluded, "that is the problem."[56]

THE DECADE OF the 1940s affected Greeley water history in many ways, not the least being World War II. Construction of Seaman Dam and Reservoir was a key feature, as well as the high mountain reservoir acquisitions. An expanded water supply allowed the City to lease more water to irrigators and other communities. This generated additional revenue, but also caused controversy with some people in Greeley.

Into this situation stepped Greeley business leaders who wanted to see Greeley grow. They included direct descendants of the original Union Colonists whose focus, sharpened by lessons of the past, riveted attention on the future. How would the Greeley City Council and the water department answer hard questions regarding the city's water supply? The 1950s—and another period of prolonged drought—would shine a spotlight on these intriguing challenges.

CHAPTER EIGHT

1950-1970
Postwar Growth and Greeley Water

A Small Town No More

THE FORCES OF war and peace, natural abundance and scarcity, and good and bad economic times had shaped each generation that lived on the fertile lands at the confluence of the South Platte and Cache la Poudre Rivers. As Greeley looked forward to its centennial in 1970, it had grown to almost 40,000 people, with population and economic booms yet to come. Many credited the region's temperate climate, job opportunities, and optimistic outlook as lures to this productive and prosperous city.

The Eisenhower era of the 1950s brought more changes to Greeley, as did the turbulent 1960s. Not since the early 20th century, when the Great Western Sugar Company attracted hundreds of families to Greeley and surrounding farm communities, did the city witness similar expansion. Evans—Greeley's small neighbor to the south—had grown by 200 percent, which required its water contract with Greeley to be restructured accordingly. Surprisingly, Windsor grew by a mere 16 people in the years 1950-1970. By comparison, Denver's population during the same period increased by over 80 percent, to 514,678 people.[1]

At the start of the 1950s, Greeley residents seemed content with the services and rates charged by the water department. Upon reflection, in a 1999 interview, however, W.D. Farr, the future water board chair, noted that "the City had a bad water system." The original water treatment facility at Bellvue, and its pipeline, had aged with "very little attention." Leadership in Greeley's water department, according to Mr. Farr, "had depended on two men, a father and son, to run it for 50 or 60 years." With the death of Milton Seaman in 1940 and the departure of son, Roy, in 1949, said Farr: "All [of a] sudden there was no water department anymore."[2] W.D. Farr knew that Greeley's water system operated on borrowed time.

In May 1951, a retaining wall of the 7.5-million-gallon Greeley Reservoir Number 1, constructed in 1906-1907 at 23rd Avenue and Reservoir Road, collapsed. Water gushed onto city streets, into Glenmere Lake and the Greeley Number 3 Ditch, flooding crops in nearby fields.[3] Rectifying the "bad system," as Farr described, needed a new management structure to oversee maintenance and water supply acquisition. In 1958, the hallmark achievement of the decade would be voter approval of a city charter, with a provision to create the Greeley Water Board. This new administrative process would be instrumental in planning and analyzing water supply opportunities, as well as handling aging infrastructure and water quality issues.

WHILE WATER SUPPLIES needed attention, a critical issue in the 1950s was wastewater treatment. It had proven inadequate for the growing community because Greeley's 1935-era sewer plant, funded by the City and the federal Public Works Administration, was a "primary treatment facility" which only removed solid waste from the effluent. This meant that partially treated sewage was still discharged into the Cache la Poudre River. In November 1955, a "Citizens Advisory Committee concerning the Improvement of the Greeley Sewage Treatment Plant and the installation of some trunk sewer lines" was established. This group, along with city officials, drafted a plan to spend up to $876,000 (over $8 million in 2020) for a project that included a "secondary treatment" facility. This new wastewater plant would have "trickling filters," comprised of layers of rock with attached clusters of micro-organisms to adsorb toxins and pollutants in the wastewater.[4] This would greatly reduce pollutants released into the river, and would have a capacity to serve approximately 25,000 people.

THE FIRST DELIVERIES of Colorado-Big Thompson (C-BT) water created new challenges and opportunities for the Greeley City Council. With the

Figure 8.1 In 1955, Greeley's population was 24,000 and 32 percent of the city's raw sewage still flowed into the Cache la Poudre River. Of necessity, the original sewage treatment plant was expanded in 1955-1957. This aerial view is looking west towards downtown Greeley. In the foreground are five sludge drying beds, two circular biological trickling filters, and settling tanks. The small circular anaerobic digester on the north end was built in 1936. City of Greeley Museums, Permanent Collection, C-1.1995.51.0006B.

exception of 500 acre-feet, the initial allotment of 4,839 acre-feet (which became available in the spring of 1956) could not yet be used by the city. Four ditch companies subsequently requested to lease the City's excess C-BT water that year because of the ongoing drought. Councilors agreed to rent 1,000 acre-feet each to the Platte Valley Irrigation and the Larimer and Weld Irrigation Companies. The Greeley and Loveland Irrigation Company also received 839 acre-feet, while the Cache la Poudre Irrigation Company received 1,500 acre-feet, the largest allocation. All recipients were charged $2.40 per acre-foot (equal to $22.60 per acre-foot in 2020 dollars). The city council then requested a study of future water needs of area ditch companies to anticipate rental requests for the following year.[5]

Greeley's C-BT allocation continued to generate interest throughout the region as the drought persisted. By December 1956, councilors learned that five ditch

Figure 8.2 On June 23, 1947, an enthusiastic crowd gathered at the east portal of the 13.1 mile long Alva B. Adams Tunnel, part of the Colorado-Big Thompson project, and witnessed the arrival of West Slope water. The tunnel is 9'9" in diameter and cost $12.8 million ($189 million in 2020 dollars). At the time, it was the longest tunnel in the United States that delivered irrigation water. Courtesy of Northern Colorado Water Conservancy District.

companies sought supplemental water from the City. Even though the Northern Colorado Water Conservancy District had not yet determined its quota allocation for 1957, the City decided on January 15, 1957, to divide its surplus waters among the interested parties. The Milton Water Users Association, located southeast of Greeley along the South Platte River, received 25 percent of Greeley's allocation, the Greeley and Loveland and New Cache la Poudre Irrigation Companies each received 19 percent, the Larimer and Weld Irrigation Company, 18 percent, and the Platte Valley Irrigation Company, 14 percent. The Water Supply and Storage Company received the remaining five percent of Greeley's 1957 C-BT water available to rent.[6]

IN DECEMBER 1951, City Manager Ray Case stood before the Greeley Kiwanis Club to review the activities of all city departments. He also outlined plans for a proposed new structure of municipal government in Greeley. Said Case: "I was associated with the City of Lincoln, Nebraska, for 12 years and thought they had a complicated water department, but it's simple compared to Greeley's." Noted the city manager: "Greeley has a fine water department and plenty of water. If an oil boom comes and the community continues to grow, we'll need the water. Someday an industry will locate here and we can say, 'Come ahead. We got the Water.'"[7] Case's prediction would indeed come true, as subsequent oil production and new industrial growth both required more water for the growing community.

For the next few years, Greeley's leaders and citizens explored new ways to manage the city's vital water system. Then, in February 1958, voters approved a referendum to create a new governing charter for the City. One major task was the complete reorganization of the water department. Jack Clayton, a member of the city council at the time, agreed to chair the "Water, Waterworks and Sewer Committee" of the charter convention. Two months later, Clayton guided the discussions that resulted in Article XVII of the new City of Greeley Charter. This section of the Charter outlined the duties of the water department.[8]

The Clayton committee summarized the water situation of Greeley in one sentence: "Greeley's problem is not one of supply, but one of transmission." The newly-formed water committee believed that "Greeley is in the most favorable situation of any Eastern Slope town in Colorado." The City owned water rights "sufficient to support a town in excess of 100,000 population if properly developed and conserved." Given that Greeley's future growth depended heavily on its water system, the charter committee called for the creation of a "water board" for the city.

W.D. Farr, then a member of the Northern District board, recalled in a 1997 interview: "Because of my interest in water and early association with Northern, I knew a good deal about the Denver [water] system." Farr also had acquaintances on the Denver Water Board, established in 1918, and the only such water management entity in Colorado. Farr obtained a set of their rules and regulations.

He also wished to avoid confrontations that the Denver and Northern District water boards had faced. "We thought that the only way we could solve the Greeley problem," said Farr, "was to get it [the water board] out of city politics,"[9] echoing the sentiments of the 1941 *Greeley Tribune* proclamation he and other Greeley businessmen had sponsored.

The new city charter called upon the water board "to build, maintain, operate, and acquire additional water." Farr wanted no taxes levied against the department, "and the water board had to be self-sustaining." For the first time, said Farr, the water department had supervision that ensured "that our funds were balanced," water rates were established equitably, "and the city council couldn't change the rates." If councilors had concerns that the charges recommended by the board were too low, said Farr, they could raise them "if they wanted to."[10] The city council could not, however, lower water rates established by the Greeley Water Board.

On June 24, 1958, Greeley voters went to the polls and approved the new city charter by a wide margin. On July 1st, the *Greeley Tribune* editorialized that of the three boards created under the new structure of municipal government, selection of the five members for the water board mattered most. Mayor Oscar Beck and the city council interviewed candidates for the board, which the *Tribune* called "a tough task," as qualified board members had to be "experienced in water matters, [and] to serve without pay." Yet another challenge, said the *Tribune*, was that the Charter called for board members who "lack private water interests that conflict with the City's."[11] The selection of the first citizen board would set the tone and direction of water management and policy for the City of Greeley for decades.

Within weeks, city officials selected Irving Cannon, W.D. Farr, Robert Davis, John R.P. Wheeler, and Roy L. Smith. Non-voting (*ex officio*) members were Mayor Oscar Beck, City Manager Ben Cruce, and City Clerk Mort Balch. At their inaugural meeting on July 30, 1958, W.D. Farr became the first board chairman, a position he would hold for nearly four decades. Under Farr's leadership, the board began its work by developing a series of six studies and reports to be conducted by consultants of the Greeley Water Department. The first was a survey of water rates.[12]

This document addressed the "projection of Greeley's future population." Farr and his colleagues recognized that this data needed to include "the probable expansion of Colorado State College [now the University of Northern Colorado] in the early 1960's." Demographers had warned that public agencies such as universities and school districts should anticipate an influx of new students created by the "Baby Boom;" the surge of 76 million children born to families of service men and women after World War II. States like California and Colorado braced for large numbers of young people in their public schools and colleges. The new Greeley Water Board also faced challenges created by the Servicemen's Readjustment Act of 1944, commonly referred to as the G.I. Bill, that included low interest housing loans which would lead to future population growth.[13]

The water board studied the economic patterns of the water department, reviewed its current operations, and devised a plan to "project these costs over the next 10 years." Farr and his colleagues wanted the water rate survey to examine "the addition of waterworks facilities necessary to meet the city's growth needs." The board then asked a consultant to "review existing data and reports on requirements for capital improvements and additions needed in the future, and to establish a 10-year budget of capital expenditures."[14]

Knowing that expert legal advice was necessary for a variety of water issues, the board discussed hiring special counsel "to study Greeley's water rights and legal possibilities in using and relocating existing water rights." The city's attorney, Thomas Richardson, had advised the water board that his other duties precluded devoting time to this matter. City Manager Ben Cruce, and Board Chairman Farr, solicited the services of William R. Kelly, the former city attorney who had helped craft legislation that led to the creation of the Colorado-Big Thompson Project. In August 1960, Cruce and Farr noted in a story for the *Greeley Tribune* that they needed a water attorney and engineering assistant to investigate "the present cost of repairing the City's high mountain lakes and the possibility of transferring these rights downstream, possibly to Seaman Reservoir."[15]

Within a month, Kelly appeared before the board and reported his preliminary findings. It became clear that the City also needed an engineering expert to review water facility operations. The board turned to William G. (Dugan) Wilkinson, the water commissioner for the Cache la Poudre River, as their engineering consultant. Wilkinson's findings formed the basis of a "long-range and short-range program for developing the water resources of the city."[16] William Kelly's primary concern was the reliability of the high mountain reservoirs to yield adequate water supplies. "They are a problem," the board attorney stated bluntly.

"They have relatively late [junior] priorities," Kelly wrote, not to mention their "inaccessibility, in distance and roads and shortness of periods when work can be done at such 9,000 to 10,000 feet altitudes." The board attorney made special mention of the "lack of finished features of [the] dams, such as deficiencies in outlets and in riprapping and spillways." Timberline Dam, "begun in 1901," said Kelly, "is so remote and so long left with its dam washed out [40 years]," that it should be abandoned. Big Beaver and Hourglass reservoirs "may offer good justification for money outlays in betterment." Only the prospects for Comanche Reservoir appealed to Kelly.[17]

The board attorney closed his 1960 report with recommendations for future acquisition and management strategies. Of all sources remaining for the city, said Kelly, the C-BT system remained the best option. At $45 per acre-foot on the open market, this water was much less expensive than in urban centers like Denver, which paid between $160 and $500 per acre-foot for water from its transmountain diversions.[18]

THE EARLY 1960S saw a new user of Greeley water emerge, one which would create both enormous opportunities and challenges for the community. In 1958, Clinton "Clint" J. Mayer, manager of the Greeley Chamber of Commerce, assembled a group of citizens "to inspect a packing plant similar to the one contemplated in Greeley." Mayor Beck, Dr. William G. Ross, president of the Colorado State College, former Mayor Gordon Rissler, and Mildred Hansen, publisher of the *Greeley Tribune,* drove to Scottsbluff, Nebraska, with local cattleman and farmer, Warren Monfort. He hoped to expand his family's feedlot in north Greeley and incorporate meat processing facilities nearby.[19] While this was welcome news for Greeley, the first issue addressed by the group was air quality. "There was no odor outside the [Scottsbluff] plant that you can detect," said the mayor after his trip to Nebraska. He noted that Swift and Company owned the 210-employee facility in Scottsbluff, and paid an average wage of $90 per week for 40 hours of work at a time when the minimum wage was 75 cents per hour (or $30 per week).[20]

Of particular concern to Mayor Beck was the disposal of animal waste. "Sewage from the plant," he noted, "is dumped directly into the [North Platte] river at Scottsbluff." Mayor Beck did not observe "a great deal of sewage, since the blood and [inedible] parts of the animals killed are processed for tankage and fertilizer." The Greeley visitors asked workers at "very close industrial businesses" whether they disliked the smell of the processing plant, finding that "the comments were all favorable." Soon thereafter, Greeley signed a contract with Warren Monfort and his son, Kenneth, to lease city water to their fledgling operation.[21]

Food processing had been an important part of Greeley's local economy, and cattle feeders Warren and Ken Monfort wanted to construct a packing plant near their finishing lots. This would increase both efficiency and profits as the company moved toward a vertically integrated business model. In the summer of 1959, the Monforts partnered with Meyer and Dave Averch of Denver Capitol Pack to initiate construction of a $2 million, 92,000 square foot meat processing plant. It would be located a mile south of the family's feedlot, east of U.S. Highway 85, adjacent to the Cache la Poudre River and with Union Pacific rail access. Greeley-Capitol Pack, Inc., opened on May 16, 1960, and was touted as the most technologically advanced cattle and lamb slaughtering facility in the country. In addition, it was hailed as the biggest industrial development in Greeley since the construction of the sugar factory in 1902. The Monforts subsequently purchased the Averch's interests and became sole owners and operators of the plant, renamed Monfort Packing. They immediately initiated plans for expansion.[22]

The packing plant was not the only big news in Greeley in 1959. In an effort to shore up national security, caused by international tensions during the Cold War era, Weld County was selected as the location for several strategic missile site pads. In 1959-1960, an Atlas E missile site (Site L) was constructed on a 20-acre site ten miles west of Greeley on a bluff near the intersection of U.S. Highway 34 and Colorado Highway 257. The facility was under the command of Warren Air Force Base in Cheyenne, Wyoming.

The City provided a 4-inch water tap and meter that connected to the existing water line, at the former World War II prisoner of war site (Greeley Camp 202), about one mile down the road from the missile site. The construction company for the project paid the "outside of the city limits" water rate, and its contract was terminated upon completion of the site.[23]

THE AREA WEST of Greeley was getting a lot of attention, and on April 13, 1959, City Manager Ben Cruce, in a memorandum to the city council, described his study of the expansion of water districts in the area west of Greeley. He had noticed a change in federal government programs, designed to assist urban areas, as they accommodated growth and transitioned from agricultural lands. "The ideas which I am about to express," wrote Cruce, "are different from those I have always considered proper for a municipality." Yet "because of many modern developments in road building, sanitation disposal, water treatment, the automobile and home buildings," said the city manager, Greeley needed to "reconsider traditional extensions to municipal services."[24]

Cruce's focus was on the "three-mile zone" surrounding the city limits. "Greeley now serves water to most of the area [outside the city limits]," he wrote to the city council, and "it serves sewer to most of the area, [and] has made or is making a drainage study of most of the area." Cruce pointed out that the City should "own all water and sewer taps in the unincorporated parts within this area." Said the city manager, "Greeley must take the lead in promoting such." This "would make it easier to plan and design one large water system and one large sewer system rather than several separate such systems" created by special water and sewer districts.[25]

Cruce's intent with the "three-mile zone" plan was to prevent a ring of unregulated development on the fringes of Greeley's city limits during a time of unprecedented growth. Building permits and inspection fees were now mandatory to ensure that contractors complied with uniform building codes and the City's safety and sanitation requirements. In the 1930s, the Greeley Chamber of Commerce had expressed concerns about substandard houses being constructed north of downtown, many without water or sewer connections. Twenty years later, Greeley residents supported the leadership of Cruce and city departments for their long-range planning initiatives and zoning requirements to avoid unregulated, haphazard development around their city.

Conversations about the "three-mile zone" naturally focused on the future of agriculture lands west of Greeley. W.D. Farr recalled in a 1997 interview that he began noticing the transition of farming to urban land uses, along U.S. Highway

34 in the mid-1950s, after he became a Northern District board member. Farr also served on the board of the Greeley and Loveland Irrigation Company. That company's president, Carl Mossberg of Greeley, joined Farr in the late 1950s on the Northern District board, and they often discussed the future of the region as they drove to Loveland together for meetings.

The Greeley and Loveland Irrigation Company had purchased a large quantity of C-BT shares in the 1950s, which it stored in Lake Loveland and Boyd Lake. Mossberg expressed concerns that farmers in the Greeley and Loveland system, like their peers elsewhere in Colorado, would be unable to sustain the high costs of operations of their irrigation company. Farr and Mossberg were also disturbed about the encroachment from rural water districts, particularly the Little Thompson Water District, which was created in 1961. Farr, realizing that "the City was going to take [annex] more of that farmland," agreed with Mossberg that Greeley should become a partner with Greeley and Loveland in the sale and distribution of the shares of water stock owned by farmers.[26]

AS THE YEAR 1960 ended, the Town of Windsor announced it would seek independence from the Greeley water system. The following year, the Town of Evans also advised Greeley that it planned to develop its own municipal utility. The Evans Town Council, representing 1,453 people, voted to issue $450,000 (nearly $4 million in 2020) in revenue bonds for an independent water system that could serve 2,300 residents, with expansion to 5,000 over time. Real estate developer Roy Lundvall, owner of land for the future "Arrowhead" residential subdivision, had agreed to construct a dam and reservoir three miles west of Evans. There the new water system would emerge with a treatment plant and an 85,000 gallon elevated storage tank. Evans already had acquired water rights directly from the increasingly popular Greeley and Loveland Irrigation Company.

Town officials told the *Greeley Tribune* that, like Windsor in 1960, "restrictions of new water taps in Evans by the City of Greeley have been the cause of the controversy." Mayor Ben Reichert said, "Evans didn't have the opportunity to grow because of the water tap restrictions." He predicted: "Evans will really boom

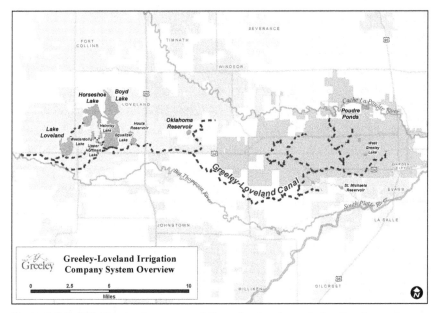

Figure 8.3 In 1961, Greeley began acquisition of water shares in the Greeley and Loveland Irrigation Company (GLIC) and created a secondary municipal supply of water from the Big Thompson River Basin. The GLIC is comprised of three companies and associated reservoirs: Boyd Lake (GLIC), Lake Loveland (Loveland and Greeley Reservoir Company) and Horseshoe Reservoir (Seven Lakes Reservoir Company). The GLIC added operational versatility and increased water supplies for the city. City of Greeley, Water and Sewer Department/Geographic Information Systems.

as a result of having its own water system," citing as evidence several industrial firms that had contacted his office "about the possibility of locating there after the water system is in operation."[27] Neighboring communities were growing, and ready to create their own water departments.

IN MAY 1961, the Greeley Water Board initiated discussions about a potential Greeley and Loveland Company partnership. The *Greeley Tribune* reported on May 10th that over two hours of the meeting was devoted to the idea of constructing a water pipeline from Boyd Lake in Loveland to Greeley (a distance of 15 miles) instead of a new pipeline from the existing Bellvue Water

Treatment Plant at the mouth of the Poudre Canyon. The route from Boyd Lake also had more open space (and less expensive land) between Loveland and Greeley, said Chairman Farr, which would simplify the acquisition of rights-of-way for a new pipeline.

The City also discussed the feasibility of a new filtration plant at Boyd Lake to serve customers along and near U.S. Highway 34. "As the city grows west," Farr told a *Tribune* reporter, "it could acquire Greeley and Loveland water rights and eventually obtain rights to a large amount of water at Boyd Lake." This facility, Farr noted, would also provide "an alternate water supply in the event some disaster interrupted the water flow in the present transmission lines from Bellvue" on the Cache la Poudre River.[28]

The Greeley Water Board recommended that the city council approve the pipeline proposal to support future growth and expansion. Councilors agreed, and on June 30, 1961, approved construction of a water transmission line from Boyd Lake that would deliver up to 10 million gallons of treated water daily to the city. "Greeley's growth potential has been tremendously increased," said the *Greeley Tribune* on July 1st, as this new water source would provide 50 percent of the city's maximum daily supply. In addition, all shareholders of the Greeley and Loveland system would be eligible for City services, since Greeley would construct a "water distribution grid" from Boyd Lake to near the campus of Colorado State College in Greeley. This venture confronted and limited the efforts of the Little Thompson Water District, whose recruitment of farmers and households south and west of Greeley (to join their drinking water system) threatened to "adversely affect the potential growth of the city."[29]

Publication of the Greeley and Loveland Company agreement gave readers of the *Greeley Tribune* much to celebrate during the 4th of July holiday. "A lack of water has not been among the problems Greeley has faced during its postwar growth," declared the *Tribune*. The editor attributed this good fortune to "farsighted planning over many years," which had "provided the city with sufficient water for expansion." Board chairman W.D. Farr, who had "put the City in the position of being able to add to its water supply as the [dominant] pattern of growth to the west continues," was thanked for his vision. As Greeley accumulated more shares in the Greeley and Loveland system, said the editor, "these water rights, when added to the present supply sources, would enable the

Figure 8.4 The original Boyd Lake Water Treatment Plant (Plant No. 2), and its transmission line, were completed in 1968. A substantially larger plant was constructed in 1976 and called Plant No. 1 (due to its larger size and capacity). City of Greeley Museums, Lew Dakan Archive, 1979.06.0007.

City to provide water for a population as high as 100,000." Another benefit of the filtration plant and transmission system in the Big Thompson Valley was that it would allow the City to obtain its C-BT water through Boyd Lake "in case of a breakdown in the Bellvue facilities or the transmission line from there."[30]

In May 1962, the engineering consulting firm of W.W. Wheeler & Associates of Denver recommended that the City of Greeley allocate $675,000 (around $6 million in 2020 dollars) to construct a six million gallon per day filter plant on the shores of Boyd Lake. This plan allowed for expansion of up to 10 million gallons per day. The previously authorized water pipeline would carry treated Boyd Lake water to the west side of Greeley, costing $1,002,000 (around $9 million in 2020). Water users of the Greeley and Loveland system would gain access to a potable (treated) water distribution grid system. The Wheeler consultants did warn city officials that "because of the hardness of the water," Greeley should obtain its water supply for the proposed filter plant directly from the Big Thompson River by means of the Greeley and Loveland Ditch, rather than diverting it from Boyd Lake.[31]

Design and funding strategies for the Greeley and Loveland project continued to occupy much of the Greeley Water Department's time during the first half of 1963. Board members requested that the current city ordinance, which required developers to provide the city with one acre-foot of water for each acre of land developed, be revised upward to three acre-feet per acre—a policy that would endure for the remainder of the 20th century. The water board also approved the idea of attaching water rights to the land, so that this water could not be sold, and would be available to potential subdividers and homebuilders in the future.

IN THE EARLY 1960s, the Greeley Water Board dealt with other concerns. The Board voted to increase water rates by 50 percent to pay for work that included the new Boyd Lake Treatment Plant. That action sparked much discussion in the community. The *Greeley Tribune* asked its readers on July 9, 1962: "Is the proposed Boyd Lake water project of such vital importance to Greeley's future to justify an immediate 50 per cent hike in water rates here?" Mayor Gordon Rissler acknowledged: "I can't see us selling a 50 per cent rate increase to our flat rate users." This water board action, said the mayor, "really shook me," as did the assertion that "Boyd Lake was no good for storage [due to the water quality issues]." Surprised by his colleague's opposition to the project, W.D. Farr called upon Mayor Rissler to analyze the various reports. "If this is what is needed," said the water board chairman bluntly, "and it takes a 50 percent increase in rates to do it, then that is what we need."[32]

The mayor's stance prompted Farr to write a lengthy letter to the city council that appeared in the September 12, 1962, issue of the *Greeley Tribune*. Farr prefaced his remarks by saying that the board attorney, William R. Kelly, had called attention to "the problem of suburban water districts [like the Little Thompson] being formed on the west side of Greeley." The longtime advocate for northern Colorado water interests, said Farr, "had warned that this problem could literally stop the growth of our city."[33]

Farr explained that little water remained in the Cache la Poudre Basin to develop. He also dismissed calls for acquiring additional water rights in the Greeley Number 3 Ditch. The City would have to seek court approval to move its diversion point about 40 miles upstream on the Poudre River, and would be eligible for only six percent of the ditch water for municipal purposes. By comparison, the Greeley and Loveland project offered 19,000 acre-feet of C-BT water, which would be stored in Lake Loveland, and not commingled with irrigation water from farms along the

Big Thompson River. Farr explained that the advantages of Lake Loveland and the Boyd Lake Water Treatment Plant "are many." Primary among these was the source of the Big Thompson itself, a river "which heads [begins] in a National Park where very strict supervision [of water quality] is practiced."

With most C-BT project water delivered directly via pipeline or concrete canals, Farr claimed that Greeley users would have "better water than you are now getting or can get in the future from the Poudre." The board chairman believed that "the cost to the City of Greeley will be the cheapest water ever developed for a Colorado municipality in modern times." Farr and his fellow board members took great pride in the fact that "this action will assure future generations that Greeley will have without question the best water system in the West."[34]

The water board's position prevailed, and the Boyd Lake Treatment Facility was completed in 1964. Today, it continues to supplement the Bellvue Water Treatment Plant and also serves as an emergency back-up facility.

Seaman Dam and Reservoir, which city officials had partially pursued for its job creation opportunities in the depths of the Great Depression, now had become a liability for the water department. Denver engineering firm W.W. Wheeler had been hired to conduct a preliminary design and cost estimate to completely rebuild the spillway. City Manager Cruce noted that previous studies revealed that "heavy flows of water through the spillway have caused extensive erosional damage particularly in the downstream half of the spillway." Facing these conditions, and their attendant costs, Cruce had previously recommended that "if the City goes ahead with the Boyd Lake project, it would not need the Seaman Reservoir water."[35] This was an important statement that would be revisited in the 1980s, but for now, the City would continue to own and operate the reservoir, even after the Boyd Lake project was completed.

NO RAIN FELL from mid-June through early August of 1964, the prime season for irrigation of farm fields and watering lawns and gardens in town. As early as May 21st, Water Director Olin Shaffer had echoed the same concerns of his predecessors, sounding the alarm about wastefulness. His staff noted that customers used an average of 20 million gallons per day, which threatened to drain the four storage reservoirs that held treated water at 23rd Avenue, and the new reservoir on the west side of town.

By early July, conditions only worsened, as Shaffer recorded on July 7, 1964. Greeley hit its all-time record for water use: 21,150,000 gallons in a single day. One week later, the City restricted all outdoor water use for a full 24 hours. Sprinkling was banned from noon on Wednesdays until noon the next day. Greeley had gone through its driest July since 1927, and the water situation was serious. Once again, the citizenry responded, as it did in other moments of water crisis, and the reservoirs began to recover by month's end.[36] This situation was a reminder of the issues faced by the city and water superintendent Milton Seaman during the Dust Bowl years of the 1930s. Greeley's abundance of municipal water did not mean an unlimited supply in a land bound to wet and drought cycles. Again, Greeley's problem (as stated in 1958 by city council member Jack Clayton) was not one of supplies, but one of transmission.

The City had successfully expanded its water portfolio in the early 1960s, so it came as a surprise in early 1965 when the *Greeley Tribune* carried a story about the failure of Greeley to attract a major employer because of the high cost of water. The Shwayder Brothers of Denver, manufacturers of Samsonite luggage, was selected by the LEGO Company, a family-owned Danish company, to open a fabrication plant in northern Colorado. Their product, the small, colorful interlocking plastic blocks that could be assembled into a variety of shapes, required a large volume of water for production. When the Shwayders came to Greeley to negotiate the purchase of water for the factory, they learned, according to the *Tribune,* that nearby Loveland could offer them a contract that was $10,000 per year less.[37]

This news led City Manager Cruce to investigate the water rates of northern Colorado communities. He learned that "Greeley has the lowest inside the city rate of any of the five cities reported on for metered customers whose usage is 30,000 gallons or less per quarter," the minimum rate for Greeley customers. Cruce then compared industrial water use patterns in Loveland, Longmont, Boulder, Fort Collins, and Greeley. This study revealed that the Shwayder request was for over 68 million gallons of water annually, approximately half the amount used by the Monfort Packing Plant (136,623,000 gallons). Cruce then reported that the City of Loveland made its more generous offer, which was accepted, just before it planned to increase its mill levy for new water bonds.[38]

While the city manager's comments suggested a logical explanation of the Shwayder contract with Loveland, others in town wanted better answers to prevent the loss of future potential employers. The local board of realtors called for a community meeting, and 150 business leaders assembled on January 12, 1965, at the American Legion Club. Cruce reminded the audience that he presented "the City's view of what Greeley can do to attract major industry." He also said, "Greeley residents drink the best water available and drive on the best streets among the five cities." Cruce was proud that "Greeley is neither high nor low in its cost of government but is at the top of the heap as the best place to live when compared to its four sister cities in northern Colorado."[39]

IN THE SUMMER of 1962, the Monfort Packing Company was again the focus of attention, and this time the reports were not positive. In spite of assurances from citizens in Scottsbluff, the packing plant in Greeley caused pollution problems in the Cache la Poudre River. Better sewage disposal methods were needed, so the City of Greeley proposed treating the packing plant wastewater for $24,000 per year (around $200,000 in 2020). City officials were directed to "confer with the Monforts regarding this [proposal] before expanding the [existing] sewage treatment plant." Such negotiations would determine "if the packing firm would pay this amount or planned to take care of its sewage itself."[40]

In early 1964, the expansion of the wastewater treatment plant became a critical issue. The original plant, constructed in 1936 at 1st Avenue and 10th Street as a federal public works project, needed expansion.[41] The city council had discussed the prospects of building a treatment plant on the Monfort property in north Greeley. However, in January 1964, the council authorized negotiations with the other large food processing company in town, Great Western Sugar, to purchase land east of the Cache la Poudre River. Some citizens disliked what seemed to be a slow pace of planning and construction of the expanded sewage treatment facility, as became apparent in the pages of the *Greeley Tribune*. In a series of columns in March, the *Tribune* reported that Greeley's plant, built with Public Works Administration money, "isn't big enough to handle it all." The result, said the *Tribune*, was "tremendous quantities of raw sewage dumped directly into the river."[42]

Figure 8.5 Aerial view, looking northwest, Greeley Wastewater Treatment Plant. In 1964, the plant was expanded and included activated sludge (secondary biological wastewater treatment facilities—two primary and two secondary clarifiers) constructed on the north side of the Cache la Poudre River. Collection of the City of Greeley Water and Sewer Department.

The Monfort Packing Company, one of the city's largest employers, recognized the importance of proper sewage disposal. Likewise, the company wanted councilors to recognize the high costs of wastewater treatment for a large enterprise. When the Monforts opened their facility in north Greeley, their beef finishing lot had a capacity of 32,000 head, which had expanded by 1968 to 100,000 head, becoming the largest in the nation. Appearing before the city council on May 10th, Ken Monfort told councilors that "he would be willing to construct pre-treatment facilities and comply with the [1964] agreement." In return, Monfort asked that the City "load the treatment facilities to capacity and treat all of his waste for a period of time." In exchange, the company "would be willing to pay an additional fee which would save him an immediate outlay of a large amount of cash to construct the pre-treatment facilities." Councilors agreed to the proposal, even as some questioned the company's delays in compliance.[43]

IN 1966, THE city water department witnessed a series of events that shaped its decisions for the rest of the decade. The City joined the conversation with northern Colorado communities to initiate a collaborative project with five other northern Colorado cities, known as "Windy Gap." Concurrently, Greeley agreed to assist Windsor with water related planning following the closure of the town's Great Western Sugar factory. In addition, the Greeley Water Board contemplated selling several of the high mountain reservoirs to the Water Supply and Storage Company (WSSC) of Fort Collins to generate revenue. The WSSC owned Chambers Lake in the upper Cache la Poudre Canyon, near Greeley's Barnes Meadow and Peterson Lake reservoirs. WSSC had also expressed interest in the Columbine and Bob Creek transmountain ditches on the Laramie River. By selling these assets, said Chairman Farr, Greeley would have money to purchase more C-BT water which could be stored either at the Greeley and Loveland facility or in the Cache la Poudre Basin. Water Department Director Olin Shaffer also liked the reduction in the city's maintenance and overhead costs if the high mountain reservoirs could be sold.[44]

Another high mountain issue that year was Seaman Reservoir. It had experienced a leak in the earthen dike, which forced the water storage pool level to be lowered by eight feet due to safety concerns. For these reasons, the water board agreed to sell, to the Water Supply and Storage Company, the system of high mountain reservoirs and ditches that Greeley no longer wished to maintain. WSSC could have Peterson Lake, Barnes Meadow, and the Columbine and Bob Creek ditches for the sum of $300,000 ($2.4 million in 2020). Greeley had stored about 200 acre-feet annually in each of the lakes; a fraction of the 900 acre-feet of total storage capacity for each reservoir.

The water board's reasoning included the $300,000 price tag needed to rehabilitate the dams at Peterson and Barnes Meadow Reservoirs. The same held true for the ditches that had a combined capacity of about 525 acre-feet during the irrigation season. The WSSC planned to abandon the ditches and redirect the 1,000 acre-feet of water, to which they were entitled, through its Laramie River tunnel.[45] Negotiations eventually faltered, however, and rather than sell the high mountain reservoirs that were purchased in 1947, the City ultimately decided to rehabilitate them, as well as Seaman Reservoir. These were short-term solutions, and the debate regarding the sale of these high mountain assets would re-emerge again in the 1980s.

ON JUNE 27, 1968, the Eastman Kodak Company announced plans to expand its operations to Colorado with a 2,400-acre land option near Windsor. The Fortune 500 company was listed as 29th in sales ($2.3 billion in 1967), ninth in net earnings, and was the maker of America's most popular camera film. For a decade, it had searched for a location west of the Mississippi River for a new plant. As the economic and population boom of the 1960s continued, Kodak's sales projections were expected to rise significantly as it introduced new films and cameras. Norman Beach, vice-president of the Rochester, New York, company told audiences of business and civic leaders in Greeley, Fort Collins, and Loveland that by 1990, Eastman Kodak would sell half of its products to buyers in the American West. Offering a payroll of $10 million per year at the start, with plans to hire up to 5,000 workers by the mid-1970s, Beach's company would contribute much to a bright future for northern Colorado, if adequate water supplies could be secured.[46]

Eastman Kodak's arrival would develop the Cache la Poudre Valley in ways not seen in decades. The primary reason why Kodak considered Weld County for its multi-million dollar facility was the apparent abundance of water. In that regard, the City of Greeley, which had provided water services to Windsor for over six decades, played an instrumental role in attracting Kodak to Windsor. W.D. Farr recalled in 1997 that Colorado Governor John Love approached him, in the Spring of 1968, about Kodak's interest in constructing a manufacturing facility in Colorado. Governor Love had met with two employees of Kodak, Robert Sheridan and Bruce Becker, who wished to remain anonymous as they traveled through-out the Mountain West in search of a site for their 500,000 square foot facility. A realty company in Denver had alerted them of 3,000 acres in the Windsor area offered for sale by Great Western Sugar, which no longer needed it for growing sugar beet seed for contract farmers.[47]

Fortunately for the Kodak representatives, W.D. Farr not only served as chairman of the Greeley Water Board, but also knew that particular property well. Farr informed "Bob" and "Bruce," as the agents were known, of the ease of access to the Bellvue pipeline on one corner of the property. The Kodak officials invited Farr to visit their headquarters in Rochester, New York, to assist with negotiations. Once there, a Kodak official asked how the City of Greeley could guarantee a stable supply like the massive amount of water available from nearby Lake Erie at Rochester, New York. "We're going to spend a lot of money to build big plants," Farr recalled being told in Rochester. The executive feared that "we're going to be high and dry [without enough water]."[48]

Realizing that the Kodak initiative hinged on the availability of a stable source of water, Farr offered to show Kodak's representatives Greeley's extensive water system. He personally escorted three company officials through Rocky Mountain National Park, driving over Trail Ridge Road and along the Colorado River to Grand Lake. There they spent the night, touring the C-BT project the next day. "There was still a lot of snow on Trail Ridge," recalled Farr, a key selling point for the Kodak visitors, since "it was June." Another important stop was at Lake Granby. Once the representatives saw the volume of water available for their operations, said Farr, "then they understood that they could get water year-round." The certainty of Greeley's cache of water, upon which each generation had depended for nearly a century, as well as its quality, led to the signing of pledges to build the Kodak plant at Windsor.[49]

The announcement was made at the Brown Palace Hotel in Denver on June 27, 1968. Because he did not publicize his role in the delicate negotiations over Kodak's water supply, W.D. Farr did not earn recognition for his efforts. Yet the future did indeed look bright for the partnership with the City of Greeley, as well as the Town of Windsor.[50] By summer's end, the City of Greeley had emerged as the most logical vendor of water for Kodak's operations.

On September 20th, the Denver law firm of Dawson, Nagel, Sherman and Howard drafted a water contract for the Greeley City Council to review. Kodak's engineers and planners had determined that they would need an escalating scale of purchases, beginning with 500,000 gallons per day through 1980. Within ten years, the company anticipated consuming one million gallons per day; an amount that Kodak noted "will be needed during the life of the plant." Then there was the matter of film production. By 1980, Kodak would use an average of six million gallons per day, with a peak demand of eight million gallons per day. The City offered to provide the plant with water from its Bellvue and Boyd Lake facilities to ensure a steady supply year-round. Kodak could also seek its own water from other providers, such as the C-BT system.[51]

Finding these terms satisfactory, the city council authorized city attorney William Bohlender and water board attorney William Kelly to draft an agreement. The Greeley Water Department had the capacity to serve the needs of Kodak as well as existing customers, said Willard Quirk of the engineering firm, Nelson, Haley, Patterson and Quirk. Since Kodak would start operations by June 1969, Quirk felt confident that no new supplies would be needed, at least not until 1975. At that point, the second transmission line from the Boyd Lake Treatment Plant, with its 10 million gallon capacity, would double the available supply. Kodak had advised the City of its need to sign the contract quickly, so as not to delay construction.[52]

Greeley water officials could now focus on maintaining and expanding its water storage facilities. Projections of future urban growth accelerated calls for collaboration among regional communities; this to maximize full use of the C-BT's water delivery system. The converging point would become the "Windy Gap Project" proposed in 1969 by Greeley, Loveland, Fort Collins, Longmont, Estes Park and Boulder. This project would make up for an annual average of 48,000 acre-feet of water that would have been provided by unbuilt features of the original C-BT Project.[53]

IN 1958, GREELEY voters seized the initiative, for better management and water planning, when they approved the new city charter and created the Greeley Water Board. The latter added an important feature to the City's water system when it negotiated the agreement with the Greeley and Loveland Irrigation Company. The Boyd Lake treatment system on the Big Thompson River now paralleled the City's Cache la Poudre River system. Greeley's C-BT water could be delivered through either or both sides of this versatile water storage and delivery system.

In a fitting epitaph to the decades of the 1950s and 1960s, the Six Cities

Committee was created to add Windy Gap water to the C-BT system, bringing to mind the cooperative spirit of Greeley's Union Colonists. They realized early on the necessity of working together to acquire water that residents, living on Colorado's semi-arid Front Range, could share. The *Longmont Times-Call* editorialized on December 17, 1969, about the merits of collaboration in water planning. "The life blood of this area is water," wrote the *Times-Call* editor. "Without water," said the editor, "the future will be very bleak."[54]

The decade of the 1970s would challenge the adaptability of the Greeley Water Board. The board and the staff would face several environmental issues, along with state and federal regulatory mandates, that would stretch their water management and collaboration skills. Population growth, and degraded water quality in the South Platte and Cache la Poudre Rivers, would test Greeley's water and wastewater systems with new, unforeseen challenges.

CHAPTER NINE

1970-1980
Cleanliness, Abundance, and Affordablity

Keeping Meeker's Promise

THROUGH THE YEARS, Greeley water has been used for a variety of endeav-ors—irrigation, washing and cleaning, refining sugar, butchering cattle, and drinking. However, in 1969, on the brink of Greeley's centennial, 99 years of limited alcohol (drinking only water, coffee, tea, or in limited locations 3.2 beer), a well-known and sometimes ridiculed hallmark of the Union Colony was again in the news. Temperance was frequently cited, along with water and irrigation, as the basis for the community's wholesomeness and astound-ing agricultural success. Now, on November 4, 1969, voters would determine whether Greeley would adhere to its conservatism and strict temperance principles and remain a "dry" community, or whether it would "modern up" like Boulder and other neighboring towns and cities, to become a "wet" community—where the sale and consumption of a wider variety of alcoholic beverages would be allowed.

Greeley was divided into two camps: those who supported the Keep Greeley Great Committee (anti-alcohol) and those more inclined toward the Help Greeley Grow Committee (pro-alcohol) groups. Both sides solicited donations to advance their causes, and letters to the editor of the *Greeley Tribune* flowed like water from a headgate, filling column after column in the newspaper. The Help Greeley Grow Committee placed a large ad in the September 27, 1969, edition that included a photograph of W.D. Farr, chairman of the Greeley Water Board as well as chair of the Help Greeley Grow Committee. His letter supported the repeal of Greeley's liquor prohibition laws, as they were in his words, a "handicap to progress" and growth.

Allowing liquor to be sold within Greeley's city limits, according to Farr, would be sensibly planned for and regulated, would encourage more businesses to locate here, and increase tax revenues through liquor licensing fees and sales. Farr (Greeley's long-time champion of water acquisition and development to encourage growth), along with 33 other businessmen named in the Committee's pro-liquor brochure, believed that after almost 100 years of temperance, it was now time for liquor, like water, to flow freely in Greeley. A record 8,202 citizens cast their ballots, and by a margin of only 235 votes (51-49% margin), liquor won—an indication that Greeley's "old guard" would need to adapt, accept, and ultimately embrace change as Greeley grew from a small town into a more modern, mature city.

The election results were a significant break from Nathan Meeker's vision of the past, and signaled new perspectives for a majority (albeit slim) of Greeley's citizens. Times were changing and the 1970s would usher in sweeping transitions, for social change and also water management, in Colorado and the nation. The environmental movement of the new decade signaled a major shift in how water and wastewater utilities operated, and Greeley would need to adopt new practices to adapt to these changes on the horizon. The temperance election results were a forecast that more "contemporary" trends were forthcoming.

Greeley pursued a strategy of planned growth in the 1970s through water acquisition and delivery system improvements. Its population would increase by 36 percent (to 53,006) from 1970 to 1980. Fort Collins was now the region's largest community at 87,758 people, nearly one-third larger than Greeley. Longmont's population exploded by 85 percent in response to the International Business Machines (IBM) plant which located in nearby Niwot. Loveland, at 37,352 citizens, had grown at the fastest rate (230 percent), in part, due to the Hewlett-Packard plant locating there.[1]

The environmental movement's impact came as a surprise to many communities that had not considered, or perhaps simply dismissed, wastewater treatment as a critical aspect of public health and safety. Historian Martin Melosi stated: "Implementation of new sanitary services and maintenance of existing systems faced serious challenges after 1970." In particular, "metropolitan growth became more complex, [while] urban fiscal problems, and environmental concerns intensified."

One of Greeley's perennial attractions, offered since 1907, was its "pure mountain water." For the town's residents, access to Cache la Poudre River water meant no need for chlorination. The City also owned enough water to allow almost unlimited use on resident's lawns and gardens in most years. But episodes of drought rudely suggested otherwise, and a brace of federal legislation during the decade required American cities to comply with the Federal Water Pollution Control Act Amendments (1972), the Safe Drinking Water Act (1974) and the Clean Water Act (1977), along with the National Environmental Policy Act of 1969 of the previous decade. These ushered in a new generation of water resources design, construction, funding, and maintenance requirements. By adjusting its planning strategies, Greeley would earn much praise and national acclaim by complying with these new water regulations.

IN THE SPRING of 1971, city water officials wisely drafted a five-year plan for operations and maintenance. The Barnes Meadow and Peterson Lake Reservoirs received $480,000 ($3.1 million in 2020 dollars) to improve their storage capacities. At Boyd Lake, the water department called for doubling the filter plant's output from 10 to 20 million gallons per day, at a cost of $862,500 ($5.5 million in 2020). In turn, this required another 10 million gallon-per-day transmission line, which cost $1,197,900 ($7.6 million in 2020). The Bellvue treatment facility on the Cache la Poudre River needed micro-strainers and chlorination equipment for the new Kodak film-processing facilities in Windsor. These were important measures, but water treatment upgrades were expensive to do properly.

Within the city limits, the water department recommended multiple improvements that included construction of a 15 million gallon storage reservoir at the 23rd Avenue location. Also needed was a $115,000 expansion of the pumping station and storage reservoir in the Highland Hills neighborhood. The City's water distribution system on the north side of the Cache la Poudre River warranted a new $304,750 pipeline to the Monfort Packing Company, along with $197,000 of new transmission and distribution lines in the growing Delta neighborhood southeast of downtown. Total expenditures would be $5,426,850 (approximately $35 million in 2020).[2]

Water use within the city limits also occupied the department's attention for much of 1970. Some residents, who now measured their water use with meters, criticized rising water rates. Julius Thompson of Greeley wrote to the *Greeley Tribune* on May 2, 1970, about conditions Union Colonists had known a century before. "In this fast-growing, semi-arid region of our country," he said, "where water consumption is expected to increase faster than the acquisition of new supplies, conservation of water should be of utmost concern to every resident." Thompson argued that the City's flat-rate fee schedule led to "excessive lawn watering" because customers had "no incentive to turn off a faucet or to repair leaking faucets, toilets, appliances or underground pipes."[3] These concerns echoed similar sentiments expressed by Water Superintendent Milton Seaman in the early 1900s, and showed the challenge of adopting water conservation ethics while trying to maintain green lawns.

Water Department Director Olin Shaffer confirmed that excessive water usage caused significant shortages at times. "The city has lots of water if it isn't wasted," Shaffer told the *Tribune*. "Every gutter in town," said the director, "has enough water running down it on watering days to water several lawns." This he attributed to "people who let their sprinklers run for hours in one location until the ground becomes saturated and the water runs off the lawn into the street." Shaffer feared his staff could not provide sufficient water at this rate, and would need to ban outdoor water use for periods of 24 hours. Shaffer hoped that this would not occur more than once a week.[4]

At the water board meeting on August 7, 1971, two other matters altered the course of the water department's operations. The board's attorney produced a draft ordinance requiring all new customers to install water meters. "This would apply to all new buildings, everyone inside and outside of the city, and any reconstruction." Board Chairman Farr questioned whether a town that had existed for a century without universal metering actually needed it: "Spending $1 ½ million at this time to convert the flat rate users to water meters would in effect be a waste of money." Farr reasoned that "the meters likely would reduce water use and, consequently, the City's water revenue." When asked if meters could address the matter of excessive watering of lawns and gardens, George Underwood, a consulting engineer with Nelson, Haley, Patterson and Quirk of Greeley, explained that "wasting of water by users here is about normal as compared with the waste in other cities."

Water Director Shaffer supported Farr's suggestion about delaying installation of meters citywide. "Presently the flat rate users pay the same rate the year round," said Shaffer, "regardless of the amount of water they use." The City had relied upon this steady source of income for the calculation of bond payments. "Meter users, on the other hand," said Shaffer, "pay only for the amount of water they use each quarter." This would create a more volatile water use pattern between summer and winter. "If everyone was on a meter," Shaffer concluded, "and we had a wet year which reduced sprinkling drastically, you couldn't pay off your bonds."[5]

This concern about meeting financial obligations led the *Greeley Tribune* to editorialize about the rate-increase dilemma. On February 5, 1972, the newspaper offered its readers a contrast between higher charges or less outdoor water. "Apparently we are going to experience some regulation this summer," wrote the *Tribune* editor. "For a city used to sprinkling freely and having velvet-like lawns," the editor wondered, "how many would be content with the even more stringent sprinkling regulations likely if the [mandatory metering] improvements are not completed by 1974?" These would include limitations on outdoor use to once every four days.

Water use efficiency was not the only topic of discussion, and the issue of wastewater treatment and efficient government surfaced as well. In 1970, City Manager Jack Huffman reported to the water board that "the sewer system was taken out of the Water Department but there is not an ordinance recorded providing for this action." He wanted the sewer operations restored to the supervision of the water department. Huffman declared that "civil engineers trained in this field have basically the same technical education and background which can be applied to either the water or sewer facilities." He also wanted a new generation of department staff, trained in the latest methods and practices. "With interchanging personnel and equipment," said Huffman, "we could have a more efficient department." He told the board: "The problems presently are in the sewer division; the water problems have been handled quite well."

Board Chair Farr agreed. Like water operations, sewer facilities "should be taken out of politics and placed under the Water Board to keep up the quality."[6] This led to the 1973 City Charter Revisions adding the Sewer Department to the water board's responsibilities, creating the Greeley Water and Sewer Board. It would continue to collaborate with the city council and city manager to meet the public's needs.

Important water debates continued into the spring of 1973. The Greeley

Chamber of Commerce organized an effort called "Forward Together." The Forward Together team saw merit in water metering and "strong enforcement of city lawn irrigation standards." Another innovative practice that Forward Together advocated was a "dual water system for household and lawn irrigation purposes." Should the water users of northern Colorado implement some or all such practices, they would be guided by the "'vision and competence' which has brought the Greeley water supply to its current condition," said J.E. Husted, chair of the Forward Together water subcommittee.[7]

AT ITS MARCH 13th meeting, water and sewer board members called once more for a $6.5 million ($37.6 million in 2020) sewage treatment expansion project. The city manager, aware that Greeley had outgrown its facilities, commented, "The sewer system is one of the most critical areas where capital improvements are needed." Huffman also saw challenges with traffic, parks and open spaces, plus fire and police services. Water and sewer director Shaffer agreed: "The sewer situation is the limiting factor in Greeley's growth at this time." It would take two to three years for the engineering and construction work to bring the wastewater treatment system up to code.[8] The reorganization of the sewer department was beginning to pay dividends with improved management and sound planning practices.

As Greeley approached the mid-1970s, major expansion of its overall water and wastewater system required resolution of three critical issues. First would be the Kodak plant in nearby Windsor, which affected how the community planned for its future water needs. Next, the Six Cities Project (known as the "Windy Gap Project" by decade's end) needed funding, study, and authorization by its urban partners, who would equally share 48,000 acre-feet of West Slope water annually. Wastewater treatment became the third major challenge; in particular, how best to accommodate major food production facilities such as Great Western Sugar, the Monfort Packing Company, and local dairies. Operations for the remainder of the 1970s depended upon how the City's water and sewer department responded to these challenges.

ON MARCH 23, 1981, W.D. Farr reported that the Windy Gap Project "after all these years, has finally been cleared." Hank Brown knew that W.D. Farr had been a key component of its progress during the decade of the 1970s and its completion in 1985. In a 2009 interview, former U.S. Senator Hank Brown recalled: "I'm convinced Windy Gap never would have happened without him."[9] From its outset, Greeley owned a one-sixth equal interest in the Windy Gap project, as did Boulder, Longmont, Loveland, Estes Park, and Fort Collins. The Platte River Power Authority became a major participant when four of the cities, Longmont, Loveland, Estes Park and Fort Collins assigned shares to it for the Rawhide Power Plant, which served those communities.

The Six Cities Committee envisioned Windy Gap as an extension of the Colorado-Big Thompson Project. As Farr explained, the C-BT system had delivered no more than 250,000 acre-feet per year, through the Alva B. Adams Tunnel, to Northern Colorado Water Conservancy District farmers, cities and businesses; not the 310,000 acre-feet of water originally calculated. A new river diversion structure, just below the confluence of the Colorado and Fraser Rivers in Grand County, and a pipeline to Lake Granby would make up most of the difference by diverting up to 48,000 acre-feet of water per year. Windy Gap would be valuable water because it would be totally reusable transmountain water, imported from the West Slope to Front Range cities. The C-BT contract between the Bureau of Reclamation and the Northern District allowed only one use of that project water. Return flows were legally dedicated (earmarked) to downstream water users, at-large within the boundaries of the Northern District, wherever and whenever those waters arrived at their headgates.[10] Windy Gap water, by contrast, could be captured and used multiple times under Colorado water law.

Not so fast and not so easy, however, as many challenges awaited those who promoted the Windy Gap project.[11] The Six Cities had commissioned an October 1969 preliminary design study regarding water availability at the proposed diversion point along the Colorado River. The analysis cautioned that water, for the relatively junior Windy Gap water rights, would be highly variable; from 63,000 acre-feet in a wet year to none during a drought, depending on snowmelt runoff conditions in any given year.[12]

On September 17, 1979, the Colorado Supreme Court had delivered a potentially fatal blow to the Windy Gap water rights. It ruled that, in order to export Colorado River water from its natural basin, a conservancy district's water decree must include a detailed plan demonstrating "that any project works or facilities will be designed, constructed and operated in such a manner that the present appropriations of water, and in addition thereto prospective uses of water . . . within the natural basin of the Colorado River . . . will not be impaired nor increased in cost at the expense of water users within the natural basin."[13]

Now the resolve of the Six Cities partnership would be tested. Prior to creation of Northern's Municipal Subdistrict, the Six Cities had entered into a February 24, 1969, agreement pledging themselves "to join in the development of water rights to be used by all and each of them" and "take all action necessary by all and each of them to develop and secure said water rights and supplies of water for the benefit of the Cities, as expeditiously as possible."[14] Greatly concerned, Grand County insisted that Northern's new Municipal Subdistrict comply with its "House Bill 1041" regulations to ensure protection of the area's interests. Greeley's potential new source of water was now in jeopardy as things did not look good for the project.

The Six Cities elected to proceed with settlement negotiations with the objecting groups. At the helm of the Municipal Subdistrict as president was W.D. Farr, also the chair of Greeley's Water and Sewer Board.[15] At his side, as a member of the Northern Colorado Water Conservancy District and Municipal Subdistrict board, was Greeley lawyer William "Bill" Bohlender. He had served as Greeley's city attorney from 1965 to 1970 and became the water and sewer board's legal counsel in 1970. Bohlender was appointed to the Northern District board in 1968 and was elected its president in 1992.[16]

BETWEEN SEPTEMBER 1979 and June 1980, under Farr and Bohlender's leadership, the Municipal Subdistrict worked to reach a comprehensive settlement. After strenuous negotiations, the Windy Gap Settlement Agreement was signed by all parties on April 30, 1980, and serves as a prototype for navigating local, state and federal permitting requirements of a major water project.[17] Several important

Figure 9.1 In 1967, Greeley and five other Front Range cities formed a mutually beneficial alliance to acquire additional water. Known as the Windy Gap Project, this transbasin diversion project from the Colorado River would use the Colorado-Big Thompson infrastructure to deliver West Slope junior water rights to the Front Range. In 1985, the project came online and its major features are seen on this map. Courtesy of Northern Colorado Water Conservancy District.

innovations in Colorado law and policy came into play with this agreement.

First among the enduring Windy Gap settlement innovations was its implementation of Colorado's 1973 Instream Flow Program. The Municipal Subdistrict took the extraordinary step of making its Windy Gap diversions subject to three new instream flow rights appropriated by the Colorado Water Conservation Board (CWCB) and adjudicated in the Water Court Division No. 5 in Glenwood Springs: from the Windy Gap diversion point to the mouth of the Williams Fork River, 90 cfs; from the mouth of Williams Fork River to the mouth of Troublesome Creek, 130 cfs; and from the mouth of the Troublesome Creek to the mouth of the Blue River, 150 cfs.[18] The CWCB made these appropriations[19] and the Water Court Division No. 5 issued decrees for them.[20]

Second among the enduring Windy Gap settlement innovations was its implementation of Colorado's House Bill 1041 through regulations adopted by Grand County. The criteria for approving or denying a Grand County 1041 Permit included a substantiated "need for the proposed water project" and "assurances of compatibility of the water project with federal, state, regional and county planning policies regarding land use and water resources." Northern District General Manager Larry Simpson spent much time meeting with ranchers, downstream of the Windy Gap diversion point, who worried about adverse impacts to their water rights and the use of their properties, "particularly irrigation uses and fishing."[21] To address their concerns, the Municipal Subdistrict (of which Greeley was a member) spent approximately $600,000 for modification of rancher diversion works. In addition, the Subdistrict paid Grand County $25,000 for salinity studies and compensated the Town of Hot Sulphur Springs $420,000 to improve the town's water and wastewater treatment facilities.

The Municipal Subdistrict also agreed to provide 3,000 acre-feet of water annually, from Lake Granby for use in Middle Park, for water supply protection to Western Slope water users. In addition, it subordinated the Windy Gap decrees to all present and future in-basin, domestic, and municipal uses on the Colorado and Fraser Rivers (excluding industrial uses) upstream of the Windy Gap diversion point. For water quality protection, the Subdistrict agreed to a water quality classification for Granby Reservoir, Shadow Mountain Reservoir and Grand Lake to protect "all present beneficial uses of these reservoirs or lakes"—and to work with the Three Lakes Sanitation District to improve its water quality treatment facilities. For recreational use, it opened the Windy Gap Reservoir for a public bird viewing area. To satisfy the Colorado River Water Conservation District's insistence on a new compensatory reservoir, the Municipal Subdistrict committed to pursuing the construction of the 30,000 acre-foot Azure Reservoir for the Western Slope, but, if that reservoir proved infeasible, it would make a payment of $10 million dollars towards an alternate reservoir.[22]

Third among the enduring Windy Gap settlement innovations was the impetus it gave to what would eventually become the Upper Basin Recovery Plan for the Endangered Colorado River Fishes. The Municipal Subdistrict needed a Section 404 Dredge and Fill Permit, from the U.S. Army Corps of Engineers under the federal Clean Water Act, to construct the Windy Gap dam and diversion works on the Colorado River. In turn, this required consultation with the U.S. Fish and Wildlife Service. The Subdistrict was facing a possible jeopardy opinion, under the Endangered Species Act in connection with the habitat needs of the

Colorado River Squawfish and Humpback Chub, downriver near Grand Junction. Following Subdistrict discussions with the U.S. Fish and Wildlife Service and Colorado's Division of Wildlife, the Fish and Wildlife Service issued a non-jeopardy opinion. This decision ratified the Subdistrict's agreement to implement the instream flows below the Windy Gap diversion. In addition, the Subdistrict agreed to contribute $100,000 for fish habitat improvements and $450,000 over three years for field research for conservation of the fishes. This was the start of what became the Upper Colorado River Endangered Fish Recovery Program, which continues today.[23]

The relationships built through Grand County's 1041 permit process extended into 2012 when Grand County issued its permit for the Windy Gap Firming Project. This was part of the East Slope Chimney Hollow Reservoir project near Loveland to improve its firm yield of water from Windy Gap. At the County's permit hearing that year, Nancy Stuart, Chair of the Grand County Commissioners, reported that "Grand County has secured protections for water quantity and quality in the Colorado River that never would have happened without the project and this permit."[24]

There were many reasons for the Greeley Water and Sewer Board to celebrate the start of Windy Gap construction in 1981. On July 11, 1981, with local, state and federal permits and approvals in hand and 175 persons in attendance, Colorado U.S. Congressman Hank Brown threw the switch to ignite dynamite charges to start the work. W.D. Farr spoke about the importance of Windy Gap water to the East Slope to slow down the conversion of agricultural water to municipal use.[25] This marked an emotional moment for the 71-year-old water statesman. Farr had also been present at the east portal of the Alva B. Adams Tunnel, near Estes Park 25 years earlier, to witness the first release of C-BT waters to the Front Range of Colorado. Once again, W.D. Farr was an eyewitness to Colorado water history.

As pipeline construction from the Windy Gap diversion site to Granby Reservoir was underway, archaeological investigations revealed an astounding find. Wattle and daub living sites (a prehistoric construction method that used woven lattice strips called wattle, which were daubed with a combination of sticky material such as wet soil, clay, sand, animal dung or straw) were uncovered, along with 100 stone artifacts. This placed Middle Park human occupation as far back as 6,000 B.C. As such, U.S. Secretary of Interior James Watt took a personal interest in the implications of these discoveries. He noted, "First, consider the time frame. These dates go back beyond the time of the North American Indian basket makers, beyond the construction of the great pyramids, and even beyond the time of Ancient Mesopotamia. The remains we have discovered date back to more than 5,900 years before the birth of Christ."[26] The Windy Gap pipeline was channeling both water and human history along its corridor.

In the early 1970s, in spite of the City of Greeley's involvement in the Windy Gap Project, the Town of Windsor expressed concerns regarding the reliability of Greeley's water sources. Greeley had provided water to Windsor for over 60 years prior to the arrival of the Eastman Kodak manufacturing facility. However, the new industry changed the water relationship between the two communities, and Windsor needed more water. In March 1970, Windsor approached the Fort Collins-Loveland Water District to explore boring a new tunnel into the Northern District's Horsetooth Reservoir to gain access to its water. The *Fort Collins Coloradoan* learned that Windsor's "secrecy" was due to its existing water contract with the City of Greeley. "Windsor is able to purchase water so long as Greeley has extra," reported the *Coloradoan*. New growth caused by the Kodak operations led Windsor town trustees to seek a more stable and independent source of water, and one which they would own. The Bureau of Reclamation approved Windsor's request, to obtain its own C-BT water, which Windsor would finance.[27]

As the Kodak plant emerged from the fields around Windsor, rumors began to circulate that the company's ultimate goal was to relocate all operations to Colorado. In June of 1971, the *Greeley Tribune* dispatched a reporter, Paul Edscorn, to Eastman Kodak headquarters in Rochester, New York. He reported that these rumors were "wishful thinking and unbridled optimism." The Colorado Division was but one of 14 Kodak manufacturing units, totaling 43,000 employees in Rochester alone. "Neither all nor part of this vast complex," said Edscorn, "is moving to Windsor." Company representatives did agree that its Windsor operations were essential to Kodak productivity and marketing, given its work in "packaging and distribution of photographic films, paper and lithographic plates and some chemicals."[28]

What limited Kodak's further expansion in Colorado, wrote the *Tribune* reporter, was "a simple reason—water." Edscorn learned from company sources in New York that "Greeley is able to supply the amount and quality of water needed in the foreseeable future for the planned operations at Windsor." Should Kodak wish to transfer its pulp mill and manufacturing processes, said Jon Walsh, assistant general manager of Kodak Park, it would need access to at least 50 million gallons of water per day. "At Rochester," wrote the *Tribune* reporter, "Kodak Park can draw its water supply from Lake Ontario, only five miles away." That alone, said Edscorn, should convince Coloradans that "the Windsor facility remains but a small part of Eastman Kodak."[29]

IT WAS NO coincidence that the Colorado Division of Eastman Kodak emphasized good water quality, in the Cache la Poudre River Basin, when they investigated Windsor for its operations. After enactment of the 1969 National Environmental Policy Act (NEPA), the U.S. Environmental Protection Agency (EPA) took steps to address questions of air and water pollution across the nation. Greeley's attention focused first on the city's wastewater facility, which was expanded in 1964, to provide secondary treatment capacity to the 1936 primary treatment plant. The City was encountering ongoing citizen complaints about odor from the numerous food processing plants on the east side of town; among these were the Great Western Sugar factory and the Monfort Packing Plant. City Manager B.H. Cruce noted in a January 26, 1970, memorandum that Greeley had spent $4,000 in 1968 (about $30,000 in 2020), and again in 1969, to control the sewer plant's smell, achieving "unsatisfactory results."[30]

Aware of odor complaints directed at food processing in general (and the Monfort operations in particular) Ken Monfort decided in early 1970 to build a new cattle finishing lot 15 miles south of Greeley near Gilcrest. This site, employing 80 to 90 people at full capacity, would have the latest computerized equipment to regulate feeding of up to 100,000 head of cattle.[31] However, it would be several years before Monfort made this finishing lot operational.

In the meantime, the packing plant sent an average of 2.5 million gallons per day of effluent to the city's wastewater plant, reaching peak flows of 4.3 million gallons per day. Plant operations showed the need for 800 gallons of potable water for each head of cattle and 143 gallons for each sheep processed. In 1970, a decade after the plant came online, two shifts per day processed 2,500 cattle and 3,500 sheep daily. City officials agreed that this volume of waste required a second treatment and recommended that the Monfort Company pay a sewer service fee for its operations and bond retirement.

More money was needed for these improvements, prompting the City to apply for a grant from the Federal Water Quality Administration for one-third of the construction costs.[32] The outlay ($660,000—around $4.4 million in 2020) for a second treatment plant would be funded by the sale of bonds. Water and sewer department personnel also explored other options for wastewater treatment, and considered the relatively new concept of outdoor holding ponds ("sewage lagoons") as a better and less expensive alternative.[33] These were later built at the Lone Tree facility east of Greeley, but only served the Monfort packing plant, and would later be owned and operated by the JBS-USA Company.

During the 1970s, pride in Greeley's drinking water system was offset by the aging and inadequate wastewater treatment facilities. In December 1970, publication of the state health department's findings stunned Greeley citizens as the report was very critical of the city's wastewater treatment operations.[34] The Colorado Water Pollution Control Commission notified City officials that they had until October 31, 1971, to bring the Greeley wastewater facility into compliance with state regulations. This would require reductions of dissolved oxygen content in sewage effluent by at least 80 percent. Howard Lewis, of the Colorado Water Pollution Control Commission, visited Greeley that fall to review the findings of state health department engineers.[35]

For the next two years, the City and Monfort Company representatives discussed efforts to reduce the volume of effluent being treated by the outdated wastewater plant. They also sought to address air and water quality concerns raised over other cattle finishing lots located just north of the community. Monfort had more plans for expansion after learning that 1972 had been a year of record profits, at $1.20 per share, after a loss of 15 cents per share the previous year. The company announced that "income from the company's cattle feeding operations continued to represent a significant proportion of the total earnings." The company still had a 100,000-head cattle feedlot north of the city limits, relying on a combination of water sources: groundwater wells, raw water purchased from irrigation companies, and municipal supplies from the City.[36]

A STAFF PROPOSAL to add a north sewer line along the Cache la Poudre River raised concerns among members of the Greeley Water and Sewer Board. Peter "Pete" Morrell, who became city manager in 1974, advised the board in June that "water projects would be influenced by sewer projects," and could result in a serious financial burden on rate payers. Darryl Alleman, administrative engineer for the department, reported to the board that the state water pollution control commission had reviewed Greeley's proposal for funding $7.5 million in wastewater projects. Alleman had been advised by state officials that they would support 75 percent of the cost of a "regional sewage facility;" this to also serve the smaller communities that purchased water from Greeley, in addition to the city itself.[37]

Greeley's inadequate sewer system continued to dominate the water and sewer department agenda. As city officials drafted revisions to their EPA proposal for a new wastewater treatment system, the water and sewer board learned on October 6, 1974, that the Colorado Water Pollution Control Commission had issued yet another "Cease and Desist Order" for the lagoons east of town that Monfort operated. Concluded Mayor Hall, "Monfort's waste was transferred out to the lagoons along with the sulfate water and that is when problems began."[38] In January 1975, Mayor George Hall spoke optimistically about reports that the City had met state standards for sewage treatment for the month of December 1974, conditions that Hall hoped would prevail in the future. However, Mayor Hall conceded that residents had legitimate complaints. Greeley's 1965 wastewater treatment plant had been built to meet existing state and federal standards at that time. The mayor noted that "it was overloaded so rapidly and standards changed so rapidly that it could no longer meet State [water quality] standards."[39] City officials sought advice from eastern cities (as water superintendent Milton Seaman had done decades earlier) that used lagoon systems as "the only way to treat packing house waste." In April 1975, the city council also hosted a public meeting in its chambers to discuss the "Wastewater Regional Facilities Plan" under section 201 of the 1972 federal Water Pollution Control Act Amendments. This public meeting focused on several options for a new Greeley sewage treatment plant. Consultant Ron McLaughlin told the audience that they were witnessing "the beginning of a new era with regard to water pollution control facilities." Mayor Hall acknowledged that "the Greeley treatment facilities and trunk sewer system have been inadequate for some time." Hall told attendees from federal, state, municipal, and private entities that "the plan must be comprehensive and far-reaching in order to ensure that funds will be used most effectively in the future."[40]

Nothing like the April 8, 1975, meeting had ever been recorded before in the Greeley Water and Sewer Board meeting minutes. The EPA obligated applicants for federal funding to conduct these hearings, and list the concerns and recommendations of the citizenry, along with those provided by consultants and public officials. The audience heard from McLaughlin that the federal government would fund up to 75 percent of approved projects. Any wastewater treatment plant constructed would require a permit from the Colorado Water Quality Control Commission to discharge pollutants into the waters of the state, in this case the Cache la Poudre River.

All of this activity pointed towards the stipulated federal goal "to eliminate all water pollution by 1985." The EPA would oversee planning, construction, and operation of wastewater treatment facilities, according to McLaughlin. In addition, successful bidders for federal funds needed to demonstrate "a comprehensive cost-effective analysis to ensure wise use [of] dollars on a long-range basis." Perhaps more difficult was the criteria that "an environmental assessment is required to check the overall effects of any plan."[41]

For the audience gathered in city council chambers, McLaughlin explained the National Environmental Policy Act strategy, which included four options for public works projects that required access to the nation's "navigable" waters. The State had contracted for a "South Platte Basin Water Quality Management Plan." From this would come the concept of a "massive regionalization with one [wastewater treatment] plant located just below Greeley serving as far upstream as Fort Collins and Loveland." This plan also created a 60 square mile planning area for Greeley's potential alternatives, with the Poudre River to the north and the South Platte on the south side of the study area. State officials predicted that this region would grow from the current 60,000 residents to as many as 266,000 people.[42]

The second half of the 1970s focused on addressing sewer treatment facility funding. Everything required more funding at a time when inflation kept spiraling upward—including the cost of borrowing money for public works projects. By 1979, the nation had witnessed a decade-long 7.5 percent inflation rate, with a peak at the end of the decade of 11.4 percent. For a city more accustomed to interest rates in the low single digits, the challenge of retiring bonds for ever-more expensive facilities and equipment placed burdens on water customers. The 1958 Greeley City Charter considered interest rates above six percent as usurious (exorbitant). Yet the growth of the city, and the demands of its residents for clean and abundant supplies of water, had to be met.[43]

ON JULY 31, 1976, just as Colorado prepared to commemorate its 100th anniversary of statehood, a torrential evening storm dropped 12 to 14 inches of rain on the Big Thompson River Canyon downstream of Estes Park. As walls of water surged through the canyon, this proverbial "100-year flood" destroyed everything in its path. The Big Thompson flood claimed 143 lives and injured 150 others, as few were prepared for such a deluge. As the river was an important source of Greeley's drinking water, debris and toxic waste carried downstream required the city to treat water at its Boyd Lake facility at three times its normal costs.

The impact of flooding from this same storm, at the Cache la Poudre River high mountain reservoirs, required additional water department study, with about $40,000 needed for repairs of six storage facilities. The bulk of these funds went toward Seaman Dam. Flood water had undercut the massive concrete sections of the spillway, with one section uplifted by 18 inches. That structure would require over $30,000 for repair costs, while the remaining facil-ities at Barnes Meadow, Peterson Lake, Hourglass, Twin Lake, and Comanche Reservoirs required debris removal. City officials hoped that some or most of these costs could be reimbursed by the U.S. Army Corps of Engineers, the agency tasked with flood protection in the nation's waterways.[44]

In March 1977, the issue of water quality in the Cache la Poudre River Basin resurfaced for city officials. The new administration of President Jimmy Carter identified environmental quality as a primary concern of its domestic policy. This included strengthening regulatory agencies, like the EPA, to improve the health of the nation's rivers. The Cache la Poudre had what the Colorado Water Quality Control Commission called a "B-2" status. This required "strong controls on Fort

Collins, Greeley and other municipal, industrial and agricultural wastewater releases." Aligning with local water users, instead of the Carter administration, the State of Colorado sought a temporary "C" classification for the Cache la Poudre River, "with no limit for ammonia." The State also wanted a permanent classification for the same region to be designated as "agriculture," or "agricultural and recreational." On March 1, 1977, the Greeley City Council agreed that "under present conditions," any classification of the lower Cache la Poudre River "which contemplates a fishing stream, will impose a severe economic hardship on water users, with little hope of achieving a fishery."[45]

The Greeley Water and Sewer Board moved forward and endorsed a $5.1 million ($21.6 million in 2020) menu of six projects. These included new filtering equipment at the Bellvue treatment plant to meet state and federal water quality standards, a large Gold Hill water storage reservoir west of town, a new distribution line to the industrial sector of southeast Greeley, and completion of pipeline installation and repairs from Bellvue. To accelerate this work, the city council discussed issuing multiple bonds, and also the sale of water taps to Windsor and Evans to generate more revenue.[46]

Seaman Reservoir also came to the attention of city councilors in the summer of 1977. Floods of the previous year had required a thorough survey of the dam, and while doing so, the City's consulting engineers examined the drainage basin above the spillway to determine whether it could handle a future major storm event. "The conclusion of the study was that a larger spillway at Seaman was probably needed." Board chairman Farr agreed with the finding: "There is a tremendous silting problem at Seaman and the possibility of abandoning the reservoir may have to be considered." He wanted a full study of Seaman Dam conducted, but in the interim, said the consultants, the State Engineer's Office would not insist upon immediate repairs while "progress is being made to remedy the situation." The U.S. Army Corps of Engineers had included Seaman Dam in its flood control study of the Cache la Poudre Basin, the outcome of which would affect any decisions Greeley might make.[47]

In fall 1977, the city council also addressed critical issues at the Bellvue treatment plant. When water and sewer board members authorized its five-year plan that spring, they thought the only concern for the Cache la Poudre treatment plant was "to meet the requirements of the Safe Drinking Water Act, which involved the addition of chemical feeders and process modifications to reduce turbidity." But after further review, new analysis led the City's consultants to change their minds about its status and future. "The filter portion of the plant," said director Alleman, "was built in the 1920's and has basically lived its service life from the standpoint of the equipment and controls." More troubling, said the water director, was the consultant's judgment that "the heating system and boilers cannot pass safety inspections."[48]

THROUGHOUT 1978, CITY water and sewer officials continued discussions with neighboring communities on common issues. One of the most alarming concerned draft plans for "reserved rights in the national forests and parks" proposed by the U.S. Forest Service. Ward Fischer attended the January 30th meeting of the Greeley Water and Sewer Board, and warned that "the United States could claim the rights to any diversions or reservoirs . . . which have priority dates subsequent to the creation of the national forest." Should the U.S. Forest Service be successful in court, the Fort Collins attorney predicted, "tremendous dangers to the water users of this area, particularly to the cities of Fort Collins and Greeley and the Water Supply and Storage Company," whom he also represented.

Fischer asked that Greeley contribute up to $5,000 towards a legal defense for the water users' association. The City agreed, and appointed its water and sewer board attorney, William Bohlender, to assist Fischer in opposition to the reserved rights case. Their defense, said Fischer, would focus on the argument that "the main purpose for creating the [national] forest was to preserve the watershed for the benefit of irrigators, cities and industries." The Forest Service's interference with the water rights of Greeley, Fort Collins, and others "would conflict with the act of Congress."[49]

At that same board meeting, Ward Fischer spoke on behalf of the City of Fort Collins and the Water Supply and Storage Company, both of which had joined the Greeley Water and Sewer Board, to study the conditions of all high mountain reservoirs in the Cache la Poudre Basin. The *Greeley Tribune* learned earlier that Fort Collins would offer to purchase Greeley's rights and property at Barnes Meadow and

Peterson Reservoirs. Fort Collins also wished to acquire the Columbine and Bob Creek ditches that transferred water from the Laramie River to the North Fork of the Cache la Poudre River. The *Fort Collins Coloradoan* sent a reporter to the February 2, 1978, meeting in Greeley expecting that an offer would be made by Roger Krempel, director of Fort Collins' water utility. "We were almost in a desperate situation in 1977," Krempel told his hometown newspaper, "because we had no raw water storage of our own;" a condition that made his city "vulnerable and dependent." Fort Collins "shouldn't find itself in that position," the utility director stated.[50]

Once the conversation between the northern Colorado utilities began, it became clear that more was at stake than purchasing or trading a few water rights. The *Greeley Tribune* noted that both cities wanted "a study of vastly expanded water use trading and cooperation among users in the drainage." Ward Fischer called upon the Greeley Water and Sewer Board to consider a "cross-tie between their two treated water transmission lines." His community could then provide Greeley with up to 2,000 acre-feet of water in winter. "This would allow the City of Greeley to have a continued, high quality, supplemental water supply during the winter months if they were to sell Barnes Meadow and Peterson Reservoirs to the City of Fort Collins." Then, speaking for the Water Supply and Storage Company, Fischer offered an exchange of the Columbine and Bob Creek ditches for 2,000 acre-feet of the company's water stored at Chambers Lake and Long Draw Reservoir. The water and sewer board considered this to be of "excellent quality," and the City could repay Fort Collins in the summers with water from storage at Seaman Reservoir.[51]

To this discussion, Chairman Farr wondered if the amount of water exchanged between the cities and the irrigation company "might not be enough as Greeley grows in the future." His particular concern was the status of the Seaman facility. "It is a very valuable reservoir," Farr told his colleagues, "as far as controlling the river," and it had "the capacity to store valuable water." His suggestion was to study converting the reservoir to irrigation storage, "since it has a large amount of mineral deposits and is often difficult to filter." Farr predicted that "as the demands of cities increase, the Poudre River won't be able to supply the total amount needed." To operate the reservoir properly, Farr recommended that a water users association should "share some of the expenses and use it as a river regulator."[52]

As discussions continued with Fort Collins, work with the Town of Windsor on its water contract proved more difficult. That community disliked paying

Greeley's perceived high rates for treated water, and believed it could acquire less expensive water from local water districts. The Fort Collins-Loveland Water District was of primary consideration. Windsor customers also complained about low water pressure in areas of their community, and Greeley officials acknowledged this was a function of the overtaxed Bellvue pipeline. City councilors recognized the inevitability of Windsor's departure from their system, but agreed to accommodate most of these concerns in the interim.

Windsor's plans for an independent water system proceeded as the summer of 1978 approached. On May 23rd, the Windsor Town Board voted unanimously to seek its own water system, connecting with the Fort Collins-Loveland District at its Donath Lake site (north of Greeley's Boyd Lake plant). "Our water pressure now is too low," said Windsor Town Board member Wayne Lutz. "With the development that's going on now," Lutz warned, "we can't go for another summer." As Greeley's water and sewer board had done for two decades, Windsor officials adopted policies similar to those of Greeley. These included an approved list of water providers, and for developers in Windsor to bring raw water in advance of building subdivisions.[53]

On August 8, 1978, none of these concerns mattered to the majority of Windsor voters when they affirmed, by a margin of nearly 3-to-1, to end their reliance on the Greeley water system. The existing contract did not end for another decade, but Greeley agreed to negotiate Windsor's departure in an orderly manner. For their part, Greeley water officials had expected and anticipated Windsor's actions. Irving Cannon of the water and sewer department told the *Tribune*: "I don't think Windsor's decision will affect Greeley to any great extent, because [the town] doesn't use a great deal of water," he said. "They have been dissatisfied and have wanted their own system." Yet, the Greeley water director could not ignore the challenges ahead for Windsor, telling the *Tribune*: "It will probably be a little more trouble than they thought."[54]

With the close of the 1970s, city water and sewer department staff had accomplished a great deal. A decade that began with water quality challenges ended with an amicable dialogue among treatment experts, financial planners, political leaders and community members to upgrade the outdated and overloaded system. The City had navigated the first generation of environmental regulations and found common ground with the EPA on best practices and economical solutions.

This partnership became apparent in 1979 when the state water quality control commission approved Greeley's decision to develop land treatment strategies for its sewage problems in the Cache la Poudre River.

The City's consultants, CH_2M Hill, had concluded that a state-of-the-art wastewater treatment plant would cost between $21 and $26 million dollars. The water department had not considered land treatment when it first designed its new facilities because few municipalities had attempted this new technology. In the meantime, Muskegon, Michigan, had installed a $42 million land treatment operation that showed much promise. Greeley officials traveled to Muskegon, observed the site, and were impressed with its efficiency.

Greeley faced challenges to acquire enough land to process the estimated 32 million gallons of liquid waste generated daily by the city. However, the water and sewer department discovered it could purchase property about 10 miles east of town that would accommodate such a land treatment facility, with longer intercept pipelines to carry effluent from existing capture points in east Greeley. This plan, said water director Alleman, would help the City meet EPA regulations scheduled for implementation in 1983. The savings in operational costs also appealed to Alleman, who advised the city council that Muskegon paid only 18 cents per 1,000 gallons for their land treatment process.[55]

WHILE CITY OFFICIALS worked on the issues of wastewater treatment, so too did the department staff continue to seek solutions to the challenges at Seaman Dam and Reservoir. At the April 5, 1979, water and sewer board meeting, Eric Wilkinson of the State Engineer's Office presented the State's position. His immediate concern was repairing the existing structure "where it could stand to discharge water without becoming a safety hazard within itself." Then the State Engineer's Office needed to see "a definite schedule" within six months for "a watch or warning system that would indicate when the dam would go out." The State also wanted "an evacuation plan and an engineering study that would show a loss of life because of the failure of the dam."

While these tasks were ongoing, Wilkinson called for Seaman to be "regulated in such a manner that flows will not go over the spillway at all if possible."

Wilkinson did not want to present the city with "a threat or cause for alarm." Instead, the son of the former Cache la Poudre water commissioner, Duggan Wilkinson (who was a former consultant on Greeley water project studies), "wanted to be frank that it is a possibility to have restrictions which could result in severe limitations."[56] The City responded by adopting all of the recommendations of the State Engineer's Office, including "riprapping" (adding a stabilizing layer of rock) to the upper nine feet of the dam.

WHEN CITY PLANNERS reviewed options for Greeley's growth northward, their conclusions encountered historical and environmental conditions that had faced city residents since the days of the Union Colony. The U.S. Soil Conservation Service told the planning staff that 99 percent of the land in the study area was "prime agricultural." Eighty-seven percent of the sector was owned by 14 landholders, with one-third of all acreage owned by Monfort of Colorado. Industry would find this area in north Greeley appealing with its access to rail and vehicle transportation corridors. "The abandonment of the [Monfort] cattle feedlots," said the report, "has improved the attractiveness of the area for the more image conscious industries in particular." For its part, Greeley would need to alter its policy of not extending utilities and streets north of the Cache la Poudre River.[57]

Of these municipal services, the most critical would be water. A rural domestic provider, the North Weld County Water District, currently delivered water to this area. Planning commission staff considered this a drawback to growth for this northern sector, as it had a "low delivery capability and very low line pressure." Should Greeley decide to annex the land, most owners would not have the quality of water required of developers. Staff research found that the study area included 1,038 acre-feet of C-BT water. City standards called for three acre-feet of water to be provided for every one acre of development. This meant that C-BT water covered only nine percent of the land. Concerns extended to sewer service as well, with the report finding that nearly all landowners relied on septic tanks for their waste disposal.[58]

As the planning staff collected information on other options for north Greeley expansion, they were guided by an April 17, 1979, letter written by W.D. Farr. The water and sewer board chairman had excused himself from the initial meeting, but wanted the staff to know his thoughts on the role of water in their deliberations. Farr saw "some definite potential for expanding [north] across the river and perhaps up the Mumper Hill [around 11th Avenue and O Street]. There is no reason," said the board chairman, "why the City of Greeley cannot take some sewer and water over to some of the area that is close to Greeley."[59]

More concerning to Farr was his firm belief that "we cannot expand to the north very much without jeopardizing the Greeley water system." Instead, "our water system is based on the fact that as Greeley grows to the west and gradually absorbs the land that has been under the Greeley and Loveland Irrigation Co., then these water rights become the property of the city." Should Greeley move north of the Poudre River, "the water rights in that particular part of the area do not have a value to the city." Farr's blunt assessment of this situation was that "we cannot utilize that water."[60]

Problematic for any landowner wanting to be annexed to Greeley was the cost of C-BT water, which was becoming more expensive. There was also the issue of the quality of the land itself. Properties adjacent to U.S. Highway 85, Farr claimed, "are low value lands and the amount of water these installations would use would be no problem at all." As one headed north towards Lucerne and Eaton, however, "you are taking some of the finest irrigated farmland in the world out of agricultural production." Farr did not consider such development in the best interests of Weld County, the state of Colorado, or "the world in total when you look ahead to future food needs." He then compared the north Greeley sector to the lands west of town. This acreage [west of Greeley] was "very low in quality irrigated land in most instances," with its production "not very great." Farr cited this "big difference" in economic productivity when he concluded: "That is the reason Greeley should grow west rather than north."[61]

The less-productive land to the west of town caught the attention of Greeley Mayor Richard "Dick" Perchlik. Through the years, the Greeley Water Department had provided water for a wide range of uses—lawn irrigation, sugar refining, Victory Gardens, meat processing, a prisoner-of-war camp, and a missile launch facility. Now, Perchlik wanted to add snowmaking to the list, and created the Sharktooth Ski Area overlooking the Cache la Poudre River. In 1971, it had the distinction of being only the second ski area in Colorado to use snow-making technology (Loveland Ski

Area was the first). It was also located at the lowest elevation of any ski operation in the state. Greeley water and snow-making technology made possible the vision of the "World's Smallest Ski Area."[62]

THE 1970s marked a time of continued growth and change for the Greeley Water and Sewer Department. Wastewater treatment issues and permitting of the Windy Gap Project were two of the major challenges. The new federal environmental laws compelled all urban utilities to concentrate on meeting new obligations. The days of focusing only on the acquisition, treatment, delivery, storage, and exchange of water supplies, were over.

Now wastewater was the focus of attention as new federal environmental regulations required significant efforts to comply with regulations. In 1973, as part of this new and enhanced focus, the Greeley Water Board became the Greeley Water and Sewer Board. Combining water and wastewater management, into a single municipal department, provided better and more efficient financial, policy, and governance oversight. Planning for the major expansion program was implemented, and major improvements were made to the wastewater treatment plant.

The Windy Gap permitting process generated intense local, state and national dialogue, negotiations, and eventually creative legislative solutions, but it was a decade-long process. It would become another important component of Greeley's water supply portfolio.

Continued population and industrial growth also necessitated additions and expansion to both the Boyd Lake and Bellvue Water Treatment Plants during the 1970s. This increased volume of water would be stored in the newly constructed 15 million gallon treated water reservoir at Gold Hill west of Greeley. These investments in new infrastructure were impacted by the high inflation and interest rates of the decade. There were dual impacts, and major challenges—for both financing and funding—for new projects.

Greeley was growing. The Greeley Water and Sewer Department and Board were expanding their roles, system capacities, and agency capabilities to continue to meet the challenges ahead.

CHAPTER TEN

1980-2000
Along the Cache la Poudre River

Currents of Controversy

RECURRING THEMES, ALONG with new challenges and new leaders, have flowed from decade-to-decade through Greeley's increasingly fascinating and complex water story. By the 1980s, the city's role as the commercial, cultural, and social hub for the surrounding agricultural economy had significantly expanded. With its commitment to food production, banking, and legal services for area farmers—and its prominence in the water markets of northern Colorado—Greeley was now a well-established player in the shifting economic and social fabric of Colorado and the nation.

In addition, Greeley was a leader in the legal legacy of managing water in a semi-arid environment, one that placed it on the national stage. The U.S. Congress and the U.S. Supreme Court were venues for extraordinary activities by Greeley's water attorneys, engineers, elected officials, and water management professionals. Fortune 500 companies relocated to the area due to the robust water system maintained by the Greeley Water and Sewer Department.

The decades of the 1980s and 1990s saw dramatic changes in the nation's industry and commerce. Unemployment reached 10.8 percent in 1982; a figure not seen since the dark days of the Great Depression. Inflation in 1980 (an indicator of the value of money) spiked to 11.3 percent. These events compelled the Greeley Water and Sewer Department to refinance its debt almost annually, with additional fees for banking services added to the burden on ratepayers.

Of greater economic significance was the historic prime lending rate of 21.5 percent, driving up project planning and development costs beyond the limits of many household budgets. The limitations posed by environmental regulations, the slowness of Greeley's growth (only 14 percent for the decade), and the reductions in federal spending during President Ronald Reagan's administration, created many obstacles for water officials. These equaled, if not surpassed, those obstacles faced by earlier generations during the Progressive Era, the Dust Bowl, the New Deal and World War II.[1]

The decade of the 1980s also witnessed protracted conflict regarding water rights along the Cache la Poudre River and other streams on both sides of the Continental Divide. Public and private interests, including the U.S. Forest Service and the Sierra Club, pressed for recognition of federal reserved water rights in the national forests; these would limit or preempt the existing water rights of irrigation companies, districts, and cities. The Northern Colorado Water Conservancy District, the City of Greeley Water and Sewer Board, and others successfully contested these claims. In the 1980s, Colorado Congressman Hank Brown was instrumental in leading a collaborative effort to create the Cache la Poudre Wild and Scenic River designation, protecting state water rights and federal interests. The next decade saw Brown create the Cache la Poudre River National Heritage Area through an Act of Congress, securing the river's political and historic national prominence.

SEWAGE TREATMENT ISSUES of the 1970s persisted throughout the 1980s.[2] While city officials reviewed the legal and structural issues of a proposed expansion of the wastewater plant, they also faced a "cease-and-desist" order from the state health department for the existing 1st Avenue facility. Water samples taken from effluent discharges to the Cache la Poudre River in January and February showed that Greeley had ". . . exceeded the maximum limits for pollutants set forth in its discharge permit."[3]

In June 1980, an analysis was completed of the impact of the new Hewlett-Packard assembly plant on Greeley's wastewater treatment system.[4] The next summer, wastewater capacity concerns increased when the City began negotiations with the Anheuser-Busch Brewing Company. The nation's largest brewing company declared an interest in Greeley because of the excellent water supplies available. Discussions focused on a site along 59th Avenue near O Street. These proved to be unsuccessful, and the company opted to build its first western brewery in Fort Collins.[5]

New industrial growth and non-compliance with water quality regulations were becoming larger issues. Population and economic growth prompted the City to improve other sections of the sewer system, including a new 6,000-foot-long sewer line, connecting the Sheep Draw sector (the area between Business U.S. 34 and U.S. Highway 34 in west Greeley) to Greeley's wastewater treatment system. Planners hoped that this project would accommodate west Greeley's projected growth and development needs for the next 50 years—to 2030.[6]

In the fall of 1981, city staff and consultants began work again on much needed expansion plans for the wastewater facility. Construction would take two to three years, at a cost of $7.7 million (around $22.5 million in 2020). In spring 1984, city officials praised the ongoing construction efforts. The water and sewer department told the *Greeley Tribune* that it was "the most expensive single construction project ever for Greeley." Its magnitude deserved a more robust name, and became the "Greeley Water Pollution Control Facility" because the new plant incorporated the best practices in wastewater management of the day. This included technology that the *Tribune* called "Greeley's response to a century-old problem, how to treat sewage effectively before releasing it into a free-flowing river."

The state-of-the-art pollution control facility included pre-treatment improve-ments, a new primary clarifier (settling tank), aeration basins, and a chlorine/dechlorination disinfection facility. This basin would add chlorine to disinfect the plant's treated water, with any residual chemicals removed before release into the river; this as a result of new state regulations to keep Colorado rivers clean.[7] After decades of wastewater issues, the health of the Cache la Poudre River would be much improved.

ON MAY 24, 1981, the Cache la Poudre River was in the news again in a *Denver Post* story, "Currents of Argument Swirl Over the Poudre River." The article quoted Greeley Water and Sewer Board Chair W.D. Farr in support of the proposed Grey Mountain-Idylwilde "pump-back" storage project. This included two proposed dams and reservoirs on the mainstem of the Cache la Poudre River, upstream of Fort Collins, to pump back stored water between

Figure 10.1 The 1984-1985 expansion of the Water Pollution Control Facility was the most costly capital improvement project ever undertaken by the City of Greeley. Included in the project were: a headworks building, primary clarifier tank, two aeration basins, blower building, two primary digester tanks, and a chlorine/dechlorination facility. The completion of this project provided Greeley with a modern state-of-the-art wastewater treatment facility. City of Greeley Museums, Permanent Collection, 1992.75.0466.

reservoirs. This would generate power and also hold water for use by cities and farms on the plains. The whole area, said Farr, "would benefit if we could manage all these tributaries;" (a reference to the upper mainstem and the North and South Forks of the Cache la Poudre). "It would make all the water supplies more stable," concluded Farr. The Northern Colorado Water Conservancy District planned to build and operate this project for the benefit of its constituents, including the City of Greeley.

Opponents of the project, calling themselves "Preserve Our Poudre," argued that the U.S. Forest Service had a legal duty, under the National Wild and Scenic Rivers Act, to study the entire Cache la Poudre River and its tributaries upstream of Fort Collins for possible designation as a wild and scenic river. "We've got about 25,000 miles of river in Colorado, and not one mile is protected," said Karen Waddell, leader of the group. She pointed out that the river flowed through Fort Collins, had significant white water rafting and kayaking in the Poudre Canyon, and that the Grey Mountain Reservoir would inundate the popular Greyrock trailhead.

Preserve Our Poudre was determined to preclude future storage of Cache la Poudre River water upstream of Fort Collins, and gained momentum when Governor Richard Lamm called for a Wild and Scenic designation totaling 83 miles in length. In response, Dick Boettcher of Greeley organized the opposing Conserve Our Poudre group to preserve reservoir development possibilities in the upper Cache la Poudre Basin. (Boettcher later served on the Greeley City Council and as a water and sewer board member, becoming the board chair when W.D. Farr retired from that position.)

On December 8, 1983, Congressman Hank Brown held a public meeting in Fort Collins to discuss "the possible Wild and Scenic designation of the Cache la Poudre River." Board Chairman W.D. Farr called this "a tremendously important issue for the City of Greeley from a standpoint of water supply, and also from a flood control standpoint." The longtime Greeley water expert encouraged "as many people from Greeley to attend this meeting as possible." Farr also "recommended that the city council issue a resolution opposing the proposed designation." Of grave concern was the negative impact of Wild and Scenic designation on any future reservoir construction in the upper Cache la Poudre River Basin, including the proposed Grey Mountain-Idylwilde project.

Chairman Farr reminded his peers that water users in northern Colorado had filed a request with the Colorado Water and Power Authority "for a very large, detailed study of the Poudre River, such as that currently underway for the St. Vrain River." Farr believed that information gathered from this initiative was needed "before any intelligent recommendations can be made concerning the Poudre River." His colleagues agreed, calling upon the City to send a representative to Fort Collins to "voice this objection."[8]

Over 40 speakers appeared before Congressman's Brown's panel at the Fort Collins City Hall, representing both support and opposition to the Wild and Scenic proposal. A reporter for the *Greeley Tribune* found striking the clear divisions between the two cities on the river, noting that "any bill to bring parts of the upper Poudre under the U.S. Wild and Scenic Rivers Act would create either the best of times or the worst of times [for Greeley and Fort Collins]."[9]

In retrospect, Congressman Brown's meeting in 1983 was strikingly similar to the meeting held at the schoolhouse on B.H. Eaton's land near present-day Windsor in July 1874. That meeting was called by General Robert Cameron to seek a compromise between the two communities. This was after Greeley irrigators had traveled upstream and discovered the Fort Collins Agricultural Colony's water diversions from the Cache la Poudre River. A little over 100 years later, Congressman Brown called a similar meeting to work out a compromise concerning the Cache la Poudre River—one that again would greatly impact Greeley's water future. Greeley citizens were passionate about protecting Greeley's water interests in both centuries. In 1983, instead of riding horses and driving buggies to a schoolhouse near Windsor, they traveled to Fort Collins in a caravan of Chevrolets, Fords and SUVs—to confront their upstream neighbors and voice their concerns and disapproval.

One month later, the importance of the situation prompted the Greeley Water and Sewer Board to convene a special workshop with their peers on the Greeley City Council. Chairman Farr asked Northern Colorado Water Conservancy District attorney Gregory J. Hobbs, Jr., to appear before the group to answer questions. Hobbs outlined the main features of the Wild and Scenic Act, noting that the Preserve Our Poudre proposal "would lock up all quantities of water, that are not being diverted, at the time the Act takes effect." This in turn "works to prevent development of conditional [water] rights."[10] This dimension of the Wild and Scenic River Act most alarmed Hobbs. "In an area like the Poudre," said the Northern District's attorney, "where there are significant undeveloped quantities of water," the law would "disallow the development of any conditional rights that have been filed, and any future filings."

Also threatened would be "present projects that are located upstream because the federal government would have the authority to determine, case by case, whether any proposed change of operation would have an adverse effect on the 'values' for which the river was designated." Greeley's high mountain reservoirs fell into this category, since their 13,000 acre-feet of released reservoir water— when commingled with the city's 9,000 acre-feet of direct flow rights on the river—"could be affected by the city's rate of withdrawal." This should concern all Greeley residents, said Hobbs, as the designation could endanger "approximately 40% of the City of Greeley's present water supply."[11]

Congressman Brown subsequently appointed a 30-member study committee of water and environmental representatives to make recommendations for the proposed legislative language to resolve the dispute. In March of 1984, believing that a firm compromise had been achieved, Brown introduced H.R. 5185 in Congress. It would have designated 72 miles of the upper Cache la Poudre River as Wild and Scenic. Left undesignated were the Grey Mountain and Indian Meadows Reservoir sites on the mainstem, the Rockwell site on the South Fork, and the enlarged Seaman Reservoir on the North Fork.

Unexpectedly, the national Sierra Club objected to the proposed legislation and it never came out of committee.[12] Brown did not retreat, and responded like Carpenter before him by exploring other options. This time he appointed a smaller six-person committee with instructions to draft a new bill to resolve differences within Colorado. He needed an agreement that would hold together all the way through Congress.[13] This new committee included Maggie Fox of the Sierra Club, Chuck Wanner of Preserve Our Poudre, and Barney White of the Colorado Environmental Coalition. Joining them were Larry Simpson, John Sayre, and Greg Hobbs of the Northern District and Municipal Subdistrict. Brown introduced the compromise in the U.S. House of Representatives while Colorado Democrat Gary Hart introduced a companion bill in the U.S. Senate.

Brown next called upon W.D. Farr to rally local support for the proposed 75-mile Wild and Scenic River designation. "I said [to Farr]," recalled Brown,

> "to get this thing done, we think we really [need] something that will ultimately be good for everybody, but we need the water groups and farm groups to sign off on it. After weeks of hard work, Farr had everybody on board. It was truly a miracle. When they knew it was okay with W.D., everybody fell in line and we got it passed." Brown added, "He never took credit for it, but he had the ability to make things [happen]."

The compromise bill endured through both chambers of the U.S. Congress.

Representative Brown obtained passage of the Cache la Poudre Wild and Scenic River Act on October 30, 1986. It protected 75 miles of the Cache la Poudre River as Colorado's first such federal designation. Two areas in the lower canyon upstream of Fort Collins—the Grey Mountain and the off-channel Glade Reservoir sites—would be left undesignated for future multipurpose water projects. Brown's careful strategy had designated 31 miles of the river as "wild," and another 44 miles as "recreational." The former category was the most restrictive, rendering the Cache la Poudre River inaccessible except by hiking trails. The recreational status of the river would allow shoreline development and the operation of existing impoundments and diversion structures. W.D. Farr praised Brown's accomplishment, calling it "wonderful" that he had found common ground between factions that had been so long at odds.[14]

COLORADO SCHOLAR DAN Tyler quotes Brown as crediting W.D. Farr for convincing farm and environmental groups to meet in the same room together to achieve Wild and Scenic legislation for the Cache la Poudre River. "It was just hell to get them to come and talk to each other, but we finally worked out a rough compromise," Brown recalled.[15] Those working sessions, in 1984-1985, produced the initial bill which national environmental groups disliked so much they spiked it. Instead of giving up, Brown appointed a smaller committee to draft the 1986 version which ultimately became law. The in-between story of the successful negotiations says much about Hank Brown's statesmanship, which paralleled Delph Carpenter's vision and resilience in forging the 1922 Colorado River Compact.

Like Delph Carpenter before him, Hank Brown (George Hanks Brown) served one term (1972-1976) in Colorado's State Senate. He was then elected to the U.S. House of Representatives (1981-1990), and to the U.S. Senate (1991-1996). Brown complemented his Congressional efforts of wild and scenic designation, ten years later in 1996, when he obtained federal legislation to establish the Cache la Poudre River National Heritage Area, from Fort Collins downstream to the confluence of the South Platte River east of Greeley.[16] His insight, congenial work ethic, and patience enabled him to successfully confront, navigate and surmount the incipient "mine fields" and regulations of the Environmental Era, and ensured recognition of the Poudre River's significance in American history.

Brown's background is an important part of the story. His maternal and paternal ancestors were rooted in Colorado agriculture (the cattle business) and Greeley's entrepreneurial energy. His grandfather, Hanks, gave Brown his middle name, shortened to "Hank" by which he was known so well. He attended high school in Menlo Park, California, but spent summers at Camp Cheley in Estes Park, Colorado. "I've never done anything that was as much fun in my life." He loved hiking, riding horseback and fishing in the mountains. "It was an introduction to what Colorado's all about."[17] Brown graduated from the University of Colorado-Boulder (and later became its president in 2005, a similar position he held at the University of Northern Colorado in Greeley from 1998-2002) and received his undergraduate and law degrees from CU. He and his wife, Nan, had moved to Greeley in 1969, where he was vice-president of Monfort of Colorado until he resigned to begin his congressional service in 1981.[18]

The issue of a Cache la Poudre Wild and Scenic River designation had been pending since the early 1970s when Colorado Senators Peter Dominick and Floyd Haskell co-sponsored a bill placing the upper Poudre River in study status.[19] Brown considered total designation of the river upstream of Fort Collins to be bad public policy. He knew that the region's historical water storage was in the upper basin and served a very desirable and productive area of Colorado. According to Representative Brown, total designation would have precluded "on-stream storage in that area" and made it "very difficult, even, to do off-stream storage." With the designation stuck in study status, "no storage could be done on the river until the study status was resolved."[20]

Dating back to his service in the Colorado Legislature, Brown was particularly concerned with protecting the existing water rights of Colorado farmers, cities and businesses. When the Cache la Poudre Wild and Scenic River Act became law,[21] it forestalled construction of the potential Elkhorn, Grey Mountain/ Idylewilde, and Indian Meadows dams and reservoirs on the mainstem.[22] However, this new federal legislation also preserved the operation of all previously decreed water rights, stating that, "Inclusion of the designated portions of the Cache la Poudre River . . . shall not interfere with the exercise of existing decreed water rights to water which has heretofore been stored or diverted by means of the present capacity of storage, conveyance, or diversion structures that exist as of the date of enactment of this title, or operation and maintenance of such structures." These existing decreed rights included the exchanges of water contained in a March 24, 1978, water court decree obtained by the Cache la Poudre Water Users Association.[23]

The newly-established junior water rights of the Cache la Poudre Wild and Scenic River were also protected. The Act carried with it an express reserved water right with a junior priority date of October 30, 1986. "The reservation of water established by the inclusion of portions of the Cache la Poudre River in the Wild and Scenic Rivers System shall be subject to the provisions of this title, shall be adjudicated in Colorado Water Court, and shall have a priority date as of the enactment of this title."[24] Water Division No. 1 Judge Robert A. Behrman entered an order on April 13, 1993, for this reserved water right. "The amount of water reserved is all of the native water arising upon or flowing through the designated segments of the Cache la Poudre River, subject to valid prior appropriations under Colorado Law." This reserved water right applies "only to native water" of the designated segments. It "shall not include, or in any way limit, either the amount or pattern of flow or releases of transbasin diverted or foreign waters," such as from the Colorado, Michigan, and/or Laramie River Basins.[25]

CONCURRENT WITH THE federal legislative efforts on the Cache la Poudre River, the Greeley Water and Sewer Board also faced the issue of much needed improvements for its high mountain reservoirs. Seaman Dam needed $870,000 in repairs and upgrades, reported Eric Wilkinson, formerly a member of the State Engineer's dam safety staff and now a member of the Greeley Water and Sewer Department staff. Barnes Meadow required $88,000 for general repairs and maintenance. The department sought approval, from federal officials, to drain Barnes Meadow to perform a thorough investigation of the facility. Peterson Lake remained unfilled, allowing the staff to solicit matching funds for a structural survey from the Colorado Water Conservation Board. Comanche and Hourglass Reservoirs operated with lower storage levels due to seepage problems, said Wilkinson, while Twin Lake held no water until it could also be assessed. The latter reservoir did not concern Wilkinson as much as the others, since the Twin Lake capacity was only 278 acre-feet of water.[26]

In January 1986, when staff and board members discussed Wilkinson's findings, an old issue re-emerged regarding the fate of Greeley's high mountain reservoirs. Director Mark Rybus explained the challenges his staff faced over the years due to heavy snows and late runoff seasons. His employees worked with irrigation companies, the City of Fort Collins, and the Cache la Poudre River water commissioner "to try to recoup as much water as possible when reservoirs need to be drained for investigation and construction work."

The conversation shifted to the possibility that Greeley could sell or exchange some or all of the high mountain reservoir sites (a topic considered back in 1966 and yet again in 1978). Rybus recommended that if Greeley decided to keep the reservoirs, then "the structures should be brought to a condition where they can be utilized for storage year-round at their maximum capacity."[27]

The board chairman offered a comment foreshadowing future controversy, over the high mountain reservoirs, in the city's water portfolio. One possibility, said Farr, was that "all of the storage could be moved downstream." This would eliminate future maintenance costs for the structures. Another idea was to sell the reservoirs and use the proceeds to acquire C-BT water. It was an intriguing idea that would come forth again three months later as a formal recommendation to the city council, but with unexpected repercussions.[28]

IN APRIL 1986, the potential sale of Greeley's high mountain reservoirs came into sharper focus. Michael Pickett, president of the Farmers National Bank of Ault, told the *Greeley Tribune* that the northern Denver suburb of Thornton "had purchased hundreds of acres of farm land and water rights surrounding the northern Weld County community." Pickett admitted that "before today there was much speculation about what was going on, but we had no inkling who was buying this land." The Ault banker conceded that "on the short haul, this will be a positive thing." As for the future, "when the water is gone," said Pickett, "this could be negative." Ault Mayor Ed Gieck echoed Pickett's concerns, saying that "no one has approached the [town] board" about the purchases. Nor did members of the Weld County Commissioners realize that the City of Thornton had ventured into northern Colorado to acquire so much property and senior water rights.[29]

Thornton's water purchases may have been an ordinary business transaction for some in northern Colorado. For others, however, the magnitude and far-reaching implications of these unexpected water acquisitions undermined the collaborative nature of sharing water in the Cache la Poudre Basin. The Water Supply and Storage Company, for its part, sent their attorney, Ward Fischer, to meet with First Interstate Bank of Fort Collins to negotiate what Fischer called "a multi-million dollar agreement" to buy back shares for the ditch company, to "keep the remaining water in the ditch."

The *Tribune* sought commentary from Margaret Carpenter, Mayor of Thornton, who expressed few concerns about her city's plan to transfer $140 million (over $320 million in 2020) in water rights to her city. Thornton already owned the water rights from 70 farms in Weld and Larimer Counties, said Carpenter. Beyond those purchases, said the Mayor, Thornton would visit with several public institutions affected by the sales, such as the school board in Ault, the Weld and Larimer County Commissioners, and the city councils of Greeley and Fort Collins. At those meetings, said Carpenter, she and her staff would declare Thornton's "intent to close on the options we have."[30]

The initial shock that surged through farming communities in northern Colorado quickly gave way to resentment and bitterness. Reporters from the *Greeley Tribune* and the *Fort Collins Coloradoan,* upon hearing about a meeting in Ault organized by dismayed Water Supply and Storage Company irrigators, learned they could not attend. Also excluded was an Ault farmer who had offered his land and water to Thornton.[31] Making matters even worse for *Tribune* readers was the discovery that Thornton wasn't the only bidder for water shares in the area.

Bill Jackson, the highly respected agricultural reporter for the *Tribune*, reached the president of Water Supply and Storage to verify rumors. To Jackson's surprise, the president told him that it was not Thornton but Denver's eastern neighbor, the City of Aurora, that first approached Water Supply and Storage to purchase its water rights. By contrast, the City of Thornton had contacted farmers directly through the brokerage services of Duane Rennels of Livermore, while Aurora had negotiated solely with the ditch company itself.[32]

From his perspective, the Thornton "water grab," as it came to be known, had "an amazing characteristic." Bill Jackson learned from his investigation that "Thornton officials were able to cloak a major municipal decision in absolute secrecy for about 10 months." He also learned that "there were few, if any, Weld County people who knew who was purchasing the farms or why." Jackson then expressed the sentiments of many in northern Colorado water circles. "Diverting millions of gallons of agricultural water for municipal purposes," wrote the *Tribune* reporter, "is a worrisome issue for this area." Even "local water experts such as W.D. Farr," said Jackson, "bemoan the proposal but see little hope of stopping it."

For its part, the Northern Colorado Water Conservancy District adamantly opposed removal of any Colorado-Big Thompson water, to places outside the district's boundaries, because its repayment contract with the federal government forbade that from happening. Northern District General Manager Larry Simpson and his staff stated, however, that they would meet with officials from Thornton, and from any other Denver communities, "to help solve their water supply problems."[33]

FEW IN THE northern Colorado water network anticipated the City of Thornton's boldness. Even fewer were ready for the next proposal. On June 5, 1986, director Mark Rybus informed Greeley Water and Sewer Board members that Thornton was offering to purchase Greeley's high mountain reservoirs and water rights for a cash payment of $6.2 million ($14.3 million in 2020). In turn, Greeley would pay Thornton $1 million ($2.3 million in 2020) "for the water rights they [Thornton] have purchased or options they intend to exercise in the Greeley and Loveland system."

Because maintenance costs and limited storage capacities had reduced the value of the high mountain reservoirs, board members seriously considered Thornton's proposal. However, the idea of the sale of the reservoirs provoked considerable controversy among Greeley residents. Once again, the *Greeley Tribune* became a platform for citizen concerns. Dorothy Strubel, a self-identified freelance writer and community activist, voiced strong opinions and objections to the proposed "water chess game."

Thornton's offer to purchase Greeley's high mountain reservoirs came just as the city learned that its longtime industrial water user, Great Western Sugar Company, planned to declare bankruptcy. During the summer of 1986, after eight decades of operations, the company prepared to close nearly all its Colorado factories. Bankruptcy would eliminate the company's need for 2,000 acre-feet of C-BT water from the Northern District and the Greeley and Loveland Irrigation Company. This water looked like a perfect replacement for the soon-to-be-sold high mountain reservoirs.

At its July 16th meeting, the Greeley Water and Sewer Board approved a contract to purchase 1,900 acre-feet of Great Western water from the Greeley and Loveland system.[34] Board Chairman Farr reminded his colleagues that, by combining Great Western Sugar's water with Thornton's 1,300 acre-feet in the Greeley and Loveland system, "approximately 2/3 of the production of the high mountain reservoirs has been acquired." This transaction would leave Greeley with about $4 million to purchase even more water rights.[35]

The Greeley Water and Sewer Board recommended that the Greeley City Council proceed with the sale of the high mountain reservoirs in what appeared to be a very reasonable transaction. To the board's surprise, however, one week later the Greeley City Council voted unanimously to reject this recommendation. Instead, they returned the sale document back to the water and sewer department. Harkening back to Greeley's historical quest for Cache la Poudre River water, council member Bruce Forbes explained the council's action. "It looks like the best quality of water we have," said Forbes, "is what you're trying to give away." Board member Robert Ruyle countered in defense of the recommendation, "a similar opportunity to sell the reservoirs may not occur soon."[36]

Two weeks later, on August 5, 1986, all other items faded from public view as the Greeley City Council gathered to discuss the reservoir transaction. Even though the city council agenda listed the proposed Thornton contract simply as "Item 18," the council devoted over three hours to listen to all sides of the argument. Council members, water and sewer department staff, and board members were surprised and perplexed by the intensity of public opposition to Thornton's offer. Joe Howard, an independent Greeley contractor, gathered "1,100 signatures opposing the sale" in less than one week. Critics of the transaction linked it, in Howard's estimation, to autocratic behavior by city officials. "It's really been pushed through like so many other things recently," said Howard. "We've had things jammed down our throats." This compounded the perception that "those high mountain reservoirs are really cherished by many residents." As for the question of repairs, Howard believed that the City "could spend the money to increase the capacity of the reservoirs and eventually get a conditional decree for more water rights." He employed a concept often cited by the water and sewer board when he concluded: "It's also important to maintain greater assets on the Poudre River system."[37]

Russ Rutten told the council that the number of petitioners opposing the sale had risen to 1,600 residents, convincing Mayor Bob Markley that their numbers could not be ignored. Council member John Kinkade spoke in favor of the proposed contract, reminding the audience that "water decisions have been a continuing process for over 100 years." A Greeley attorney, Kinkade was "convinced that the Water and Sewer Board is working toward the city's best interest." Council member Forbes admitted that he had been "brainwashed into believing the high mountain lakes provide good water." He would be "willing to consider the exchange with Thornton, but not a sale, as a dual source of water [from both the Cache la Poudre and the Big Thompson Rivers] is worth keeping and protecting." Councilor Lynn Settje agreed that the city had "a most conservative" water and sewer board.[38]

In an attempt to clarify matters, Water and Sewer Board Chairman W.D. Farr stood and addressed the gathering at city hall in what the *Tribune* called "a 45-minute history lesson and explanation." Farr believed that "the current [public] interest is due to the lack of understanding of the City of Greeley's complex water situation." He considered his board's action as "an economic decision, not an emotional decision." Repair costs would increase user rates by 20 percent, "and then there is no place to use the water." If the City were to expand its Bellvue pipeline to accommodate more supplies, it would cost over $1 million per mile for the 38-mile route to town.

Farr's lengthy explanation, however, did not satisfy Russell Rutten, Joe Howard, or their allies. The "big question," said Rutten, "is if buying the reservoirs was such a good idea 40 years ago, why is it not a good idea now?" Joe Howard had similar concerns and did not support negotiating with Thornton officials. "Why do we want to do business with Thornton," said Howard, "after all the emotions over their dealings with the farmers and Water Supply and Storage Company?"[39]

Councilors recognized the dilemma at hand that night: the wisdom and authority of the water board was being challenged by the largest delegation anyone had ever seen assembled to protest a pending city council action. Bruce Forbes told the audience that Mr. Farr "had done a good job selling the proposal, but he [Forbes] could not support the sale." Councilor Peter Boer agreed, noting "the sale may be in the city's best interest, but the council could not afford to go against public opinion."[40]

With nowhere else to turn for support, Councilor Kinkade made a motion to accept the Thornton reservoir purchase offer. Two colleagues joined Kinkade in favoring the sale while three others rejected the action. Turning to Mayor Bob Markley, the council asked for his vote to break the tie—which he cast in opposition to the agreement.

"They summed it all up," Farr told a *Greeley Tribune* reporter as the meeting adjourned. "It's obvious," said the board chairman, "what the decision is based on." Speaking bluntly to the reporter, Farr called the 4 to 3 tally "not in the best interest of Greeley." Yet he saw no other path forward, telling the *Tribune*: "If the citizens want to pay extra money to keep those reservoirs, I guess that's what we'll do."[41] This was the first time the city council had rejected a major recommendation of the Greeley Water and Sewer Board. True to his word, Farr asked the water department staff to accelerate feasibility studies underway to rehabilitate the highly regarded reservoirs.

Eric Wilkinson soon after reported his findings, as well as a list of needed repairs to Seaman Dam. In August 1987, the State Engineer ruled that the Twin Lake Reservoir must remain out of operations until required repairs were made. State estimates ran as high as $1,800 per acre-foot for those costs.[42] At Comanche Dam, with ten times the capacity of Twin Lake, the State found even more challenges. "Sand boils appeared in the outlet discharge channel," said the State Engineer's report, while "leaks in the outlet tunnel were also noted." The water and sewer department staff had already lowered the storage pool at Comanche Dam by nearly 40 percent and would have to reduce it further by nearly 10 percent to meet State safety standards. Upgrades and repairs would require significant expenditures of funds, but they were all in line with the strong desires of the community. These efforts, however, were now threatened by a new federal action;

one which could create a federal water right that would be senior to the existing water rights of Greeley's high mountain reservoirs, and other assets, on the Cache la Poudre and Big Thompson Rivers.

STATE-CREATED WATER RIGHTS, which divert and store water in the national forests, are essential to Colorado's vitality. The federal government recognized and respected this fact early in the 20th century:

> "What happens to the water [in a forest reserve]? Nothing, except that the flow is steadier. The creation of a national forest has no effect whatever on the laws which govern the appropriation of water. This is a matter governed entirely by State and Territorial laws."[43]
>
> —Gifford Pinchot
> Forest Service Chief, 1907

This policy was severely tested, however, in the 1980s. Despite the compromise which led to federal designation of the Cache la Poudre as a Wild and Scenic River in 1986, the U.S. Justice Department pressed for senior federal reserved water rights, it claimed existed throughout the Arapahoe and Roosevelt National Forests, on both sides of the Continental Divide. This effort threatened Colorado's prior appropriation water rights established under Colorado law as early as 1890, when construction commenced on the Grand River Ditch that diverted water into the Cache la Poudre from the very upper reaches of the Colorado River.

At risk for Greeley were all its water rights dependent upon the Colorado, Laramie, Big Thompson and Cache la Poudre Rivers, the four sources of Greeley's water supply.[44] The City's quest for high mountain water coincided with the creation of the Roosevelt (then called Medicine Bow) National Forest in 1905. The effort extended to the purchase of shares in the Water Supply and Storage Company, and then the Tunnel Water Company for water from the Colorado and Laramie Rivers.[45]

Imagine, then, the consternation of Greeley and other water users of northern Colorado when the U.S. Forest Service filed its reserved water rights claims in the Water Court Division No. 1 in Greeley, in the mid-1970s, and amended them in the 1980's. The U.S. Justice Department asserted forest reservation dates as early as 1891, 1897, and 1905 for a large amount of "channel-shaping flows." These reserved water rights, if recognized, would have preempted the operation of state water rights lawfully decreed to farmers and cities who had already made beneficial use of the water. Allowed and encouraged by federal law, these water users had previously constructed and operated direct flow ditches and reservoirs within the national forest.

It's necessary to understand why these claims so disturbed the equilibrium of settled expectations of water users. In the U.S. Supreme Court's 1978 decision in *U.S. v. New Mexico*, the court ruled that Congress intended that water "would be reserved [by the federal government] only where necessary to preserve the timber or to secure favorable water flows for private and public uses under state law." This precluded the U.S. Forest Service from claiming "instream flows for recreational, wildlife, and scenic purposes."[46] As the Colorado Supreme Court held in the 1983 *U.S. v. City and County of Denver*, Congress actually intended "to provide large quantities of water for the economic development of the West." This policy would be frustrated if the "many public and private appropriators" in the national forests—"cities, industries, farmers, and ranchers"—must "relinquish their long-utilized water rights" in favor of junior appropriators downstream and outside the national forest reservations.[47]

Greeley's water and sewer board voted to support the Northern District's opposition to the U.S. Forest Service's reserved water rights claims, contributing funds to the "Reserved Rights Defense Fund." The city's high mountain reservoirs were in jeopardy, said the board, for which this contribution would "support the engineering and technical analysis in opposition to the United States' minimum stream flow claims."[48]

A furious debate in Colorado and throughout the West shaped up over this federal reserved water rights issue that could leapfrog existing state prior appropriation water rights. Precluded by the highest courts of the United States and of Colorado from claiming instream flow rights, the U.S. Forest Service turned to the theory of geomorphological fluvial flushing flows (that amount of water, particularly in high flow conditions) which can transport sediment, remove vegetation, and shape stream channels. This, contended the U.S. Justice Department, meets "the favorable conditions of water flow" test for a senior federal water right reservation. It was a novel idea.

The case eventually made its way to Judge Robert Behrman, Water Judge for Division No. 1, the South Platte River, based in Greeley. He held court for 100 days of trial, and also participated in several field trips organized by the parties to the case. On February 12, 1993, Judge Behrman's decision narrowed and defined the extent of U.S. Forest Service reserved water rights to only firefighting and administrative purposes. Owners of existing water rights in these forest areas could continue to operate, repair, maintain and replace facilities, and access existing water facilities by existing routes, including the use of motorized access where necessary and customarily employed.

In reaching his decision and rejecting the U.S. channel-shaping claims, Judge Behrman concluded that the U.S. Forest Service's "elaborate methods . . . signally failed to produce a reliable quantification. In particular, the method used to estimate bank full at the quantification points is fatally flawed." The water court weighed, as well, the devastating impact granting the claims would have on the cities and farmers whose state water rights were long-operating within the forests. Grandfathers of the forest reserves, such as Gifford Pinchot, had stressed the importance of water storage at the time of spring runoff. Judge Behrman found that:

> "Municipalities need water all year long, and agriculturalists gener-
> ally have better supplies of water in the spring but are particularly
> in need of irrigation water later in the growing season. Water
> storage in the upper part of the watershed promotes these equable
> flows. Such equable flows were sought by those whose ideas are
> reflected in the creation of the national forests and are exactly what
> they meant when they referred to 'favorable water flows.'"

The judge's decree did grant, to the United States, reserved water rights the water court found to be within the primary purposes of the national forests; namely, for firefighting and for administrative uses—including groundwater and surface water for domestic water at ranger and guard stations, stock water for Forest Service animals, reforestation, erosion control, road construction and maintenance, and vehicle maintenance, not to exceed 100 acre-feet annually in each of the forest reservations. For firefighting, the Forest Service could use water from any stream or lake in the forest. The priority date for these reserved rights is "the date the land containing the particular source of water was reserved from the public domain."[49] The Colorado Doctrine of Prior Appropriation, adopted into the state constitution of 1876, had been upheld and preserved.

AS GREELEY AND northern Colorado entered the last decade of the 20th century, the water and sewer department encountered yet another dry cycle in the mid-1990s. Fortunately, the inflationary spiral of the 1980s had abated and allowed city officials to sell bonds for infrastructure expansion and replacement of aging facilities. Regional collaboration, in matters of water quality and quantity, helped buffer the persistent competition for increasingly scarce water rights. The water and sewer department could now plan for its future with the confidence that comes from the lessons of the past.

In the first years of the 1990s, the City engaged in a series of issues that had persisted for a decade and more. The high mountain reservoirs, now considered essential to Greeley's water portfolio, would need over $3 million in upgrades; a figure that the City funded at an interest rate of seven percent (a marked decline from the double-digit inflation rates of the 1980s). The department also wanted to acquire the remaining 288 shares of the Mountain and Plains Irrigation Company (for a total of 1,000 shares). One reason that the board sought resolution of these water issues was the constant rise in price for water in northern Colorado. Higher quality Colorado-Big Thompson Project water now cost as much as $1,500 per acre-foot.[50]

In December 1990, the City learned that Hourglass (one of Greeley's high mountain reservoirs) had lost seven acre-feet of water per day due to the State-required lower storage levels for dam safety concerns. Staff members estimated that Hourglass Reservoir upgrades would range between $2 million and $40 million—depending upon issues encountered during construction repairs. This led city staff to recommend that Hourglass be used only to retain spring runoff water to earn "credits" for storage (within the State of Colorado's water accounting system), and then release that water quickly to spare the facility from further damage.[51]

In 1991, as the analysis of the high mountain reservoirs continued, city officials completed their negotiations with the Greeley and Loveland Irrigation

Company to acquire majority control of that organization. The City agreed to sign contracts with individual shareholders and offered them "lease-backs" for up to 15 years; a process whereby the landowner could sell water to the City, then pay a water rental fee to continue to irrigate their lands. This allowed the City to gain a predictable supply of water for future demands without the burden of building new storage reservoirs. It was a good arrangement for both parties. The Greeley and Loveland Company also agreed to have a member of the Greeley Water and Sewer Department serve on its board of directors. The City chose its water department director for the post, with the responsibility to represent the majority of shares now owned by Greeley.[52]

The water and sewer department staff next drafted contracts to purchase 1,061 acre-feet of Greeley and Loveland Company water, with an additional 2,507 acre-feet under study. The price for these shares totaled $4 million; an amount that some on the water and sewer board believed should be met by selling a portion of the Windy Gap water owned by Greeley. The city's usage of Greeley and Loveland water, the following year, was over one third (14,000 acre-feet) of its total supply of 41,000 acre-feet.[53]

Collaboration with Greeley and Loveland Company water users had its parallel with a concurrent planning process for regional water facilities sponsored by the Northern Colorado Water Conservancy District. In 1989, the Northern District had approached officials, in all seven counties within its boundaries, regarding serving their water needs. This network would have included other counties northeast of Denver. Among the ideas suggested by the Northern District was adaptation of Greeley's Boyd Lake and Bellvue water treatment facilities into a regional system. This did not occur.

Another collaborative effort involved the U.S. Forest Service, which now sought to obtain instream flows below reservoirs in the upper reaches of the Cache la Poudre River. Instream flows would enhance water quantity during the wintertime months for fish and other aquatic life. The federal government delayed renewal of Greeley's special use permits, for its high mountain reservoirs, as these discussions proceeded. The Forest Service wanted the City to provide bypass flows by allowing reservoir outlets to remain open during winter months; this to increase the volume of water in key segments of the upper Cache la Poudre River.

As Greeley attorney Jim Witwer explained in his *Colorado Lawyer* article, "the term 'bypass flow requirement' refers to the mandatory abstention from diverting water which, under state water law, would otherwise be diverted in priority." If not coordinated with decreed water rights released from storage for delivery to downstream water users, imposition of bypass flows by the Forest Service could result in injury to water rights. This is because storable water, bypassed by a reservoir owner, is deducted from the amount of water that can later be stored under the water storage right of Colorado water law. In addition, other downstream water rights may be able to intercept the bypassed water under their priorities that were adjudicated in Colorado's water courts. This would result in the loss of valuable beneficial use water rights to the original owner of the bypass flow.[54]

State Senator Tom Norton, who later served as Mayor of Greeley, had sponsored Senate Joint Resolution 92-15 in the Colorado General Assembly. This measure opposed imposition of bypass flow, or other water release requirements, as a condition for federal special use permits and easements for water facilities on U.S. Forest Service Lands.[55] In August 1992, Northern District President Bill Bohlender and Municipal Subdistrict President W.D. Farr wrote to U.S. Forest Service Supervisor Skip Underwood. The Greeley officials argued that the "Arapaho/Roosevelt National Forest plays a key role in supplying water rights whose storage and diversion points exist on the Forest." Bohlender and Farr called upon the Forest Service to "renew the permits of Boulder, Loveland, Greeley, Fort Collins, and the Grand County Water and Sanitation District without restrictions which impact the yield of their water rights."[56]

A month later, Senator Hank Brown wrote U.S. Secretary of Agriculture Edward R. Madigan, and included the correspondence from the City of Greeley, the City of Loveland, and the Grand County Water and Sanitation District. Brown contended that Greeley could be forced to spend up to $9 million to replace the water yield it would lose from imposition of U.S. Forest Service bypass flows.[57] On October 22, 1993, Ken Salazar, then Executive Director of Colorado's Department of Natural Resources, urged the Forest Service to explore mitigation solutions that do "not impose conditions on permits for existing water supply facilities that would reduce their yield or substantially increase the cost of the yield."[58]

As previously occurred with the Wild and Scenic River compromise, a federal/state standoff was successfully negotiated. "The security of existing water supplies," reported the Greeley City Council at their meeting on February

7, 1995, "and the health of the Poudre River were maintained without litigation thanks to the inquiries and contributions of these officials."[59] Key figures were U.S. Senators Hank Brown and Ben Nighthorse Campbell, U.S. Representative Wayne Allard, and Colorado Governor Roy Romer.

On January 4, 1995, the U.S. Forest Service issued a 50-year easement for Greeley's Barnes Meadow Reservoir after intense negotiations at the local, state and federal level by representatives of the City of Greeley. This document incorporated a Joint Operations Plan proposed and developed by Greeley, Fort Collins, and the Water Supply and Storage Company. Under this plan, a constant release of 10 cfs of water, from November 1st through March 31st, would enter the mainstem of the Cache la Poudre River downstream of Barnes Meadow Reservoir and/or Chambers Lake. A total of 3,000 acre-feet would augment a 50-mile stretch of the Cache la Poudre River to Greeley's Bellvue treatment plant. This benefitted aquatic life during the naturally occurring low flow season, all without endangering Greeley's decreed water rights. Barnes Meadow Reservoir already supplemented the City's wintertime water supply, making the proposed agreement a logical compromise.[60]

DURING THE 1990S, water and sewer department staff could take significant pride in the advances made with wastewater treatment at the Greeley Water Pollution Control Facility. In October 1992, the City learned that it had won the "Plant Performance Award" from the Rocky Mountain Water Pollution Control Association. The following September, the City earned a regional award from the U.S. Environmental Protection Agency and a second place national award for operations of its water pollution control facility. On August 11, 1994, bolstered by this regional and national recognition, the Greeley Water and Sewer Department announced that it had accepted the bid of the Hensel Phelps Construction Company to build additional capacity and treatment capabilities for water pollution control. This work was estimated to cost $10.7 million. Odor control measures were a key part of the work to be done. When completed, the project would alleviate recurring complaints regarding odors emanating from the plant.[61]

Planning for enhanced regional water supplies also continued. City officials entered into negotiations with the U.S. Forest Service to exchange 1,000 acres of forest land at the Rockwell Reservoir site; this in anticipation of a joint storage facility for Greeley and Fort Collins along the Cache la Poudre River. The City also purchased 1,000 acre-feet of C-BT water from Kodak of Colorado, which no longer needed it after reducing operations in the mid-1990s. Greeley also agreed to reintegrate the City of Windsor into the Greeley water and sewer system, with Windsor supplying 400 acre-feet of raw water for Greeley's treatment.[62]

The cost of facility upgrades also factored into the City's water planning as the 20th century came to an end. In November 1996, the water and sewer department joined in a study of the "North-South Pipe Line Project." This would deliver C-BT water to the Bellvue treatment plant during the winter months. Partners included Northern Water, Fort Collins, the Tri-District water system, and the North Poudre Irrigation Company. The plan called for pumping water from the proposed C-BT pipeline through the Hansen Canal, and then to Horsetooth Reservoir. This would give Greeley more usable water from Bellvue in the winter months. Greeley's Cache la Poudre River sources would also benefit from expansion of the Bellvue treatment plant, in which the department would spend $20 million to increase capacity to 30 million gallons per day.[63]

As the millennium approached, water and sewer department officials looked at plans to also expand treatment capacity at the Boyd Lake facility. The $15 million price tag included assistance from the Colorado Water Resources and Power Development Authority, which offered an interest rate of 80 percent of the market rate. The City also agreed to pay $3.1 million towards the $19 million Pleasant Valley pipeline (also known as the "North-South" pipeline project) to deliver C-BT water in wintertime to the Bellvue facility.

The Greeley Water and Sewer Board had been led with strong and visionary leadership the previous 38 years. Thus, it was fitting on May 6, 1997, that the Greeley City Council enacted an ordinance honoring the long tenure of its board chairman, W.D. Farr, with the declaration: "His foresight in the development of water projects has been instrumental in securing the water supply needed for the future." Farr's service to his hometown and to northern Colorado, said the council, "has been an inspiration and positive example to many in Colorado and the water planning field for six decades."[64]

National recognition of the Cache la Poudre River continued. With Senator Hank Brown's time in Washington, D.C., about to end, Congress enacted the Cache La Poudre River Corridor Act on October 19, 1996.[65] This completed what the 1986 Wild and Scenic River Act had started, and now the entire Poudre River, from its source high in the Rockies to its confluence with the South Platte River, would be enjoyed and celebrated nationally for all its beauty, utility, and heritage.

Of his service in Congress, Brown was typically humble about the role he had played. They were principles to live by, a way of moving forward. "One is you get people out of the framework of being on different teams, and you get them to sit down and talk to each other and listen to the witnesses. The second thing is that you put it in a framework for helping the community. All of a sudden, you've got a common goal that you share."[66]

AS THE 20TH century drew to a close, the Greeley Water and Sewer Department had matured into a highly respected water and wastewater utility. The preceding two decades witnessed major controversies at local, state and national levels that affected the planning and operations of the department. In particular, the successful defense of state-created water rights in Water Court Division No. 1, and the two Cache la Poudre River federal designations, created a whirlwind of nationally significant achievements. Greeley was once again a primary player and catalyst in the development of new and beneficial partnerships, initiatives, and water policy for the region.

As the new century arrived, it came with another drought of historic dimensions. The city's water and sewer department and board would now be summoned to provide vision and leadership for one of its most critical challenges. Nature would present the next dilemma for the people of the erstwhile Union Colony.

CHAPTER ELEVEN

2000-2020
Challenges Met, Lessons Learned

Greeley Water at 150

EACH GENERATION OF staff, management and policymakers of the Greeley Water and Sewer Department has encountered opportunities and obstacles as they strived to deliver on the "Meeker promise" of clean, sufficient and reasonably priced water. The years 2000-2020 would be no different. These two decades were marked by long-range master planning and implementation, driven as always by the challenges of a semi-arid land.

The early 21st century experienced two decades of historic drought throughout the Colorado River Plateau, interrupted only by episodes of flooding. Chronic dry weather oppressed every river basin of the state at different times, affecting city and farm families alike. In the South Platte River Basin, the years 2002-2006 marked the "well crisis." The State Engineer (of the Colorado Division of Water Resources) ordered over 4,000 "junior" water wells to cease pumping. Only very senior surface water rights, dating back to the early 1860s, were allowed to divert from the South Platte River and its tributaries, including the Cache la Poudre River. Well owners with water court-approved augmentation plans could pump only if they did not injure downstream senior water rights.[1] The City of Greeley, and its water and sewer board, were caught in the dilemma of protecting its senior water rights while seeking ways to help the struggling agricultural economy of the region.

During these extraordinary times, Greeley embarked upon its 2003 Water Master Plan and implemented four strategic initiatives critical to the City's future:

1. Continued water acquisition;
2. Construction of additional reservoir storage;

3. Investments in capital improvement projects; and
4. Water conservation.

These measures would build upon the lessons learned over the previous 130 years since Greeley's founding.

IN MAY 2000, representatives of ConAgra (one of four companies in Greeley listed on the "Fortune 500" list of largest corporations in America, and the owners of the former Monfort Packing Company), sought a new location for their ConAgra Beef Company Headquarters. Through a series of incentives, Greeley officials convinced ConAgra to not move to another community, such as Loveland, which offered cheaper land, or to the larger city of Fort Collins. These incentives included a waiver of the raw water surcharge for the company's 8th Avenue meat processing plant, and the sale of 1,000 acre-feet of C-BT water at $2,200 per unit.[2]

At their May 5th meeting, city councilors recognized that this agreement was possible, in part, due to the quality and quantity of water made available to ConAgra. The importance of a reliable high quality water supply, to the agricultural processing industry, harkened back to 1902 with the establishment of the Greeley Sugar Company factory.

In 2009, lessons learned from retaining ConAgra were helpful in creating an economic development incentive package for Leprino Foods of Denver. A key factor in bringing their mozzarella cheese plant to Greeley was the attractive pricing of raw water provided to the company. Dairy herds within a 50-mile radius would provide the required milk, and that demand ultimately doubled the number of dairy cows in Weld County. Furthering the tradition of Greeley's support of the region's agricultural economy, Leprino constructed its facility on the site once occupied by the 1902 Greeley Sugar Company. This collaboration underscored the necessity and tradition of using Greeley water, from field to factory, to sustain Weld County's agricultural economy.

Figure 11.1 In 2007, Denver-based Leprino Foods acquired the Great Western Sugar Company site and constructed a 1.26 million square foot plant in three phases from 2010-2017. One of the company's largest plants in the country, it manufactures block mozzarella cheese and dairy-based nutritional products (whey protein isolate, lactose, non-fat dry milk and micellar casein). Courtesy of Leprino Foods.

THE DROUGHT OF 2000 to 2003 stressed Greeley's water supplies in magnitudes not seen since the 1930s and 1950s. This latest episode sternly tested the actual drought-year yields of Greeley's water rights, and shaped planning for future dry cycles. Board members heard from department staff that Greeley consumers had increased their usage by 15 percent in one year, while the City of Evans had experienced a 20 percent rise in water demand.[3]

In April 2002, the City discussed a "Drought Emergency Plan," with four levels of reductions and conservation. The following month, W.D. Farr called that year's spring snowpack the worst since the Northern Colorado Water Conservancy District started keeping records in the 1930s. By June, streamflows in the Cache la Poudre and Big Thompson Rivers were the lowest in recorded history. Water and sewer board members were forced to restrict outdoor watering to two days per week, with no watering at all between 10:00 a.m. and 6:00 p.m. The Northern District advised the City in July that C-BT water releases could be as low as 30 percent, a drastic measure dictated by the drought. Climate experts believed it to be the worst in over 300 years. The low water level of Boyd Lake caused algae blooms to flourish, resulting in taste and odor problems that also had not been experienced in recent memory.[4]

Dry conditions in northern Colorado had not improved by the winter of 2003. In response, Director Jon Monson ordered a 15 percent reduction in water deliveries compared to the year 2000, a strategy designed to save 2,000 acre-feet of water. He had studied Denver Water's ongoing efforts to reduce usage by 30 percent, which allowed outdoor watering every third day. The City also explored the option of requiring better soil preparation for new lawns. That spring, Monson and his staff heard from the Northern District that C-BT allottees would receive only one-third of average deliveries. Lake Granby, the primary C-BT storage reservoir, neared what Northern District officials called its "dead-pool stage." Staff worried that it would take years to restore the reservoir to its full 465,000 acre-foot capacity. The water and sewer board learned that in 2002, only 8.5 inches of moisture had fallen.[5]

On April 1, 2003, responding to this crisis, the city council passed an ordinance limiting outside water use to every 3rd day. The goal was to save 1,000 acre-feet by allowing residents to water only once during the work week and once on Sundays. Fines between $100 and $500 would be levied on those violating the ordinance. Director Monson wanted to conserve up to 5,000 acre-feet that year, although city councilors agreed that this would reduce revenues for the water and sewer department by as much as $2 million. Monson advised the council that his department had reserves of $6.5 million, from which funds could be drawn to cover any shortages. Citizens responded willingly to the conservation appeal, and water use declined by 40 percent through May.[6]

Greeley residents were reminded that they lived in a land of climatic extremes. The spring and early summer of 2003 produced a striking increase in moisture. The first event was a major snowstorm in March, (Greeley received about a foot, while the mountains above Denver received as much as 11 feet of new snow), followed by rains that enhanced streamflows over the short-term. Water users throughout the Cache la Poudre Basin reveled in rainfall amounts in May that exceeded the entire 2002 calendar year. Whereas the city in the spring of that year had received less than four inches of precipitation, totals by mid-2003 were 8.5 inches, around 60 percent of normal.

Despite this relief, city water officials persisted with use restrictions and the goal of saving 6,000 acre-feet of water by year's end. To help with this campaign, seven temporary employees were hired for Greeley's "water patrol" (reminiscent of the young men hired in 1893, including Delph Carpenter, to patrol the town's water supplies at night). The patrol, also known as the "Green Team" wrote over 600 warnings by mid-July, and by October reported 1,200 citations for abuse of watering regulations. The city concluded its water year with over 4,100 acre-feet of water saved for use in the coming year.[7]

IN OCTOBER 2003, coincident with the improved water conditions, Greeley released the final draft of its Water Master Plan. The authors reported the city's good fortune over the years in having a "safe, good quality, plentiful water supply." Yet, as the 21st century dawned, the challenges of infrastructure age, population and economic growth, new regulations, and increasingly limited opportunities to acquire new water supplies could not be ignored. Greeley's water demands had tripled in the past 50 years, as had its population. The next half-century was predicted to witness another tripling of people and their demands for water. Projections for 2050 would require an overall water supply of 74,500 acre-feet.[8]

As discussed earlier, the 2003 Water Master Plan contained four strategic action areas: continued water acquisition, construction of additional reservoir storage, investments in capital improvement projects, and water conservation. To meet these long-term goals and prepare for the next drought, the City created a 10-year, $247 million Capital Improvements Plan as a first step. Board Chairman Harold Evans outlined a series of tasks for the water and sewer department. These included participation in the Windy Gap Firming Project, establishment of a 6,000 acre-feet Water Acquisition Fund, construction of a new transmission pipeline from the Bellvue Water Treatment Plant, winterizing the Boyd Lake Plant, upgrading the capacity of the Bellvue Plant, and continued improvements at the water pollution control facility.[9] The 2003 Water Master Plan also provided a comprehensive look at these future action areas to meet the City's 2050 water needs.

The first strategic action item of the 2003 Water Master Plan was continued water acquisitions. As part of the first initiative, department staff spent time in 2004 analyzing how to fund Greeley's participation in the Windy Gap Firming Project and ways to acquire more water supplies. A decision was made to sell 20 of Greeley's 64 Windy Gap water units to generate additional revenue. The City of Evans offered to acquire five of these units, at a cost of $3,038,000. Fort Lupton wanted three units, offering $1.88 million. Next, the Little Thompson Water District requested 12 units. By year's end, the City retained ownership of 44 of its original 64 units in the project. In August 2004, the water and sewer board recommended a new 10-Year Capital Improvement Plan to the city council. This called for $164 million dollars to initiate projects identified and recommended in the Water Master Plan. The Board also planned to sell, over the next decade, an additional $36 million in bonds to acquire new water rights and to construct additional storage.[10]

One effort toward acquisition of new water rights began with the North Weld County Water District and the Fort Collins-Loveland Water District. The plan was to jointly acquire a total of 150 shares of the Laramie-Poudre Tunnel transbasin water from the Windsor Reservoir and Canal Company. In their 2005 report, department staff conceded that "the purchase agreement proved to be far more complex than originally thought." It was believed that, by April 2006, the City would have access to an additional 1,100 acre-feet from this transaction. According to one staff member, this would be one of the last large blocks of wholly consumable water available in the entire Cache la Poudre Basin.[11]

In 2006, department staff informed the board that the current portfolio of 36,500 acre-feet would provide an adequate supply of water only until the year 2021. After the Future Water Account funds were used to purchase the targeted 6,000 acre-feet of water, the city's supply would be adequate until approximately 2030. Staff estimated that Greeley's water demand in 2050 would approach 65,000 acre-feet. This would require even more water supplies and the construction of a regional storage project.[12]

These scenarios prompted the water and sewer board to convene a "Future

Water Supply" workshop on November 1, 2007. Discussion focused on the assumption that supplies would be maximized by the year 2030. Population growth levels, based on the department's predictive models, did not correspond to historical patterns. Staff members observed that customers had reduced consumption, by 18 percent in 2003, through watering only twice per week in the summer. If the City ordered a 20 percent reduction in usage, it could anticipate meeting demand through 2038 without new supplies. This strategy, however, "would change landscaping," the staff predicted.[13]

Board members also discussed the Master Plan's call to purchase 6,000 acre-feet of water, for the Future Water Account, to accommodate growth. If water became too expensive, the only alternative would be a "regional reservoir" for storage. The City's options were limited. Most appealing was the advance purchase of water, which was estimated at $90 million. Such an expense would require raising water rates by 84 percent over the coming 10 years; a substantial increase for rate-conscious customers.

This was troubling news as the City surveyed water markets for additional supplies. "For many years," according to its 2007 annual report, "the Cache la Poudre basin was geographically far enough to limit attempts by the Denver Metro area to acquire water." Now, the emergence of cities and special water districts, with offers to purchase water at $30,000 per acre-foot, reminded Greeley that it faced stiff competition. Then there was the matter of "private equity investors." A staff report noted that such groups had "floated a prospectus in an unsuccessful attempt to corner the market on Colorado-Big Thompson units." With the City of Thornton poised to use its Cache la Poudre Basin purchases, "it is becoming clear that those water supplies may no longer be available in as little as 10 years."[14]

At an October 2015 water and sewer board meeting, a comprehensive review of the City's water dedication policy and cash-in-lieu policy was presented. The raw water dedication policy, for residential units, was shown to be close to the median of 22 neighboring communities, and only slightly higher than average. Staff recommended that the raw water dedication policy (of three acre-feet per acre) for residential units not be changed. They also recommended that the calculation of the cash-in-lieu price be based on a 3-year rolling average of the Colorado-Big Thompson (C-BT) market price. This was in recognition of the continued escalation in the market price of C-BT water. Staff was directed by the

board to make additional refinements to these policies and bring them back to
the board for adoption at a future meeting.

By 2016, Greeley's population growth rate had recovered to pre-recessional
rates. In tandem, however, the raw water market price increased substantially,
while water acquisition competition also increased. Department staff suggested
that "for their own long-term benefit, the current ratepayers have and may have
to continue to act now to secure an adequate water supply for the next fifty years."
The City now returned to its projected growth schedule of 2.0 to 2.5 percent
annually. More concerning was the pressure on water sales propelled by suburban Denver metropolitan areas and special water districts. "Large municipalities
such as Aurora, Arapahoe County and Cherry Creek," said the report, "are still
acquiring new supplies in the basin." In 2015, market data showed that "C-BT
water has become scarce and the price of C-BT water has risen to more than three
times 2008 prices to $25,000 per unit."

Due to the competition for water and escalating prices, the Future Water
Account acquisition goal was increased from 6,000 acre-feet to a total of 10,000
acre-feet. This was accomplished with the purchase of 15 shares of Water Supply
& Storage Company (WSSC), 203 shares of the Boyd and Freeman Irrigation
Company, 90 shares in the North Poudre Irrigation Company (NPIC), 45 shares
of Larimer & Weld Irrigation System, 16 shares of New Cache la Poudre Irrigation
Company and Reservoir Company, two shares of Windsor Reservoir and Irrigation
Canal Company, and five units of Windy Gap water. By 2019, the City's water
portfolio included 38.5 shares of WSSC, a small number of the Larimer-Weld
shares, 505 shares of Greeley and Loveland stock (11,000 acre-feet), 82 shares of
the Greeley Irrigation Company (the Greeley Number 3 Ditch), and 22,565 units
of Colorado-Big Thompson water. The City now had 38,700 acre-feet of "firm
yield," a term used to describe water available in the worst periods of drought.[15]
The 75 shares of water rights acquired from the Laramie-Poudre Tunnel Company
had cost $6 million, and the purchase included 806.5 units of C-BT water.[16] (One
unit of C-BT water yields, on average, 0.7 acre-feet.)

On another front, said the 2016 staff report, water quality regulatory demands
"continue to be tracked with potential impacts from changes by the Colorado
Department of Public Health and Environment for disinfection [of water treat-
ment]." The Bellvue and Boyd water treatment plants continued to age, along

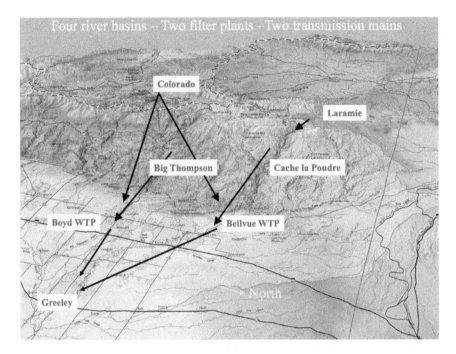

Figure 11.2 This map illustrates Greeley's "long reach" for water, from four river basins; the Laramie, Cache la Poudre, Colorado and Big Thompson. Water is treated at the Bellvue and Boyd Lake plants, with transmission lines from each facility delivering potable water to Greeley. City of Greeley Water and Sewer Department Collection.

with the transmission and distribution systems. Department plans called for several replacement projects to keep the system in good condition.[17]

In 2019, according to staff reports, 82 percent of city water was consumed within the city limits, with 62 percent dedicated to residential customers. The latter applied 55 percent of their water to outdoor landscaping, with a peak summer season (May through October) of 75 percent. Since 2003, the City has purchased 8,000 acre-feet of water through its Future Water Account. This strategy had countered the ever-increasing cost of water, which by 2020 had reached $60,000 per unit for C-BT water.

The second goal of the 2003 Water Master Plan was the construction of additional reservoir storage. In July 2000, Greeley had committed to the Phase II study of the "Chimney Rock Reservoir" project, later renamed the Chimney Hollow Reservoir.

The project would "firm up" the Windy Gap water rights that Greeley had acquired three decades earlier, through the Six Cities plan (now called the Windy Gap Project). The new reservoir would be located in a valley west of Loveland and Carter Lake. Greeley would own 10 percent of the 90,000 acre-feet of storage in the new reservoir.[18] It was anticipated that the Windy Gap Firming Project would not become operational until at least 2010 or later. This led to the search for additional storage that could be constructed in a shorter time frame.

The proposed expansion of Seaman Dam and Reservoir drew attention. A report included raising the dam's height by 105 feet, which would increase storage capacity to 38,000 acre-feet of new water. As designed, this project would cost the City $49 million. W.D. Farr called for acceptance of this report. City leaders also investigated the possibility of partnering with the City of Fort Collins on a joint expansion project for both Halligan and Seaman Reservoirs. On January 6, 2004, the city council unanimously accepted the recommendation of the water and sewer board "to pursue expansion of the Milton Seaman Reservoir, instead of continuing participation in the Northern Integrated Supply Project (NISP)." The latter is a project that would divert flows from the Cache la Poudre River for storage in the proposed Glade Reservoir north of Fort Collins. Additional capacity would be created at the "Galeton Exchange Reservoir," located northeast of Greeley.[19]

Federal and state regulations played a major role in pursuing additional reservoir storage, and the proposed enlargement of Milton Seaman Dam and Reservoir was no exception. Of particular impact was the need to protect the endangered species known as the "Preble's Meadow Jumping Mouse," found in the area of the North Fork of the Cache la Poudre River, between the city's Seaman Reservoir and Fort Collins' Halligan Reservoir. This area had been listed by the U.S. Fish and Wildlife Service as prime habitat for this species. Studies conducted by the Denver Museum of Nature and Science contended that the Preble's mouse faced no more impact from water projects than other North American variants of the species. Should the Preble's mouse be delisted, said staff members in 2003, the uncertainties attendant to planning for Seaman Reservoir expansion would be eliminated.[20] If the mouse remained as a "protected" species (which did occur), it would pose a major obstacle in the permitting process.

In early 2004, Greeley formally began the National Environmental Policy Act (NEPA) 404 permitting process, with the U.S. Army Corps of Engineers, for the enlargement of Milton Seaman Reservoir from 5,000 acre-feet to as much as 53,000 acre-feet. This expansion project would be designated as the "Preferred Alternative" (a technical term within the NEPA guidelines for the permitting process). In September 2004, Greeley entered into an Intergovernmental Agreement (IGA) with the City of Fort Collins for the joint permitting of the Halligan-Seaman Water Management Plan. This would be a cooperative effort until the 404 permits were issued, with the final goal of obtaining individual approvals for Milton Seaman and Halligan Reservoirs. The plan was for the two cities to maintain ownership of their respective dams and reservoirs, and to fund their own project construction costs. Evaluating the cumulative impact on the North Fork of the two projects was a key consideration in the decision to move forward with a joint permitting strategy.

In 2007, at the request of the U.S. Army Corps of Engineers (Corps), Greeley joined the City of Fort Collins and several non-governmental entities to form the "Shared Vision Planning" (SVP) effort. Funded by the Western Governors' Council and monitored by the Corps, this group sought "to determine if there were opportunities to enhance the flows in the North Fork and the mainstem Cache la Poudre River below the North Fork confluence without sacrificing the yield of the project." Much like earlier generations of Greeley water officials, the City pursued a collaborative strategy to explore "a better way of permitting large water projects."[21]

At the conclusion of the two-plus-year effort, the Corps of Engineers requested that the two cities formally incorporate the Shared Visioning Process into the NEPA permitting process. The Greeley Water and Sewer Board voted unanimously in favor of continuing with this effort. The City of Fort Collins, on the other hand, chose not to continue. The outcome led to dissolution of the joint permitting process agreement for the two reservoir projects. Fort Collins and Greeley then proceeded with individual permitting plans.

In 2019, the Windy Gap Firming Project, with Chimney Hollow Reservoir as its centerpiece, received approval from federal and state regulatory agencies. Local environmental groups, however, had filed suit to halt construction. A decision on this legal action is expected sometime in 2020.

By 2020, gravel pit storage materialized into viable water projects. The City had acquired the right to store water in what became known as the "Poudre

Ponds" located along 35th Avenue at the Cache la Poudre River. The cost to convert the Poudre Ponds gravel pits to state-approved, lined gravel-pit storage was $2,863,000. The project required minimal effort for permitting, although the gravel pits required expensive bentonite lining to keep stored water from percolating into the groundwater table and returning back to the river. While the Poudre Ponds had only junior 1999 and 2006 storage rights, it could obtain water from the Greeley Irrigation Company, Windy Gap Second Use, and also reusable effluent from the city's water pollution control facility. The lined gravel pits provide 1,600 acre-feet of storage, with the potential to add 1,000 acre-feet at an adjacent site.

Greeley also joined the Tri-District water agencies to purchase the Overland Trail Gravel Pits, located northwest of Fort Collins, from the LaFarge Construction Company. The City had gained access to five parcels of land near Fort Collins with this purchase; an area that covered some 36 acres, with an anticipated date of 2022 for full completion.[22] It is anticipated that a total of 5,000 acre-feet of storage will be available. Greeley's portion of this total is 50 percent or 2,500 acre-feet. The Overland Trail ponds hold a junior 2000 storage right with up to 5,000 acre-feet of potential storage available by 2022. All gravel pit storage could be used to meet historic return flow and stream augmentation obligations. There also could be exchanges made of city water upstream to the Bellvue treatment plant.

IN MAY 2012, wildfires in the upper Cache la Poudre River Canyon threatened the city's water supply reservoirs and direct flows from the river. Dry weather contributed to 95,000 acres of grass and timber burning around the city's Seaman Reservoir. The massive High Park and Hewlett Gulch forest fires sent debris and ash down the Poudre River and into Seaman Reservoir, threatening the city's water treatment structure at Bellvue. Also endangered were the City of Fort Collins' water supply intake near Seaman Dam. Utility officials throughout the canyon implemented their early warning system, whereby treatment operators could block the flow of water into their facilities.[23]

The Cache la Poudre River carried higher loads of debris and ash as the runoff season advanced, causing the City to restrict the use of the polluted water at its

Bellvue drinking water treatment plant for over a month. To accelerate the mitigation of erosion around Seaman Reservoir, as the summer rainy season loomed,
Greeley and Fort Collins partnered with Larimer County to spend $5 million to
drop and spread ground cover by helicopter on the burned hillsides.[24]

In mid-September 2013, while engaged in the issue of fire damage restoration at
its largest storage reservoir, city officials witnessed the most devastating floods experienced in northern Colorado in a generation. Not since the deadly Big Thompson
River flood of July 31, 1976, had so much precipitation fallen on the watershed as
it did from September 13-15. When the 15-inch deluge subsided, and damage to
homes, businesses, farms, and oil fields was assessed, the Greeley Water and Sewer
Department discovered that the amount of water stored in Boyd Lake had increased
from 28,000 acre-feet to 37,000 acre-feet in a matter of days.

A THIRD STRATEGIC area of the 2003 Water Master Plan was its call
for expanded and upgraded infrastructure. These capital improvements
included investments at the Boyd Lake and Bellvue treatment plants. The
water and sewer department also implemented a network of projects to
provide non-potable water to major outdoor landscapes throughout the city,
such as parks and other recreation areas. To meet current and future water
demands, department staff drafted plans for facilities' enhancement. The
Bellvue treatment plant had been slated for a $14 million expansion by 2008.
Further data analysis revealed that rehabilitation of the existing sedimentation and filter systems, as well as replacement of smaller pipes, would enable
the plant to produce 32 million gallons per day, at a cost of $6 million. The
savings of $8 million could be reinvested in a new Bellvue water transmission
line to the city's Gold Hill storage reservoir. In March, the City announced
the sale of $17,210,000 in bonds for the construction of the 60-inch pipeline.

Crews began installation of the "Chimney Park Phase I" section of the pipeline
over a 2.2-mile sector near the former Kodak of Colorado plant in Windsor. This
new treated water line would connect the Bellvue plant to the Greeley distribution
system.[25] In addition, it would solve the decades-long dilemma of the Greeley
water system described by the Water, Waterworks and Sewer Committee of the

Figure 11.3 In 2005, Greeley's water infrastructure expansion continued with the construction of a $100 million 30-mile transmission line from Bellvue to west Greeley. Considered a "generational investment," the 60-inch diameter line can deliver 70 million gallons per day, a necessity as Greeley continues to grow. Greeley Water and Sewer Department Collection.

City Charter Convention back in 1958. That committee summarized the water situation for Greeley at the time in one sentence: **"Greeley's problem is not one of supply, but one of transmission."** That vexing problem, the city hoped, would now be solved for decades to come.

In 2005, work continued on a variety of water infrastructure projects for the city, among them the addition of one-third of the 30 miles of the 60-inch Bellvue transmission line. At the Bellvue plant, the City issued contracts for a $4 million renovation of the residuals handling system, a $1.2 million improvement of the flocculation-sedimentation basins; and replacement by city crews of one-third of the internal plant piping. These actions resulted in an acceleration of the treatment and transmission projects for the city. Should the process continue at this pace, staff believed that they would have the entire 60-inch Bellvue line operational three years prior to the 2015 target date. This work also allowed staff to reconsider the high costs of winterizing the Boyd Lake treatment plant. Cost estimates for improvements at the Bellvue plant had risen from an initial design estimate of $1.6 million to almost $4 million. The City believed that expanding the capacity of the Bellvue plant and its transmission line could ensure a supply of 17 million gallons per day during the winter.[26]

The Bellvue transmission line also had been extended from the plant to some 4,000 feet south of the town of Windsor, connecting with that town's distribution system. The next section to Gold Hill (a treated water reservoir) would be under construction in 2020. A series of projects at the Boyd plant "are part of upgrades intended to improve the finished water quality and towards winterizing Boyd Lake WTP." Among the issues addressed were "the addition of ozone to improve water quality and eliminate taste/odors, replacement of aging power infrastructure, winterizing all chemicals, and replacing chlorine gas with sodium hypochlorite for disinfection."[27]

These projects, along with efforts to replace aging water lines within city limits, did much to help the water and sewer department meet the challenges of growth in the early 21st century. At Boyd Lake, the staff also worked to reduce customer concerns about taste and odor issues; these the result of water being stored in Lake Loveland and Boyd Lake before being treated. In particular, blue-green algae blooms that formed in mid-summer's heat required more treatment to eliminate such concerns. The goal was to approximate the quality (taste and odor) of water that Greeley consumers received from the Cache la Poudre River.

By 2019, over $100 million had been expended to construct the 60-inch pipeline from Bellvue to Greeley. It would deliver up to 70 million gallons of water per day; an amount much greater than the plant's current level of 32 million gallons per day. Much like the original wooden stave line of 1907, this pipe was deemed a "generational investment" by city staff. With the addition of a pumping plant, the line's capacity could be enhanced to carry up to 100 million gallons per day, if needed. It has a project life of 75 to 100 years, making its original cost a wise investment.

In 2020, a second improvement at the Bellvue plant was the addition of a new "Treatment Train." This term describes the linear treatment process and associated equipment in the new building. Its features include flocculation, sedimentation, filtration equipment, and associated piping, pumps, and controls. The capacity of

Figure 11.4 The Boyd Lake Water Treatment Plant has the capacity to process 38 million gallons of water per day. This plant is Greeley's summer peaking plant and is not run in the wintertime. City of Greeley Water and Sewer Department Collection.

this new facility is 20 million gallons per day, with a budgeted cost of $25,458,000.

Bellvue's raw water quality issues, such as turbidity control, removal of microbial contaminants, and total organic carbon (TOC), were identified as issues which required more investigation. A water treatment study had also identified *cryptosporidium* in the river water; a bacteria that posed digestive problems for consumers. These and other issues prompted staff to seek new and better treatment methods which included replacement of chlorine gas with ultraviolet (UV) light (which scans water before it is released into the treated water pipeline). Chlorine gas, while effective at bacteria control, also had volatile side effects when released into the atmosphere. The transition to UV treatment came in response to a regulation by the U.S. EPA called the "Stage 2 Disinfection Byproduct Rule."[28]

Looking beyond 2020 at Bellvue, plans are to increase treatment capacity to 125 million gallons per day (MGD). Each of the new treatment buildings, said Adam Prior, chief engineer for the water and sewer department, has capacity for 21 MGD. They can be "pilot-tested" to expand their capacity to a range of 100 to 125 MGD. A second treatment building will be completed by 2027, a timeframe that could be

Figure 11.5 The Bellvue Water Treatment Plant can process 32 million gallons of water per day. Located on the Cache la Poudre River, it is Greeley's year-round water treatment plant. The river diversion structure, shown above, diverts water from the river to the plant. City of Greeley Museums, Permanent Collection, 1991.42.1205A.

adjusted according to priorities determined by the water and sewer department.[29]

One additional infrastructure investment would be the use of untreated water for outdoor irrigation throughout the city. The initial focus is on major turf areas such as parks, golf courses, and schools. These public spaces need up to 36 inches of water per year to maintain bluegrass turf. By 2019, Greeley had 62 sites that utilized non-potable water for irrigation.

The City also realized that an important component of its non-potable water came from its Greeley and Loveland Irrigation Company (GLIC) water supplies. To allow for easier transfer of these waters to the city system during the early and late irrigations seasons, the department announced plans in 2007 for the "Lower Equalization Project." This initiative sought "to equalize canal flows during the complete irrigation season, leading to greater efficiencies and higher potable yields of the GLIC system to Greeley." Such a facility has multiple benefits such as "water supply, water demand, exchange potential, and operational considerations." The Lower Equalizer offers "an extremely efficient way to increase the firm yield of Greeley's water system." The project will use irrigation water that would not be treated.[30]

WHILE DROUGHT, GOVERNMENT regulations, growth, and consumer demand for the "Meeker promise" influenced Greeley's water planning for the first two decades of the 21st century, the department also needed to respond to changing conditions of the wastewater section of their work. In 2011, historian Martin Melosi wrote of the new generation of science and engineering of water pollution control: "All technologies of sanitation were capital intensive, and they required continual maintenance and repair." No better evidence of this exists than the commitment of the City to fund over $76 million for improvements at the Greeley Water Pollution Control Facility (WPCF).

Under the direction of Jon Monson, the department invested in a Supervisory Control and Data Acquisition (SCADA) system. Computers can now track on a 24-hour basis the manner of treatment, waste and bacteria removal, and discharge of effluent. This method is much more advanced from the 1970s calculations, which were taken once per day. Other elements of plant operations, installed after 2000, were new blowers, digesters, clarifiers, and the installation of ultraviolet light equipment to disinfect effluent as it was released from the plant into the Cache la Poudre River. The sewer collection system also received attention from department staff, with expansion of the Poudre Trunk Line westward to 71st Avenue. More "lift stations" were constructed to serve new neighborhoods along the U.S. Highway 34 corridor, among them the St. Michael's development and the University of Colorado Health Services Hospital.

As the first two decades of the 21st century concluded, the City had embraced a vision of pollution control services that reflected its century-long commitment to clean, secure, abundant, and cost efficient drinking water. Gone were the days of direct discharge of waste to the Cache la Poudre River. Public demand for a cleaner environment, once questioned by municipal officials nationwide as expensive and proscriptive, now became a key goal of the city's best practices. Known as the "2018 WPCF Water Treatment and Nutrient Master Plan Update," the document called for "a holistic, cost effective, long-term capital improvement plan for treating wastewater." Nutrient discharges at the WPCF would be reduced to meet growth and regulatory requirements over a 20-year planning period through 2037.[31]

Reading much like the department's reports on water supply acquisition and storage capacity, the WPCF master plan calculated the need to meet an annual population growth curve of 2 to 2.5 percent. Making the city's planning process more challenging was the presence of substantial industrial wastewater from Greeley's meat packing and cheese processing plants, as well as from local dairy operators. The latter were required to manage their own treatment facilities or provide pretreatment, while the City addressed the discharge of residential and commercial customers. The city's treatment facility in 2020 has a daily output of 7.5 million gallons, with a total discharge capacity of 14 million gallons per day.

Two state regulations, in particular, influenced the wastewater planning process: "Regulation 85," whereby the Colorado Department of Public Health and Environment called for reduction of levels of phosphorus and nitrogen from wastewater; and "Regulation 31," which required "tertiary filtration and chemical addition," as well as "biogas utilization improvements." At the core of the Regulation 31 standards was improving the city's effluent to a cleanliness level of 99.99 percent. The City considered this achievable, as the plant's treatment processes in 2020 averages 95 percent to 98 percent on any given day. The state's Water Quality Control Commission expected urban utilities to initiate planning and design of expansion, once an existing system had reached 80 percent of design treatment capacity. When the flow level approached 95 percent, said the commission, construction should begin to "trigger hydraulic capacity improvements across the water pollution control facility by 2027."[32] The department staff accepted this challenge as it had earlier issues of water pollution control and treatment.

Four critical elements now faced the Greeley Water and Sewer Board: 1) Fluctuating river levels caused by flooding; 2) Future land acquisition opportunities for new wastewater facilities; 3) Actual long-term growth in flows and loads relative to projected values; and 4) Specific future (wastewater) regulatory requirements. Approximately $195 million will be needed over a 20-year period to meet these wastewater treatment obligations. The City would address first the Regulation 85 issues of nutrient removal, then engage in primary treatment upgrades that included influent pumping and "digester ferric chloride." The third

Figure 11.6 In 2020, the Greeley Water Pollution Control Facility was renamed the Greeley Wastewater Treatment and Reclamation Facility, reflecting its many technological upgrades since 2000. These include 24-hour computer tracking of sewage treatment, waste and bacteria removal, and discharge of effluent. New blowers, digesters, clarifiers, and ultraviolet light ensure the highest industry standards for the safe treatment and reclamation of wastewater. Aerial photo by Stephanie Burchett.

phase of Greeley's WPCF master plan focused on capacity expansion, with an emphasis on plant-wide flow and load capacity improvements, blower replacement, "Struvite [mineral deposit] management and phosphorous sequestration," and solids handling improvements. The final stage of the master plan, to occur sometime after the year 2030, involves Regulation 31 compliance. However, this will require substantial advances in science and engineering to achieve the levels of wastewater quality expected by the State of Colorado.[33]

All of these improvements will be profoundly important to the capacity and functions of Greeley's wastewater treatment system. They marked a vast improvement from the decades of the 1950s through the 1970s, when issues with packing plant waste, and undersized and aged facilities were chronic problems. In 2020, the wastewater treatment plant became the "Greeley Wastewater Treatment and

Reclamation Facility;" a better description of the plant's overall goal to reclaim water from wastes, and to treat it for non-potable uses.

THE FOURTH STRATEGIC area of the 2003 Water Master Plan was the city's water conservation program. In April 2002, the City discussed a "Drought Emergency Plan," with four levels of reductions and conservation. When the department assessed its operations in its 2003 annual report, per capita daily usage had declined by 20 percent. This equated to 182 gallons per person per day, a substantial difference from 229 gallons per day in 2001. This prompted city officials to ask if it was wise to set future reduction rates at this level, or to work towards a sustained pattern of 10 percent below 2001's figures. Equally important was the discussion of whether drought conditions should limit the reduction in storage in city reservoirs to 50 percent of capacity.

A pilot program of water budgets, for individual customers, was developed. This innovative process calculated the "customer-specific amount of water needed for indoor and outdoor use, depending on the number of persons living at a residence, the square footage of irrigated area at each residence, and local weather data." Department staff had identified six subdivisions within Greeley for testing the water budget concept. Reports on their findings would be presented to the water and sewer board and city council before any further adoption of the strategy.[34]

In 2004, department staff observed a successful response to drought conditions; this despite a population rate of 3.4 percent, well above the master plan's projections of 2.5 percent. Citizens had reduced their summer water usage by over 25 percent from that of 2000. Equally impressive was the addition of nearly 3,000 new accounts in that same period, an increase of 14 percent. These statistics allowed the department to consider lifting restrictions on outdoor watering—from once every three days to the previous policy of alternate days. The staff was concerned about widespread damage to landscaping if limitations were not adjusted.[35]

By 2005, as the drought crisis lessened, the water and sewer department charted rising water consumption by citizens. When usage exceeded 93 percent of the system's threshold in July, staff began design work on increasing the supply as per the stipulations of the master plan. This had occurred with the addition of

655 water taps that year, a number that had declined 19 percent over the previous 12-month period.

As the year 2006 drew to a close, the local economy slowed, with impacts on water use and revenues. The City had installed 187 new water taps that year, a decline of nearly 75 percent from the 2003 total. In 2007, concerns about the declining economy became more pressing. Population projections fell for the third straight year, even as they remained within the long-range predictions of the 2003 Water Master Plan. Developers had approached the staff seeking relief from the City's water and sewer fees, and asked that such charges be lowered to make Greeley more competitive. This request, however, was at odds with the City's long-standing policy that "growth pay its own way."

The department also faced a return of high-demand days due to the summer heat. Annual usage for 2006 had reached 9.2 billion gallons, a number that the City reported did not equal the pre-drought conditions before 2000, even as the population had grown by 13,000 people. Because there had been peak consumption days above the system's 90 percent threshold, department planners, for the second year in a row, looked towards capacity increases to meet the standards of the 2003 water master plan.[36]

An interesting statistic emerged at the end of 2006. Until 1986, the average residential lot size in Greeley had been 9,640 square feet. By 2007, this had fallen by more than half, to 4,480 square feet. Changes in consumer housing had emerged as a function of the prolonged dry cycle. In 2007, city water staff reported that the high mountain reservoirs had produced only one-quarter of their 8,000 acre-feet capacity. The City decided that spring to lease only half of its surplus yield of 26,000 acre-feet to area irrigation companies; the remainder was saved for emergency use by urban consumers.[37]

In 2011, the water budget-based rate model for single family residential customers was further developed and tested. In 2017, the water-budget initiative was fully implemented across the city for all single family residential users. The individual water budgets are based on the number of persons per household, the actual irrigated area, and real time weather data. If the target water budget is exceeded, the billing rate for the excess use is increased. This additional charge encourages more efficient use of water. The staff reported that by 2018 "96% of customers stayed within their total annual budget.[38]

In 2019, the City's updated "Water Conservation Plan," initially approved by the Colorado Water Conservation Board (CWCB) in 2010, received final state recognition. Over the next decade, the department sought a reduction of 9.3 percent in water demand. Greeley's "water conservation program was one of the largest in the state with an annual budget over $500,000," noted the CWCB. Among the features praised by state officials were "residential landscape code changes, commercial audits and conservation strategies at city park landscapes." If the plan proved effective, city officials told the CWCB, Greeley would realize a reduction in demand of 3,120 acre-feet.[39]

The city's pride in its water budget, and other conservation programs, resulted from nearly two decades of planning for water conservation. In 2009 the department submitted its first formal conservation plan, as required, to the State of Colorado for approval. This plan was updated and approved again in 2014. The conservation program pointed out a 28 percent reduction in water use since the year 2000. This decline reflects the conservation efforts of the users and the effectiveness of the City's conservation programs. The department's long term plans called for further reductions in water use. The goal is to save, through conservation efforts, an additional 3,100 acre-feet of water by 2035.

IN 2011, THE issue of preserving local history came to the fore when the Poudre River Heritage Alliance issued its Guidebook for the Cache la Poudre River Heritage Area. The chair of this Colorado non-profit organization was Rick Brady, Greeley's City Attorney, a longtime member of the Alliance's board of directors.[40] This Guidebook traces the natural, historical, scenic, recreational, cultural and water right features of the river from the mouth of the Poudre Canyon at Bellvue into and through the City of Greeley. Sponsored by Senators Wayne Allard and Ken Salazar, co-sponsored in the U.S. House of Representatives by Congressperson Betsy Markey, the 2009 Cache la Poudre River National Heritage Area Act forwards the legacy Senator Hank Brown preserved with the 1996 Poudre River Corridor Act.[41]

The Heritage Alliance Board includes the City of Greeley, Weld and Larimer Counties, the City of Fort Collins, the Town of Windsor, the Town of Timnath, the Northern Colorado Water Conservancy District, the Central Colorado Water Conservancy District, and other members of the public and private sectors. The heritage area extends for 45 miles, including lands within the river's 100-year floodplain. The Alliance's Vision Statement is both straightforward and profound:

> "The Cache la Poudre River National Heritage Area is a renowned attraction that combines opportunities for education on the central theme of Western water law, with a healthy natural environment of abundant wildlife and breathtaking scenery, all supported by premiere facilities, including trails, visitor centers, and interpretive exhibits."[42]

The Heritage Area includes Island Grove Regional Park, where Delph Carpenter's boyhood home is preserved.[43] Greeley had much to celebrate and be proud of through its association with the Cache la Poudre River, and now with its Poudre Heritage Alliance. It is a fitting tribute to all who had settled, developed, and prospered in the valley of Native tribes, Union Colonists, and groundbreakers of water law, environmental protection, and technological innovation.

AS THE THIRD decade of the 21st century begins, the City of Greeley can reflect upon its successful responses to the water challenges of the years 2000-2020. Through its diligent adherence to the four strategic points of the 2003 Water Master Plan, the City has modernized its potable water and wastewater infrastructure, purchased new supplies of raw water, worked on the expansion of storage reservoirs, and reduced water demand through its water conservation campaign. Adherence to a 10-year cycle of capital-improvement projects allowed for budgeting for ever-more expensive initiatives. Building upon the heritage of its first 150 years, the water and sewer department has proof of its good work, as recipient of national awards from the U.S. EPA, for the Water Pollution Control Facility.

On the "water side" in 2017, Greeley won both the "Best of the Best" professional judges award, for the best tasting water in the U.S., and the People's Choice award (all convention attendees voted) at the American Water Works Association national conference in Philadelphia. This was the first time any city in the United States had garnered both awards in the same year.

The confluence of visionary and altruistic individuals, good planning, good fortune, and good preparations for the future remained the essence of the "Meeker Promise." Those who had worked so hard to keep these traditions alive, even as they met the challenges of a new century, guaranteed the citizens of Greeley that the next 50 years would be filled with optimism. It was the pledge that Union Colonists possessed, when they first saw the "magic touch of water" flowing past their new homes.

Chapter Twelve

150 Years Later

The Magic Touch of Water

By Harold Evans, Chair of the Greeley Water and Sewer Board

THE HISTORY OF Greeley Water has evolved over 150 years into a remarkable and award-winning water system that serves 140,000 customers today. Prior to the 1859 Colorado gold rush, this area was home to indigenous peoples—the Arapaho, Cheyenne, and Utes. Early explorers called this vast sea of buffalo grass and cactus, east of the Continental Divide, the "Great American Desert." With its challenging climate and little rain, it was considered unsuitable for farming.

In April 1870, the Union Colony of Colorado, a joint stock colonization venture, purchased land on the river delta just west of the confluence of the South Platte and Cache la Poudre Rivers in Colorado Territory. An unobstructed view of the "Shining Mountains," as the Utes called the Rockies, was an inspiring backdrop for a new community. The individuals chosen by Union Colony founder, Nathan Meeker, were of good character, financially solvent, and skilled in diverse trades and professions. Through cooperation and strenuous work, they achieved their goals of building a temperance town sustained through irrigated agriculture. Meeker, the agricultural editor of Horace Greeley's renowned newspaper, *The New York Tribune,* named the new town "Greeley," in honor of the famous journalist, who was the Union Colony's first treasurer, and enthusiastic promoter who encouraged the colonists in all their endeavors.

THE HISTORY OF Greeley Water starts with the Number 3 Canal. Construction of this irrigation system began two weeks after the colonists arrived at the town site. Eight feet wide, 15 inches deep, and 10 miles long, it was completed in 10 weeks and began carrying water on June 10, 1870. It supplied water for the colonists' yards and gardens, and small cultivated tracts and farms outside the municipal boundaries. A 3/8th undivided interest in the ditch was dedicated for use on the Colony's parks and gardens. Today, the Greeley Irrigation Company owns and operates this ditch. The City retains its original 3/8th undivided interest and has purchased approximately one-half of the company's other shares. In 2020, water diverted from the Cache la Poudre River will have flowed through the Greeley Number 3 Canal for 150 consecutive years.

In the fall of 1870, the Colony started construction on the Number 2 Canal to irrigate the higher bench lands north of the Cache la Poudre River. Completed in the spring of 1871, the Number 2 Canal operates under the auspices of the New Cache la Poudre Irrigation Company, a mutual ditch company owned primarily by farmers. The City of Greeley also owns shares in this company, which diverts from the Poudre River upstream from the Greeley Number 3 Canal.

In the summer of 1874, the Cache la Poudre River dried up at the Number 3 Canal headgate. The new Fort Collins Agricultural Colony settlers had diverted all available water from the river into their two new upstream canals. This led to an acrimonious meeting between the parties (near present day Windsor, Colorado) on July 15, 1874. "Every man to his tent, to his rifle and cartridges!" was the Union Colony battle cry at one point. Fortunately, cooler heads prevailed and shots were never fired. Later in July and early August, heavy rains ensured enough water for Greeley and Fort Collins farmers for that season. The Greeley-Fort Collins conflict was a major driver for the water provisions included in Colorado's 1876 Constitution. These provisions established the basic tenets of western water law that became known as the Colorado Doctrine.

This "first in time, first in right" doctrine prioritized a user's appropriation of water, from a stream for beneficial use or need, based on the actual date or time that use began. Though Greeley water leaders played a key role in drafting these water provisions, they were joined in common interest by members of the Constitutional Convention from throughout Colorado. Many western territories and states began to model their water laws on precedents, that originated from the 1874 conflict, concerning the rightful use and equitable division of water from the Cache la Poudre River.

Water for Greeley's domestic use during the 1870's came from individual shallow wells sunk into the Poudre River aquifer and stored in underground cisterns. Water for town lawns, gardens, and parks came through laterals (smaller irrigation channels) from the larger Number 3 Canal. At this time, there was no pressurized water distribution for the city. As more agricultural irrigation occurred, water quality deteriorated in the shallow aquifer. The town then drilled a deep artesian well in the south half of Lincoln Park in 1883-1884. Seven other artesian wells were drilled during the next two years. A subsequent loss of underground pressure diminished the availability of a reliable water supply from these wells. In 1889, the first water treatment plant was constructed on the north side of town. It consisted of a large infiltration gallery, with a steam pumping system and transmission pipe, that delivered water to an elevated storage tank on Greeley's highest hill south of town. Gravity pressure, from this tank, provided water throughout Greeley for domestic use and firefighting.

In 1902, the Greeley Sugar Factory opened. Locally grown sugar beets joined potatoes as a major cash crop for area farmers. Weld County had long enjoyed a national reputation for its potatoes. Both crops relied on irrigation water delivered via the Union Colony's Number 2 and 3 Canals. The sugar beet industry in northeastern Colorado created a population boom for the area, and Greeley's water system soon became inadequate to handle this growth. Built in 1889, the water treatment plant's capacity to serve the growing community was limited. The critical question for city officials was whether or not to expand the existing water treatment plant or look to the mountains for a new water supply.

After extensive research and analysis, the Greeley City Council decided to develop the mountain water system. Land and water rights were available for purchase on the Cache la Poudre River just west of the small community of Bellvue near the Poudre Canyon's mouth. On December 26, 1905, the citizens of Greeley approved issuing $350,000 in bonds to finance the project consisting of a water treatment plant and 38 miles of pipeline to Greeley. The pipeline was 20 inches in diameter and constructed of wood staves coated with tar and wrapped with spiral metal bands. The water rights purchased were 7.5 cubic feet per second with the number 6 1/2 priority right on the river dated August 1, 1862. These direct flow rights are still an important part of Greeley's water supplies today.

The Bellvue Water Treatment Plant delivered its first treated water in September of 1907. Greeley purchased an additional water right of 5 cubic feet per second, with the number 6 priority on the Poudre River, in 1925. Greeley has had Bellvue water deliveries (with several pipeline replacements and upgrades) for 113 consecutive years. Key individuals responsible for the mountain water system and subsequent completion of the Bellvue project included Henry C. Watson (Greeley mayor from 1901-1905); attorney Franklin J. Green (mayor from 1905-1909), and well-known water lawyer, Charles Todd (mayor from 1917-1923).[1]

Delph Carpenter, a descendant of Union Colonists, became nationally known in the 1920s. His innovative work on interstate water sharing compacts with Colorado's downstream neighbors transformed western and United States water law. He is best known for his work in crafting the Colorado River Compact, which divides Colorado River water between the upper and lower basin states. Carpenter was the Colorado commissioner on the seven-state Colorado River Commission chaired by Herbert Hoover, U.S. Secretary of Commerce. Hoover later credited Carpenter as the architect of the Colorado River Compact, signed on November 24, 1922, at Bishop's Lodge in Santa Fé, New Mexico. Colorado Governor Ralph Carr, himself a water lawyer, called Carpenter the "Father of Interstate Compacts." Measured and divided at Lees Ferry in northern Arizona, the 1922 Colorado River Compact limits the upper basin from depleting water flows below 75 million acre-feet of water over a ten year rolling average. This water flows through the Grand Canyon and is stored in Lake Mead.

The Great Depression and a major drought challenged Greeley and the Nation during the 1930s. For Greeley Water, two major problems arose—how to obtain a supplemental water supply for northeastern Colorado, and how best to deal with raw sewage discharged into the Cache la Poudre River. The idea of importing Colorado River water from the Western Slope had been considered for several decades. The federal government's funding of Wyoming's Casper-Alcova project in the 1930s spurred concrete plans for a transmountain tunnel, from Grand Lake on the west side of the Continental Divide, to the Big Thompson River on the east side. In July 1933, a group of Greeley leaders, including attorney William R. Kelly and Charles Hansen, publisher of the *Greeley Tribune*, met to discuss financing a survey that eventually led to formation of the Northern Colorado Water Users Association, and intense, but ultimately successful negotiations with Colorado's Western Slope interests. In 1937, the Colorado General Assembly adopted the Water Conservancy Act drafted by Greeley lawyers Thomas A. Nixon and William R. Kelly. In turn, this led to the formation of the Northern Colorado Water Conservancy District and Congressional funding for the Colorado-Big Thompson Project (C-BT). On July 5, 1938, the Northern District signed a repayment contract with the United States. Construction started in 1938 and was completed in 1957, almost 20 years later, due in part to labor and materials shortages during World War II. Greeley's Charles Hansen became known as the C-BT project's "Godfather."

In 1939, the City of Greeley committed to acquiring 15,000 units of C-BT water. Today, Greeley owns 22,812 units, and is the largest municipal owner of C-BT water. On an annual basis, the C-BT project delivers in excess of 200,000 acre-feet of water into the eight-county area of the Northern District, more than offsetting the loss of the 70,000 acre-feet of water that Delph Carpenter failed to acquire in the 1922 *Wyoming v. Colorado* U.S. Supreme Court case. This case dealt with the amount of water Colorado could annually divert from the Laramie River.

The second major challenge for Greeley Water in the 1930's was raw sewage being discharged into the Poudre River by Greeley and every other community and business along the river. Sewage treatment became a necessity for the area. Throughout most of the 1930's, the State Health Department had warned the cities they needed sewage treatment facilities. In 1936, Greeley constructed its first wastewater treatment plant on the east side of town which provided primary treatment of the sewage stream.

The 1940's was the decade of reservoirs for Greeley Water. In 1940, the City of Greeley started building Milton Seaman Reservoir on the North Fork of the Cache la Poudre River. Initially a Work Projects Administration financed project, the City of Greeley completed the dam using its own resources. During World War II, delays in the construction of the dam occurred due to material and key equipment shortages. The initial filling of Seaman Reservoir took place in the spring of 1948.

Storing 5,000 acre-feet of water, this reservoir is an important part of Greeley's water system due to its close upstream proximity to the city's Bellvue Water Treatment Plant. In 1947, Greeley Water purchased seven high mountain reservoirs located in the Poudre River drainage: Barnes Meadow, Comanche, Hourglass, Peterson and Twin Lake (two others were later abandoned). Together they provide

8,100 acre-feet of water storage. All have junior water rights, but provide flexibility in the management of Greeley's Poudre River water portfolio. Key structural components of these reservoirs were upgraded during the 1990s.

In addition to the Colorado-Big Thompson project coming on line, the 1950's were important to Greeley Water from a governance standpoint. The Greeley Water Board was created upon voter approval of Greeley's Home Rule Charter in 1958. Formation of the Water Board took Greeley water out of politics. Working collaboratively with the city council and city manager, the board concentrates on the complexities of water issues, rates charged, facility construction and maintenance, and delivery of high quality water to customers. In 1973, the board's responsibility expanded into wastewater treatment and collection through creation of the now-existing water and sewer board. Mr. W.D. Farr became the first chair of the water board in 1958, and served in that capacity for 39 years. As a long-time board member of the Northern Colorado Water Conservancy District, Mr. Farr was a highly respected water leader throughout Colorado and beyond.

In 1955, the city's wastewater treatment plant was enlarged to meet the needs of a rapidly growing community. The Bellvue Water Treatment Plant was also expanded during this time period. The Boyd Lake component of Greeley's water supply system came about in 1961 with an agreement between the Greeley and Loveland Irrigation Company and the City of Greeley. This agreement provided Greeley's domestic treated water service to farms under the Greeley and Loveland system. In exchange, when these farms were eventually annexed into Greeley, the farm owners supported annexation and received credit for their shares in the company. This agreement led to the construction of the Boyd Lake Water Treatment Plant, located in Loveland, along with a treated water pipeline to Greeley.

The 1970's challenged the City of Greeley to meet the wastewater treatment needs of the Monfort Packing Company, a large beef and lamb processing firm, together with controlling odor coming from the wastewater treatment plant. These challenges persisted until completion of a major expansion of the wastewater plant in 1985. The Windy Gap addition to the C-BT project, of which Greeley was one of the six original participants, wound its way through the local, state and national approval process in the 1970s and 1980s. This project, approved in 1981 and completed in 1985, brought additional Colorado River water to Greeley and its partners.

The 1980's saw increasing federal regulations and a focus on environmental mitigation. In 1986, the designation of the 75-mile Cache la Poudre Wild and Scenic River was a watershed event for the area. Greeley's U.S. Congressman, Hank Brown, obtained compromise and passage of this legislation. Later, as Colorado's U.S. Senator, Brown played a pivotal role in the creation and passage of the Cache la Poudre River Corridor Act in 1996. Together, these designations established the Poudre River's significance in the history of western water use and water law, and secured the Poudre's preservation from its headwaters to its confluence with the South Platte River.

Along with increasing focus on environmental issues, Greeley invested in the future growth of the community with major upgrades to both the wastewater treatment plant and the sewage collection system. In 1985, a $10 million expansion of the wastewater treatment plant, to accommodate future growth, also brought it into compliance with full secondary treatment standards. Installation of the Sheep Draw trunk sewer line provided the necessary infrastructure for west Greeley's future development and growth.

The early 1990's brought economic stress to farmers in Weld County and throughout the nation as many farms were threatened by foreclosure. Greeley responded by purchasing $10 million in water shares from farmers to the west of Greeley under the Greeley and Loveland Irrigation Company. An important element of these purchases was a lease back of the water to farmers for an initial 15-year time period, with options to renew if Greeley did not yet need the water. This arrangement kept the farms in production and simultaneously provided Greeley with a future water supply for annexed land. Working with the local farm community has been a hallmark of Greeley's leaders since 1870.

The first two decades of the 21st century have been dedicated to planning for and investing in the future of Greeley Water and Sewer. The 2002-2003 drought stressed Greeley's water supplies greatly. This prompted the City to analyze and confirm the actual dry year yields of its water supplies, a major benefit in planning for the future. By 2003, a new long range Master Plan for Greeley Water indicated Greeley's population could more than double by 2050. A strategic Four Point Plan identified the actions required to meet this future demand. These four strategic actions are:

- Enhanced Water Conservation Efforts
- Continued Infrastructure Investments
- Additional Water Rights Acquisitions
- Expanded Reservoir Storage

In 2006, a master plan for the Water Pollution Control Facility was also completed and updated in 2018. It focused on achieving compliance with future regulatory standards for the removal of nitrogen and phosphorus, as well as the future treatment capacity of the plant. The water pollution control facility can treat 14 million gallons of sewage per day. For several years, the U.S. Environmental Protection Agency has recognized the plant for meeting all treatment requirements. Both the Water Master Plan and the Water Pollution Control Facility Master Plan are the basis for developing 10-year capital improvement plans for the needed infrastructure. These capital improvement plans are updated annually.

Implementation of these master plans has steadily progressed. In the water arena there have been many significant accomplishments. Water conservation efforts have yielded a 28 percent reduction in water use in gallons per capita per day. A water budget program for single family residential customers has also been implemented. A new 60-inch diameter water pipeline has been installed from the Bellvue Plant to Greeley. A new 20 million gallon per day treatment facility is nearing completion at the Bellvue Water Treatment Plant to replace 1950s-era treatment capacity. Federal and State permitting activities have been underway for almost 15 years on two reservoirs. The first is the expansion of the existing Milton Seaman Reservoir. The second is participation in the Windy Gap Firming Project for the construction of a new 90,000 acre-foot reservoir at Chimney Hollow on the east side of the Rocky Mountains west of Loveland. Significant water acquisitions have also been made, including the purchase of an interest in the Laramie-Poudre Tunnel Company.

Today, Greeley Water receives its water supplies from four river basins—the Colorado, the Big Thompson, the Poudre and the Laramie. These watersheds feed two water treatment plants with a capacity to treat 70 million gallons of water per day. This treated water is distributed through 155 miles of transmission lines and 476 miles of distribution mains. The Greeley water system began in April 1870 with the construction of the Number 3 Canal. Today's system is a testimony to the ingenuity, persistence, and foresight of past Greeley water leaders. They not only provided for Greeley's water future, but they also had a major influence on the history of water in Colorado, the West and the Nation.

GREELEY WATER FACES a challenging future, as it has in the past, with an increasing urban population, a finite water supply, and an important agricultural economy to maintain. In addition to these three features, there is a practical limit on how much of the community's economic wealth can be used for water and sewer infrastructure. With a finite water supply, Greeley residents must determine how to balance the competing needs of irrigated agriculture with increasing population growth and urban development. How will the agricultural economy remain viable? How much can the urban demand be reduced by conservation and other methods? How will economic resources be obtained and used for long-term infrastructure investment? What might a sustainable water future look like? What are some of the possibilities?

Greeley's water future may well include the following:

- Enhanced water conservation
- Increased urban densities
- Xeric (lower water use) landscaping
- Additional reservoir storage
- Adaptation to climate change, and preparedness for cyclical wet and drought periods
- Creative agricultural water transfer alternatives

These possibilities include only some of the items that may be part of Greeley's sustainable water future. Looking back, and learning from the past, are an important part of knowing how to proceed into the future. The original Union Colonists who arrived in the spring of 1870 were up to the challenge and carried a visionary commitment to the future. They combined hard work, ingenuity, perseverance, and cooperation with a recognition that a vibrant community must always plan for and invest in its future. On March 29, 1941, an advertisement placed in the

Greeley Tribune by a group of prominent businessmen said it well. They advised: **"Look ahead and plan for others as others have planned for you."**

At the confluence of this 150th Anniversary year of Greeley Water, we have an obligation to do the same.

Figure 12.1 Looking to the future, in 1908, from an overlook above Greeley's Bellvue Waterworks and the Cache la Poudre River. City of Greeley Museums, Permanent Collection, AI-2490.

Endnotes

INTRODUCTION

1. See U.S. Department of Education, "Programs," https://www2.ed.gov/programs/americanhistory/2005awards.html.

CHAPTER ONE

1. Benson, Maxine (Ed.), *From Pittsburgh To the Rocky Mountains, Major Stephen Long's Expedition, 1819-1820* (Golden, CO: Fulcrum, Inc., 1988), xiv; Goetzmann, William H., *Army Exploration In The American West, 1803-1863* (Austin, TX: Texas State Historical Association, 1991), 43.

2. Crifasi, Robert R., *A Land Made from Water: Appropriation and the Evolution of Colorado's Landscape, Ditches, and Water Institutions* (Boulder, CO: University Press of Colorado, 2015), 9-12.

3. Boyd, David, *A History: Greeley and the Union Colony of Colorado* (Greeley, CO: Greeley Tribune Press, 1890), 29-32; Willard, James Field, *The Union Colony at Greeley, Colorado, 1869-1871* (Boulder, CO: University of Colorado, 1918), 231.

4. Evans, Howard Ensign and Mary Alice Evans, *Cache la Poudre: The Natural History of the Rocky Mountain River* (Boulder, CO: University Press of Colorado, 1991), 141.

5. Burris, Lucy, *People of the Poudre: An Ethnohistory of the Cache la Poudre River National Heritage Area, AD 1500-1880* (Fort Collins, CO: U.S. National Park Service, 2006), 21-28; West, Elliott, *The Contested Plains: Indians, Goldseekers, and the Rush to Colorado* (Lawrence, KS: University Press of Kansas, 1998), 18-19.

6. West, *The Contested Plains,* 22-23.

7. Louisiana Purchase Treaty, U.S./France, April 30, 1803, 8 Stat. 200; Ambrose, Stephen E., *Undaunted Courage, Meriwether Lewis, Thomas Jefferson, and the Opening of the American West* (New York, NY: Simon & Schuster, 1996).

8. Orsi, Jared, *Citizen Explorer, The Life of Zebulon Pike* (Oxford, U.K.: Oxford University Press, 2014).

9. Evans, Harold Ensign, *The Natural History of the Long Expedition to the Rocky Mountains, 1819-1820* (New York, NY: Oxford University Press, 1997), 22-24. Other members of the Long Expedition of note included Thomas Biddle, Jr., a relative of Nicholas Biddle, Director of the Second U.S. Bank (and the target of President Andrew Jackson's ire that led to the notorious "Bank War" of 1832); and Edwin James, botanist and geologist. James would climb the mountain he named "Long's Peak," offering the first scientific description of its terrain along the northern Front Range. Titian Ramsay Peale was the son of Charles

Willson Peale, a prominent Revolutionary War painter and founder of one of America's first natural history museums in Philadelphia.

10. Watrous, Ansel, *History of Larimer County, Colorado* (Fort Collins, CO: Courier Printing and Publishing Company, 1911), 23.

11. Burris, *People of the Poudre, 38*; Pelzer, Louis, *Henry Dodge* (Iowa City, IA: State Historical Society of Iowa, 1911), 121-122. Dodge grew up on a farm in Kentucky, served in the War of 1812, and in 1836 would become the first governor of Wisconsin.

12. Frémont, John Charles, *Memoirs of My Life* (Lanham, MD: First Cooper Square Press, 2001); Rolle, Andrew, *John Charles Frémont, Character as Destiny* (Norman, OK: University of Oklahoma Press, 1991). Jesse Hart Benton, Frémont's wife, greatly contributed to the highly readable literary quality of this first-person account.

13. Frémont, *Memoirs of My Life,* 180.

14. Murphy, Lawrence R., *Lucien Bonaparte Maxwell, Napoleon of the Southwest* (Norman, OK: University of Oklahoma Press, 1983).

15. Schell, Stephen C., *Following John C. Frémont's Trail through Northern Colorado, 1843* (Fort Collins, CO: C Schell Press LLC, 2010), 12-14; *Watrous, History of Larimer County,* 23; Norris, Jane E. and Lee G., *Written in Water: The Life of Benjamin Harrison Eaton* (Athens, OH: Swallow Press/Ohio University Press, 1990), 21-33.

16. Karnes, Thomas L., *William Gilpin, Western Nationalist* (Austin, TX: University of Texas Press, 1970). William Gilpin, who imagined a great center of civilization encompassing the area between the Mississippi River and the Rocky Mountains, would become Colorado's first territorial governor in 1861.

17. De Voto, Bernard, *The Year of Decision, 1846* (Boston, MA: Little, Brown, and Company, 1943).

18. Treaty of Guadalupe Hidalgo, U.S./Mexico, February 2, 1948, 9 Stat. 922; Del Castillo, Richard Griswold, *The Treaty of Guadalupe Hidalgo, A Legacy of Conflict* (Norman, OK: University of Oklahoma Press, 1990); Gomez, Laura E., *Manifest Destinies, The Making of the Mexican American Race* (New York, NY: New York University Press, 2007); Abbott, Carl, Leonard, Stephen J., and Noel, Thomas J., *Colorado, A History of the Centennial State,* 5th Edition (Boulder, CO: University Press of Colorado, 2013), 24, 462.

19. Mall, Loren L., *Public Land and Mining Law, Text and Cases,* 3rd Edition (Seattle, WA: Butterworth Legal Publishers, Inc., 1981), 4-6; See also *The Journals of Francis Parkman,* Volume II, Edited by Mason Wade (New York and London: Harper & Brothers Publishers), 471-472, 507.

20. Kansas-Nebraska Act, Chp. 59, 10 Stat. 277, 283-84 (1854).

21. Tom Cech correspondence with Dr. Robert Ward, June 13, 2019.

22. A very good discussion of the impact of the Colorado Gold Rush on the environment and Native societies can be found in Elliott West's *The Contested Plains,* 97-172.

23. Greeley, Horace, *An Overland Journey from New York to San Francisco in the Summer of 1859* (New York, NY: C.M. Saxton, Barker and Company, 1860), 98.

24. Ibid., 100.

25. Ibid., 100-102.

26. *Irwin v. Phillips,* 5 Cal. 140 (1855); *Tartar v. Spring Creek Water and Mining Company,* 5 Cal. 395 (1855); *Conger v. Weaver,* 6 Cal. 548 (1856); *Weaver v. Eureka Lake Company,* 15 Cal. 271 (1860); *Rupley v. Welch,* 23 Cal. 452 (1863). Kanazawa, Mark, *Golden Rules, The Origins of California Water Law in the Gold Rush* (Chicago, IL: University of Chicago Press, 2015).

27. Littleworth, Arthur L. and Garner, Eric L., *California Water* (Point Arena, CA: Solano Press Books, 1995), 29-30.

28. On file with the Colorado Supreme Court Law Library, Denver, Colorado.

29. Ibid.

30. Act of Feb. 28, 1861, Chp. 59, 12 Stat 172; Colorado Statehood Enabling Act, Chp. 139, 18 Stat. 474.

31. Romero, Tom L., II and Schulten, Susan, *Reconstituting the Center of the United States: The Creation of Colorado Territory in 1861* (Omaha, NE: Western History Association Newsletter, University of Nebraska at Omaha, Fall 2011).

32. Homestead Act of May 20, 1862, Chp. 75, 12 Stat. 392; Pacific Railroad Act of 1862, Chp. 120, 12 Stat. 489; Land Grant College Act of July 2, 1862, 12 Stat. 503 (Morrill Act).

33. Smith, Duane A., *The Birth of Colorado, A Civil War Perspective* (Norman, OK: University of Oklahoma Press, 1989), 32, 52, 235.

34. Mining Act of July 26, 1866, Chp. 262, 14 Stat. 251, 253.

35. Act of October 11, 1861, 1861 Colo. Sess. Laws, 35.

36. Act of November 5, 1861, 1861 Colo. Sess. Laws 67-69, Sec. 2.

37. Act of March 11, 1864, 1864 Colo. Sess. Laws 49, 58, Sec. 32.

38. Goetzmann, William H., *Exploration and Empire: The Explorer and the Scientist in the Winning of the American West* (New York, NY: Alfred A. Knopf, 1966), 390-392.

39. Fong, Kristin, "Worthington Whittredge: An Artist's Draw to Colorado," July 17, 2015, Denver Public Library, Denver, Colorado, https://history.denverlibrary.org/news/worthington-whittredge-artists-draw-colorado, accessed June 2019. General Pope had been Commander of the Department of the Missouri during the war.

40. Whittredge, Worthington, Edited by John I.H. Baur, *Autobiography of Worthington Whittredge, 1820 - 1910* (Brooklyn, NY: Brooklyn Institute of Arts and Sciences, 1942), 45.

41. Fong, Kristin, "Worthington Whittredge: An Artist's Draw to Colorado," *Genealogy News,* July 17, 2015.

42. Bauer, John I.H., Editor, *Autobiography of Worthington Whittredge* (New York, NY: Arno

Press, 1969), 64; Janson, Anthony F., *The Western Landscape of Worthington Whittredge,* 125. The artists Sanford Gifford and John Kensett had collaborated with Whittredge since the 1850s, when as young men they spent a year in Italy with Albert Bierstadt.

43. Janson, 127-129; Bauer, 64-65.

44. Trenton, Patricia and Hassrick, Peter H., *The Rocky Mountains: A Vision for Artists in the Nineteenth Century* (Norman, OK: University of Oklahoma Press, 1983), 213-214.

45. Ibid., 214.

CHAPTER TWO

1. Meeker, Nathan C., "A Western Colony," *New York Tribune,* December 4, 1869.

2. Ibid.

3. Shaw, Jhelene R., *Yours for Colorado: Applicants to the 1870 Union Colony at Greeley,* Undergraduate Honors Thesis (Boulder, CO: University of Colorado-Boulder, Spring 2016), https://scholar.colorado.edu/cgi/viewcontent.cgi?article=2413&context=honr_theses, accessed June 2019.

4. Boyd, David, *A History: Greeley and the Union Colony of Colorado* (Greeley, CO: Greeley Tribune Press, 1890), 1.

5. Boyd, *A History: Greeley and the Union Colony of Colorado,* 39-42.

6. Kelsey, Jr., Harry E., *Frontier Capitalist, The Life of John Evans* (Denver, CO: State Historical Society of Colorado) and (Boulder, CO: Pruett Publishing Company, 1969), 173-176. Boyd explains that the Locating Committee succeeded in purchasing up to 69,324 acres of railroad and government land on the Cache la Poudre River, although with some difficulty in buying up the claims of squatters. Boyd, *A History: Greeley and the Union Colony of Colorado,* 43-44.

7. Correspondence with Peggy Ford Waldo, City of Greeley Museums, Greeley, Colorado, June 14, 2019.

8. "Greeley, Colorado," UpstateColorado Economic Development, https://upstatecolorado.org/upstate-communities/greeley/, accessed September 2019.

9. Pabor, William E., editor, *First Annual Report of the Union Colony of Colorado, Including a History of the Town of Greeley* (New York: George W. Southwick, 1871), 12, 15.

10. Deed of the Union Colony of Colorado to the Town of Greeley, Colorado, February 23, 1875, Weld County Records Book 12-206, 1-14 to 1-15.

11. Boyd, David, "Irrigation Near Greeley, Colorado," U.S. Geological Survey, Frederick Newell, Hydrographer, Washington, D.C., 1897, published in the Department of the Interior, *Water-Supply and Irrigation Papers of the United States Geological Survey,* No. 9 (Washington, D.C.: U.S. Government Printing Office, 1897), 27-29.

12. See as well, Deed of the Union Colony of Colorado to the Greeley Irrigation Company, August 3, 1882, Weld County Record Book 14, Greeley, Colorado, 446.

13. Clark, J. Max, *Colonial Days* (Denver, CO: Smith-Brooks Company Publishers, 1902), 40, 68-74. For a discussion of the increasing importance of lawns and gardens to the rapidly urbanizing eastern United States, see Jackson, Kenneth, *The Crabgrass Frontier: The Suburbanization of the United States* (New York, NY: Oxford University Press, 1985), 57, 61, 72.

14. Correspondence with Peggy Ford Waldo, City of Greeley Museums, June 14, 2019.

15. Boyd, *A History: Greeley and the Union Colony of Colorado,* 76-77.

16. Ibid.

17. Pabor, William E., editor, *First annual report of the Union Colony of Colorado, including a history of the town of Greeley* (New York, NY: George W. Southwick, 1871), 12.

18. Ibid., 14-15.

19. Pabor, William Edgar, *Colorado as an Agricultural State, Its Farms, Fields, and Garden Lands* (New York, NY: Orange Judd Company, 1883).

20. "HORACE GREELEY—His Reception at Greeley," *Daily Rocky Mountain News,* Denver, Colorado, October 12, 1870, 4.

21. "From Our Traveling Correspondent," *Denver Daily Colorado Tribune,* October 15, 1870, cited in Willard, James Field, *The Union Colony at Greeley, 1869-1871* (Boulder, CO: University of Colorado, 1918), 234-237.

22. Bird, Isabella, *A Lady's Life in the Rocky Mountains,* with an introduction by Daniel J. Boorstin (Norman, OK: University of Oklahoma Press, 1960), 29-33.

23. Greenwood, Grace, *New Life in New Lands: Notes of Travel* (New York, NY: J.B. Ford and Company, 1873), 61.

24. Correspondence with Peggy Ford Waldo, City of Greeley Museums, August 27, 2019.

25. "Notes of Travel," *New York Times,* August 19, 1871; "Sara Jane Lippincott," From Wikipedia, https://en.wikipedia.org/wiki/Sara_Jane_Lippincott, accessed August 2019.

26. Hallett became Chief Justice of Colorado's Territorial Supreme Court on April 10, 1866. See Pinkney, James Faulkner, *Moses Hall,* 2 Rocky Mtn. L. Rev. 173, 175 (1930). He became a federal judge for the District of Colorado in 1877, the year following Colorado's admission to the Union. Riner, William A., Hon. Moses Hallett, 4 Wyoming. L. J. 86, 89 (1949).

27. *Yunker v. Nichols,* 1 Colo. 551 (1872).

28. Wells was one of the ten signatories to the influential Address *To The People Of Colorado* recommending that they adopt the Colorado Constitution which the Constitution Convention drafted. See *The Constitution of the State of Colorado, Adopted In Convention,* March 14, 1876; *see also The Address of the Convention to the People of Colorado, Election, Saturday, July 1, 1876* (Denver, CO: Tribune Book and Job Printing House, 1876), 65. Commencing with the April term of court in 1877, upon election by the people,

Wells became one of the first three justices of the newly-constituted Colorado Supreme Court. Frantz, Albert T., *Colorado Appellate Courts—The First Hundred Years,* 36 Dicta 103, 108 (1959).

29. Dunbar, Robert G., "Water Conflicts and Controls in Colorado," *Agricultural History,* Vol. 22, No. 3, July 1948, 181-182; Boyd, *Greeley and the Union Colony of Colorado,* 119-120; "The Water Question," *Fort Collins Standard,* July 22, 1874.

30. "The Water Question," *Fort Collins Standard;* Boyd, *Greeley and the Union Colony of Colorado,* 120; Dunbar, "Water Conflicts," 182.

31. Communication with Dr. Robert Ward, former Director of the Colorado Water Resources Research Institute, Colorado State University, Fort Collins, Colorado, June 13, 2019.

32. "The Water Question," *Fort Collins Standard.*

33. Boyd, *A History: Greeley and The Union Colony of Colorado,* 120.

34. Ibid.

35. "Vested Rights," *Fort Collins Standard,* July 22, 1874; "What Greeley Claims," *Fort Collins Standard,* July 29, 1874.

36. Boyd, *A History: Greeley and the Union Colony of Colorado,* 120.

37. Powell, John Wesley, *Report on the Lands of the Arid Regions of the United States* (Washington, D.C.: U.S. Government Printing Office, 1879), 11, 43-44.

38. Oesterle, Dale A. and Collins, Richard B., *The Colorado State Constitution, A Reference Guide* (Westport, CT: Greenwood Press, 2002), 1, 336-346.

39. Hafen, L.R., "Steps to Statehood in Colorado," Vol. III, *Colorado Magazine,* No. 3 (Denver, CO: State Historical and Natural History Society of Colorado, August 1926), 97-110.

40. Hersey, Henry J., "The Colorado Constitution," Vol. III, *Colorado Magazine,* No. 3 (Denver, CO: State Historical and Natural History Society of Colorado, August 1926), 70.

41. Foster, Edward D., "The Miracle of a Half-Century," Vol. III, *Colorado Magazine,* No. 3 (Denver, CO: State Historical and Natural History Society of Colorado, August 1926), 89.

42. "Proceedings of the Constitutional Convention," Denver, Colorado, 1875-1876, 15-17, 37.

43. Ibid., 44.

44. Ibid., 344.

45. Ibid., 392. The term "natural stream" includes seepage, return flows from prior uses, and groundwater that is tributary to a surface stream. *Empire Lodge Homeowners' Association v. Moyer,* 39 P.3d 1139, 1147 (Colo. 2001).

46. Ibid., 504.

47. "An Act To Prevent the Waste of Water During the Irrigating Season," Colorado Territorial Laws, 1876, 78-79.

48. See 1877 Colorado General Laws, 1386, Sec. 2, 37-84-108, C.R.S. (2019).

49. Colorado Constitutional Convention, 594-595.

50. Ibid., 615-616.

51. Ibid., 700-701.

52. "Section 5. The water of every natural stream, not heretofore appropriated, within the State of Colorado, is hereby declared to be the property of the public, and the same is dedicated to the use of the people of the State, subject to appropriation as hereinafter provided."

53. Schorr, David, *The Colorado Doctrine, Water Rights, Corporations, And Distributive Justice On The American Frontier* (New Haven, CT: Yale University Press, 2012).

54. Ibid., 30, 41-42.

55. Ibid., 43-44, 62.

56. Ibid., 44-45.

57. Ibid., 50, 52.

58. Ibid., 54.

59. See, generally, Hobbs, Jr., Gregory J., *"Colorado's 1969 Adjudication and Administration Act: Settling In"* (Denver, CO: University of Denver Water Law Review, Vol. 3, Issue 1, 1999), 1-19.

60. Boyd, *A History: Greeley and the Union Colony of Colorado,* 121.

61. Ibid., 122-123.

62. Act of February 19, 1879, 1879 Colo. Sess. Laws 94-108; Act of February 23, 1881, 1881 Colo. Sess. Laws 141-161; Act of March 5, 1881, 1881 Colo. Sess. Laws 119-122; *Union Colony of Colorado v. Elliott,* 5 Colo. 371, 380-381, (1880).

63. Boyd, 127.

CHAPTER THREE

1. Boyd, David, *A History: Greeley and the Union Colony of Colorado* (Greeley, CO: Greeley Tribune Press, 1890), 29-32; Willard, James Field, *The Union Colony at Greeley, Colorado, 1869-1871* (Boulder, CO: University of Colorado, 1918), 231.

2. First Adjudication Proceedings In Water District No. 3, Colorado, Book III, 597-672; Book VIII, 7-8.

3. *Decree in the Matter of Priorities of Water Rights in Water District No. 3,* Entered by the Honorable Victor A. Elliott, Judge of the Second Judicial District, Colorado, April 11, 1882, 152-153. See Hemphill, Robert G., *Irrigation In Northern Colorado,* Bulletin No. 1026, U.S. Department of Agriculture (Washington, D.C.: U.S. Government Printing Office, 1922), 15.

4. Hobbs, Justice Gregory J., Jr., *The Role of Climate on Water Institutions in the Western Americas* (Westminster, CO: Rocky Mountain Mineral Law Foundation, 2005), Vol. 42, No. 2, 273, 289.

5. *Coffin v. Left Hand Ditch Company,* 6 Colo. 443, 447 (1882).

6. *Strickler v. Colorado Springs,* 26 P. 313 (Colo. 1891).

7. Decree No. 2100, County of Larimer, Colorado, Water District No. 3, Water Division No. 1, Entered September 30, 1906, priority date August 1, 1862 for 7.5 cfs.

8. Decree No. 5326, County of Larimer, Colorado, Water District No. 3, Water Division No. 1, Entered June 19, 1926, priority date March 15, 1862 for 5 cfs.

9. Nettleton, E.S., *The Reservoir System of the Cache La Poudre Valley,* Bulletin No. 92, U.S. Department of Agriculture, Office of Experiment Stations (Washington, D.C.: U.S. Government Printing Office, 1901).

10. Ibid., 37.

11. Limerick, Patricia Nelson, *A Ditch in Time: The City, the West, and Water* (Golden, CO: Fulcrum Publishing, 2012), 32-33; Sundberg, Wayne C., *Fort Collins' First Water Works* (Fort Collins, CO: Poudre Landmarks Foundation, Inc., 2004), 13-16.

12. Melosi, Martin V., *The Sanitary City: Environmental Services in Urban America from Colonial Times to the Present* (Pittsburgh, PA: University of Pittsburgh Press, 2008).

13. Boyd, *Greeley and the Union Colony of Colorado,* 207.

14. Ibid., 209-212.

15. Ibid., 143, 211-213. The Oasis Hotel and its artesian well had an interesting history. In 1871, a building in Cheyenne, Wyoming, was purchased and moved to Greeley where it was converted into a hotel (the Greeley House) which stood on the northeast corner of the intersection of 8th Avenue and 7th Street in downtown Greeley. The fire left Greeley without a suitable hotel. Greeleyites had shown their "cooperative" spirit in the 1870s by digging community irrigation ditches, raising money for instruments needed for the Greeley Silver Coronet Band (1870), and for construction of Greeley's first jail (1874). This spirit prevailed in 1880, when a group of Greeley men formed the Greeley Hotel Company with a capital stock of $15,000 (shares $25 each). The goal was to build a new three-story brick hotel, 65' x 108' ASAP on the site of the former Greeley House. Three contractors bid on the new hotel project: W.G. Bentley, $19,380, six months to complete; S. Vaughn of Denver, $19,750, three months to complete; and Woodbury and Wyman, $22,565, three months to complete. Unfortunately, Bentley, the low bidder, fell ill with typhoid fever and the work went to Woodbury and Wyman, who started construction in October 1880. The 1880 fire transformed Greeley into a solid "brick-and-mortar" town resplendent with progress and amenities. In addition, the "Philadelphia Plan" of numbering streets was adopted by ordinance in 1884. Linn Grove Cemetery received a windmill to pump groundwater; Greeley became a "city of the second class" in 1886 with a population

of 2,177, and its municipal government was reorganized with the creation of wards, a town board and a mayor. The Greeley Board of Trade was organized to promote settlement and manufacturing in the city, and this effort produced the Kuner Pickle Works (1888) and the Greeley Water Works (1889).

16. Ibid., 218-220.

17. "Yesterday in Greeley," *Greeley Sunday Journal*, August 31, 1958; "Mr. Seaman's Story on Greeley's Water Works," *Greeley Tribune*, no date; City of Greeley Water and Sewer Department, Greeley, Colorado.

18. "Trouble with Water Consumers," *Greeley Tribune*, May 25, 1893.

19. Ibid.

20. "Greeley's Hydrant Water," *Greeley Tribune*, August 18, 1898.

21. Nash, Gerald D., *The American West in the Twentieth Century: A Short History of an Urban Oasis*, 3rd Edition (Albuquerque, NM: University of New Mexico Press, 1985), 11-13.

22. Clark, Max J., *Colonial Days* (Denver, CO: The Smith-Brooks Company Publishers, 1902).

23. Ibid., 79.

24. Ibid., 102.

25. Ibid., 103. Clark illustrated the intangibles of enterprise, talent and intellect of the Progressive Era described by Gerald Nash.

26. Mead, Elwood, *Report of Experiments in Irrigation and Meteorology*, Bulletin No. 1, State Agricultural College of Colorado (Fort Collins, CO: Larimer Bee Publishing House, 1897). See also, Mead, Elwood and Johnson, C.T., *The Use of Water in Irrigation, Report of Investigations Made in 1899*, U.S. Department of Agriculture (Washington, D.C.: U.S. Government Printing Office, 1900).

27. Kluger, James R., *Turning on Water With A Shovel, The Career of Elwood Mead* (Albuquerque, NM: University of New Mexico Press, 1922), 11-13.

28. Boyd, David, *Irrigation Near Greeley, Colorado, Water Supply and Irrigation Papers of the United States Geological Survey*, No. 9, U.S. Department of Interior (Washington, D.C.: U.S. Government Printing Office, 1897), 29-30.

29. Nettleton, E.S., *The Reservoir System of the Cache La Poudre Valley*, U.S. Department of Agriculture (Washington, D.C.: U.S. Government Printing Office, 1901).

30. Ibid., 8.

31. Ely, Richard T., "A Study of a 'Decreed' Town," *Harper's Magazine* (New York, NY: Harper & Brothers, 1903), 390.

32. Ibid., 396.

33. Ibid., 397.

34. Ibid., 396-398.

35. Communication with Peggy Ford Waldo, City of Greeley Museums, Greeley, Colorado, August 13, 2019.

36. Nathan Meeker's short tenure as Indian Agent on the White River lands of the Utes in 1879 is among the most tragic of Colorado historical events. The causes for expelling four bands of the Utes from their native grounds in Colorado to reservations in Utah were complex, disturbing, and still highly controversial. See Silbernagel, Robert, *Troubled Trails, The Meeker Affair and the Expulsion of Utes From Colorado* (Salt Lake City, UT: University of Utah Press, 2011).

CHAPTER FOUR

1. Daniel Tyler interview with W.D. Farr, Greeley, Colorado, September 22, 2003, Daniel Tyler Papers, Colorado State University Water Resources Archive, Fort Collins, Colorado. In 1900, Colorado had a total of 540,000 residents.

2. Minutes of the Greeley City Council Meeting, Greeley, Colorado, May 1, August 21, September 19, 1900; March 19, 1901.

3. *Fort Collins Weekly Courier,* Fort Collins, Colorado, May 9, 1901.

4. May, William John, Jr., *The Great Western Sugarlands: The History of the Great Western Sugar Company and the Economic Development of the Great Plains* (New York, NY: Garland Publishing, Inc., 1989), 27-29; and Gale Encyclopedia of U.S. Economic History, "Dingley Tariff," 2000, https://www.encyclopedia.com/history/encyclopedias-almanacs-transcripts-and-maps/dingley-tariff, accessed June 2019.

5. "Our Building Boom: Over One Hundred Dwellings Erected in Greeley Since January," *Greeley Tribune,* November 14, 1901.

6. May, *The Great Western Sugarlands,* 29-32.

7. Waldo, Peggy Ford with the Greeley Museum, *Images of America—Greeley* (Charleston, SC: Arcadia Publishing, 2016), 75.

8. Correspondence with Peggy Ford Waldo, City of Greeley Museums, August 5, 2019.

9. Ibid.

10. Ibid., "Dowden 4 Horse Potato Digger," B & D Lillies, https://www.bdlilies.com/a10.html, accessed January 7, 2020.

11. Tyler, Daniel, *W.D. Farr: Cowboy in the Boardroom* (Norman, OK: University of Oklahoma Press, 2011), 21.

12. "Must Have Water," *Greeley Tribune,* September 25, 1902.

13. Ibid.

14. Ibid.

15. Ibid.

16. Tyler, *W.D. Farr: Cowboy in the Boardroom*, 240.

17. Ibid.

18. Greeley City Council Meeting Minutes, May 19, June 16, October 6, 1903; April 19, May 17, June 21, July 26, 1904.

19. *Fort Collins Weekly Courier,* August 24, 1904; Greeley City Council Meeting Minutes, July 26, August 16, October 4, November 15, December 6, 1904; February 7, 1905.

20. "The Water Supply from Thompson Shaping," *Greeley Tribune,* April 27, 1905.

21. Ibid. The Boyd Lake study can be found in Hiram M. Chittenden, *Preliminary Examination of Reservoir Sites in Wyoming and Colorado . . . Letter from the Secretary of War, Transmitting a Letter from the Chief of Engineers, Together with a Report from Captain Chittenden of a Preliminary Examination Made by Him of Certain Reservoir Sites in the States of Wyoming and Colorado* (Washington, D.C.: U.S. Government Printing Office, 1898).

22. Greeley City Council Meeting Minutes, February 7, 1905; "More Water: Mayor Watson Gives Some Light on the Question," *Greeley Tribune,* February 23, 1905.

23. "More Water," *Greeley Tribune;* Greeley City Council Meeting Minutes, February 28, 1905.

24. "Nature Spares," *Fort Collins Weekly Courier,* June 7, 1905.

25. "Found Good Water," *Greeley Tribune,* July 20, 1905.

26. Greeley City Council Meeting Minutes, November 28, December 29, 1905; January 2, 1906; *Fort Collins Weekly Courier,* January 3, 17, 1906.

27. "Water System Contract Let," *Greeley Tribune,* February 22, 1906.

28. Ibid.

29. Greeley City Council Meeting Minutes, April 10, May 8, July 3, 1906; February 12, March 5, 1907.

30. "Greeley Can Lay Pipe Line in Highway," *Fort Collins Weekly Courier,* August 29, 1906.

31. "Pipe Making: Interesting Manufacturing Plant in Greeley," *Greeley Tribune,* July 26, 1906; "What is Done: Progress Made on New City Water System," *Greeley Tribune,* July 26, 1906.

32. "Water Will Be Metered," *Greeley Tribune,* July 29, 1907.

33. "Soft Water is Here: Was Turned into City Mains Last Saturday," *Greeley Tribune,* September 12, 1907; "Saw the Works for Themselves: Greeley People Go to the New Water Plant by the Train Load," *Greeley Tribune,* September 27, 1907.

34. Act of April 2, 1891, 385.

35. *Strickler v. City of Colorado Springs,* 26 P. 313,316 (Colo. 1891).

36. Act of April 6, 1899, Chp. 153, Sec. 2, 420.

37. Ibid., Chp. 105, Sec. 1, 235.

38. Act of April 11, 1903, Ch. 130, Sec. 1, 297. *See Platte Water Co. v. Northern Colorado Irrigation Co.,* 21 P. 711, 712 (Colo. 1889).

39. Ibid., Sec. 2, 298.

40. Ibid., Secs. 2 & 3, 297-298.

41. Greeley City Council Meeting Minutes, December 10, 1907.

42. Anderson, George, "A Gravity Water Supply System at Greeley, Colo.," *The Engineering Record,* Volume 56, No. 24, New York, NY, December 1907, 642.

43. May 17, 1905; land added 33 Stat. 3029. See McCarthy, G. Michael, *Hour of Trial, The Conservation Conflict in Colorado and the West, 1891-1907* (Norman, OK: University of Oklahoma Press, 1977), 139.

44. Executive Order 5826, March 28, 1932.

45. *Fort Collins Courier,* May 29, 1908; "Country Club is Organized and Directors Chosen," *Fort Collins Courier,* February 17, 1909.

46. "Timnath," *Fort Collins Courier,* November 4, 1908; Greeley City Council Meeting Minutes, September 8, 1908; February 2, June 29, November 9, November 24, 1909.

47. "Women Dig Trench for Water Main," *Greeley Tribune,* December 8, 1910.

48. Ibid.

Chapter Five

1. Speech of Charles F. Tew, "The Greeley District: The Garden Spot of the Golden West," Greeley, Colorado, April 4, 1910, 5; Greeley District 1910 File, Box 63, Papers of Delph E. Carpenter, Colorado State University Water Resources Archive, Fort Collins, Colorado.

2. "Laramie-Poudre Irrigation Company, 1902-1937," Public Lands History Center, Colorado State University, Fort Collins, Colorado, https://publiclands.colostate.edu/digital_projects/dp/poudre-river/moving-storing/let-the-water-flow-ditch-companys/laramie-poudre-irrigation-company/, accessed July 2019.

3. Senate Resolution No. 16, *Colorado Senate Journal*, Denver, Colorado, April 4, 1909, 1092-1093.

4. "Water From the Western Slope," *Denver Republican,* Denver, Colorado, August 25, 1911, Box 78, Folder 1, Water, Miscellaneous 1906-1979 File, Delph Carpenter Files, Colorado State University Water Resources Archive, Fort Collins, Colorado.

5. *Wyoming v. Colorado*, October Term 1916, No. 7, Original, Vol. I, Transcript of Record at 2-11. See the court's decision, *Wyoming v. Colorado*, 259 U. S. 419 (1922).

6. "Laramie-Poudre Irrigation Company: 1902-1937," Public Lands History Center, A Department of History Center, Colorado State University, Fort Collins, Colorado, https://publiclands.colostate.edu/digital_projects/dp/poudre-river/moving-storing/let-the-water-flow-ditch-companys/laramie-poudre-irrigation-company/, accessed June 2019.

7. Greeley City Council Meeting Minutes, April 30, May 21, July 9, 1912; "Greeley Water Main Broken—Using Ditch Water," *Fort Collins Weekly Courier,* Fort Collins, Colorado, June 5, 1912.

8. "$30,000,000 Sugar Beet Crop in Colorado This Year; Industry Has Made Farmers Richest in the World," *Fort Collins Weekly Courier,* August 15, 1913.

9. Ibid.

10. "Weld County—History of Colorado," edited by Wilbur Fisk Stone (Chicago, IL: S.J. Clarke Publishing Company, 1918), Vol. II; http://files.usgwarchives.net/co/weld/bios/seamanm.txt, accessed June 2019.

11. "Milton Seaman, Returned From Extended Vacation in Eastern Cities, Lauds Our Water System," *Greeley Tribune,* February 3, 1916.

12. "Superintendent Art Bolenbaugh to Retire from Water Department on June 2," *Greeley Tribune*, December 8, 1958.

13. Nash, Gerald D., *The American West in the Twentieth Century* (Albuquerque, NM: University of New Mexico Press, 1977), 64-68; Pisani, Donald J., *Water and American Government* (Berkeley, CA: University of California Press, 2002), 123-124; and Malone, Michael P. and Etulain, Richard W., *The American West* (Lincoln, NE: University of Nebraska Press, 1989), 18-19. Etulain was a former Director of the Center for the American West at the University of New Mexico, while Michael Malone was an award-winning historian and president of Montana State University.

14. "Master Water Storage Lake Is Suggested," *Greeley Tribune,* June 10, 1919.

15. "Water Shortage Problem Before City Aldermen," *Greeley Tribune,* July 30, 1919.

16. "Four Greeley Men File Maps of Poudre Channel Reservoir With Capacity of 46,000 Acre Feet," *Greeley Tribune,* August 29, 1919.

17. Tyler, Daniel, *Silver Fox of the Rockies* (Norman, OK: University of Oklahoma Press, 2003), 159. See also Tyler & Hinshaw, Editors, *Love in an Envelope, A Courtship in the American West* (Albuquerque, NM: University of New Mexico Press, 2008).

18. *Wyoming v. Colorado*, Vol. 1, Transcript of Record at 53. (On file with the Colorado Supreme Court Law Library, Denver, Colorado.)

19. Ibid., Vol. I, Transcript of Record at 28.

20. Ibid., Vol. I, Transcript of Record at 33.

21. Tyler, Daniel, *Delphus Emory Carpenter and the Colorado River Compact of 1922,* 1 U. Denv. Water L. Rev. 228, 230 (1998).

22. Hinderlider, M.C. and Meeker, R.I., *Interstate Water Problems and Their Solution*, 1925. (On file with the Colorado Supreme Court Law Library, Denver, Colorado.)

23. Delph Carpenter, July 29, 1921, Address to the Colorado Bar Association, Volume 24, 24th Annual Meeting, July 29 and 30, 1921 at 44-101, 89.

24. Peters, Mike, *Greeley Tribune*, 3A, reprinted November 16, 1970, https://history. weldgov.com/county_150/entertainment_in_weld/movie_history, accessed June 2019; "Local Crew Shoots Greeley Area Movie," *Greeley Tribune*, July 23, 1913; and "The Velvet Light Trap," Issues 19-23, University of Wisconsin-Madison, Department of Communication Arts, and the University of Texas at Austin, Department of Radio-Television-Film, Project Muse, 1982.

25. Act of May 18, 1920; 41 Stat. 600 (known as the "Kincaid Act").

26. Carpenter, Address to the Colorado Bar Association, 1921, 89.

27. S.B. No. 421, Chp. 242 at 795-798, 1921 Colo. Sess. Laws.

28. S.B. No. 420, Chp. 243 at 799-802.

29. S.B. No. 419, Chp. 244 at 803-806.

30. S.B. No. 422, Chp. 245 at 807-810.

31. S.B. No. 418, Chp. 246 at 811-815.

32. U.S. House of Representatives, 67th Congress, 1st Session, June 4, 1921, Hearing on H.R. 6821, Appendix 210 at A-84.

33. Hobbs, Greg, Justice, "In Praise of Fair Colorado, The Practice of Poetry, History, and Judging," *Inside the Drama of the Colorado River Compact Negotiations: Negotiating the Apportionment,* 6th Meeting, January 30, 1922, 291-92 (Denver, CO: Bradford Publishing Company, 2004).

34. Ibid., 7th Meeting, January 30, 1922, 298-299.

35. 1922 Colorado River Compact, Article III (a); C.R.S. 37-61-101 (2018). The Boulder Canyon Project Act of 1928 provided for annual Lake Mead deliveries to the three lower basin states in these amounts: 4.4 million acre-feet to California, 2.8 million acre-feet to Arizona and 300,000 acre-feet to Nevada. *Arizona v. California,* 373 U.S. 546, 565 (1963).

36. Wilcox, E.V., "The Water Oracle of Greeley: The Colorado Community is a Shining Example of Neighborly and Businesslike Teamwork," *The Country Gentleman*, Philadelphia, PA, October 9, 1920; Box 78, Folder 1: Water, Miscellaneous File, Delph E. Carpenter Papers, Colorado State University Water Resources Archive, Fort Collins, Colorado.

37. Ibid.

38. Ibid.

39. Ibid.

40. Ibid.

41. Greeley City Council Meeting Minutes, Greeley, Colorado, July 25, 1929.

42. Ibid., April 6, 13, 1920. The "Delta Pipe Line Association" was a group of residents outside the city limits to the south and east of Greeley, near the Cache la Poudre River.

43. "City Claim to Purest Water Proven a Fact," *Greeley Tribune,* April 21, 1920.

44. Ibid.

45. "Water System Has Severest Test; Is 'Okeh,'" *Greeley Tribune,* July 5, 1921.

46. "City Considers Repair Policy for Water Line," *Greeley Tribune,* October 19, 1921; Letter of Mayor Charles Todd to the City Council of the City of Greeley, Greeley, Colorado, October 13, 1921, Greeley Water and Sewer Department Files.

47. Greeley City Council Meeting Minutes, Greeley, Colorado, April 11, 22, 1922.

48. Correspondence with Peggy Ford Waldo, City of Greeley Museums, Greeley, Colorado, July 2019.

49. "Biggest Flood Since 1904 Has Swollen Poudre," *Greeley Tribune,* June 11, 1923.

50. U.S. Geological Survey, "Floods in Colorado," Water Supply Paper 997 (Washington, D.C.: U.S. Government Printing Office, 1948), https://pubs.usgs.gov/wsp/0997/report.pdf, accessed June 2019.

51. "Men Make Trip to Waterworks," *Greeley Tribune,* June 19, 1923; "Hayden Urges Water Saving," *Greeley Tribune,* June 19, 1923; "Water 'Black as Ink' Comes Thru Pipe Line," *Greeley Tribune,* June 21, 1923.

52. "Sprinkling Ban Removed by Act of City Mayor," *Greeley Tribune,* June 22, 1923.

53. "Greeley Users Are Instructed to Boil Water," *Greeley Tribune,* June 25, 1923.

54. "Pipe Line Will Be Rebuilt by Close of Year," *Greeley Tribune,* May 14, 1924.

55. "Greeley Sewer System Lacks Safety Margin," *Greeley Tribune,* January 27, 1925.

56. Hansen, James E., "Charles A. Lory and the Challenges of Colorado's Semi-Arid Frontier," Colorado State University, Fort Collins, Colorado, August 1980, https://poudreheritage.org/wp-content/uploads/charles_a_lory_paper.pdf, accessed June 2019.

57. Todd, C.D. to the Mayor and City Council of the City of Greeley, Colorado, June 28, 1926, Greeley Water and Sewer Department Files; Greeley City Council Meeting Minutes, October 13, 1925; No. 430 Transfer Decree, Greeley Pipe Line (Old) to Greeley Pipe Line (New); Also Boyd & Freeman Ditch to Greeley Pipe Line, June 19, 1926, Colorado Division of Water Resources Files, Division No. 1, Office of the State Engineer, Greeley, Colorado.

58. Todd to the Mayor and City Council of Greeley. The Boyd and Freeman ditch right held the Number 6 ranking, placing it ahead of the Number 6 ½ priority of the Whedbee Ditch.

59. Greeley City Council Meeting Minutes, October 13, 1925; Todd to the Mayor and City Council of Greeley.

60. Ibid. For more information of Todd's work on Greeley's Bellvue water rights, see *Milton*

Seaman's Story On Greeley's Water Works, on file with the City of Greeley.

61. "Collins Lawyer Urges Northern Ditch Combine to Protect Their Rights From Scenery Conservers," *Greeley Tribune,* February 19, 1926.

62. Ibid.

63. "City's Water System Not for Sale, Altho Oklahomans Make Offer," *Greeley Tribune,* May 4, 1927.

64. "Poudre Will Be Surveyed for Storage Lakes," *Greeley Tribune,* April 9, 1927.

65. Ibid.

66. Huntley, R.L., Chief Engineer, Operating Department, Union Pacific System, Omaha, Nebraska, to Elwood Mead, Commissioner, Bureau of Reclamation, U.S. Department of the Interior, Washington, D.C., November 29, 1924; Mead to Huntley, December 8, 1924, Colorado Correspondence re: "Surveys and Investigations," Cache la Poudre Report, RG 115, DEN NARA.

67. "Use of Water Restricted as City's Supply Line Blows Up," *Greeley Tribune,* August 14, 1928.

68. "Water Supply Discussed at Exchange Club by LaFollette," *Greeley Tribune,* August 18, 1928.

69. "Council Opposed to Logging on Poudre," *Greeley Tribune,* February 7, 1929; "Kreutzer Tells How Poudre Lumbering Can Be Developed," *Greeley Tribune,* February 15, 1929.

70. Greeley City Council Meeting Minutes, Greeley, Colorado, February 14, 1928, June 18, 1929.

71. Carpenter, D.E., "Reservations to Cession of Park Urged by D.E. Carpenter," Letter to the *Greeley Tribune,* January 17, 1929.

72. "Reservations to Cession of Park Urged by D.E. Carpenter," *Greeley Tribune,* January 17, 1929, *Greeley Daily Tribune:* Reservations to . . . 1924, Delph E. Carpenter Papers, Box 135, Colorado State University Water Resources Archive, Fort Collins, Colorado.

CHAPTER SIX

1. U.S. Census, 1950, Table 6-8. Drought severely impaired crop production in the dryland areas of Weld County, but had little effect on the prolific rabbit population. It was a curse and a blessing. In December 1934, in the middle of the worst drought in memory, 800 hunters from Denver and northeastern Colorado traversed 36 sections of land west of Briggsdale. Approximately 10,000 jackrabbits were shipped free of charge on a Union Pacific freight car and given to Denver's poor. The charity of neighbors and municipal governments was tested during the 1930s.

2. Nash, Gerald D., *The American West in the Twentieth Century* (Albuquerque, NM: University of New Mexico Press, 1977), 136-144.

3. The first wave of sugar beet harvesters in Colorado were Russian Americans; increasingly, Mexican Americans and Japanese Americans also contributed greatly to the workforce despite low wages. The depression had a deep impact on all laborers; Mexican Americans were particularly hard hit when Governor Ed Johnson in 1935 ordered a halt to Latinos entering Colorado to work (soon rescinded in the face of the producer need for these workers). See Romero II, Tom I., *A War to Keep Alien Labor out of Colorado, The 'Mexican Menace' and the Historical Origins of Local and State Anti-Immigration Initiatives*, in Hessick, Carissa Byrne and Chin, Gabriel J. (Eds.) *Strange Neighbors, The Role of States in Immigration Policy* (New York and London: New York University Press, 2014), 63-96. For the role of Japanese Americans in agriculture and sugar beet production, see Wei, William, *Asians in Colorado, A History Of Persecution And Perseverance In The Centennial State* (Seattle and London: University of Washington Press, 2016), 151-177.

4. Deutsch, Sarah, *No Separate Refuge: Culture, Class, and Gender on an Anglo-Hispanic Frontier in the American Southwest, 1880-1940* (New York, NY: Oxford University Press, 1987), 162; Nash, *The American West in the Twentieth Century*, 138-142; Interview by Michael Welsh with W.D. Farr, Cache la Poudre Oral History Project, National Park Service, Greeley, Colorado, October 16, 2002; Thomas McKee, Nolan Doesken, and John Kliest, Colorado State University, "Historical dry and wet periods in Colorado," Colorado State University Water Resources Archive, Fort Collins, Colorado, no date.

5. "Weld to Try to Get Work for Farmers," *Greeley Tribune*, September 15, 1933. In 1933, the Weld County Commissioners lobbied for state funds to employ farmers in the drought-stricken areas of eastern Weld to help during the winter months with the reconstruction of Highway 14 from Buckingham to the Logan County line. In September, 40 teams were working on the road, and crews were rotated every two weeks to provide others with employment and wages. Some who received pay warrants from the county, for road work previously completed, planned on using the warrants to pay the delinquent taxes on their properties. Commissioner S.K. Clark noted that without state money to employ farmers to complete badly needed road work, direct payment of limited relief money would still be necessary to assist the residents of this district.

6. "Access Colorado Data," Colorado Climate Center, Colorado State University, Fort Collins, Colorado, https://climate.colostate.edu/data_access.html, accessed July 2019.

7. Greeley City Council Meeting Minutes, January 28, 1930.

8. "City Put on Water Ration as Safeguard," *Greeley Tribune*, February 3, 1930; "Miles of City Water Lines Said Frozen," *Greeley Tribune*, February 4, 1930.

9. "Water Waste Goes on Says Seaman," *Greeley Tribune*, February 25, 1930; Greeley City Council Meeting Minutes, February 11, 18, 1930.

10. "City Officials Survey New Pipe Line to Town," *Greeley Tribune,* March 13, 1930; "Wooden Pipe Will Be Used Near Greeley," *Greeley Tribune,* March 15, 1930; "Double Pipe Line West of City Is Plan," *Greeley Tribune*, April 23, 1930.

11. Annual Reports, Water Department, City of Greeley, Colorado, 1930-1947, Records of the City of Greeley Water and Sewer Department, Greeley, Colorado.

12. "Rainfall Way Below Normal Figures Show," *Greeley Tribune,* May 7, 1930.

13. Greeley City Council Meeting Minutes, April 21, 1931.

14. Ibid., May 19, July 14, 1931.

15. "City Losing Heavily from Storage Leaks," *Greeley Tribune*, March 7, 1934.

16. Greeley City Council Meeting Minutes, July 29, August 4, 11, 1931. Greeley businessmen D.R. McArthur, H.F. Wheeler, Joseph C. Ewing, Fred Norcross and H.P Ketelson founded the Greeley Greasewood Oil Company on January 3, 1931, and purchased land and mineral leases, constructed pipelines and sold stock. For good luck, the company christened its rotary drill with a Greeley Wonder cantaloupe, a hybrid developed by Union Colonist James Max Clark in the 1890s. Jay Taylor, superintendent of the Halliburton Oil Well Cementing Company visited Greeley in September 1931 and "gushed" that Weld County's oil fields would become the most important in the State and Greeley was the most "cordial, friendly city that I'm acquainted with." Taylor proclaimed, "You have the prettiest crude oil at Greasewood I have ever seen and I believe that you have the beginnings of a big oil industry right at Greeley's back door." This was good (and prophetic) news, and no one could foretell the explosion of oil and gas development that would occur in the coming decades. During the 1930s, workers were glad to have these jobs (similar to those who found energy industry jobs at the turn of the next century as well). Water, of course, was and is essential to drilling operations. The Greasewood Lakes, although filled with enough water to "float a battleship" in the 1890s and again in 1933, were completely dry lake beds during the oil boom of 1930-1931. A pipeline from Jackson Lake (Morgan County) to the Greasewood oil field was constructed to provide water for the large rotary drilling rigs.

17. Ibid., October 6, December 29, 1931.

18. Greeley City Council Meeting Minutes, October 6, December 29, 1931.

19. "City Losing Heavily from Storage Leaks," *Greeley Tribune*, March 7, 1934.

20. Greeley City Council Meeting Minutes, January 19, February 2, 9, 16, 1932.

21. Ibid., August 2, 1932.

22. Ibid., December 13, 20, 27, 1932.

23. Ibid., "Seaman Came To Greeley 50 Years Ago," *Greeley Tribune*, August 23, 1934.

24. Greeley City Council Meeting Minutes, December 20, 1932, January 10, 24, 1933.

25. Ibid., April 25, May 9, 1933.

26. Ibid., August 15, 1933.

27. Ibid., May 29, 1934.

28. Ibid.

29. Greeley City Council Meeting Minutes, October 2, 1934.

30. Ibid., November 6, 1934.

31. "Greeley Might Purchase Lofty Mountain Lake as Protection Against Severe Water Famine," *Greeley Tribune*, March 28, 1935.

32. Ibid.

33. Ibid.

34. Greeley City Council Meeting Minutes, March 5, 1935.

35. Ibid., May 14, 21, 28, 1935.

36. Ibid., September 3, December 3, 10, 1935.

37. Ibid., March 3, September 8, 1936.

38. Tyler, Daniel, *The Last Water Hole in the West, The Colorado-Big Thompson Project and the Northern Colorado Water Conservancy District* (Niwot, CO: University Press of Colorado, 1992), 28-29.

39. Autobee, Robert, "Colorado-Big Thompson Project," U.S. Bureau of Reclamation, https://www.usbr.gov/projects/pdf.php?id=97, accessed August 30, 2019, 5-6.

40. Ibid., 6-7.

41. Greeley City Council Meeting Minutes, October 27, 1936; T.B. Moodey, City Engineer, City of Greeley, to the Northern Colorado Water Users Association, Greeley, Colorado, October 30, 1936, Northern Colorado Water Conservancy District Files, Berthoud, Colorado. Mead told Charles Hansen in 1935: "Your county has a special meaning to me. I made the first gauging of all the ditches in northern Colorado, working during vacations [from his teaching position at Colorado Agricultural College] for the State Engineer . . . You have a great county and you need more water, and I feel a personal satisfaction in being able to work with you [as USBR] commissioner toward getting it." (Tyler, *The Last Water Hole in the West,* 39). The planning, design, and construction of the Colorado-Big Thompson Project is thoroughly documented in Daniel Tyler's book.

42. Moodey to Northern Colorado Water Users Association, October 30, 1936.

43. Greeley City Council Meeting Minutes, February 2, 1937.

44. "Editor of 'Nation's Business' Notes Rapid Gains in Weld," *Greeley Tribune*, August 27, 1937.

45. Ibid.

46. "United Against a Common Enemy," *Greeley Tribune*, October 1, 1937.

47. Ibid.

48. "New Frontiers in Colorado," *Greeley Tribune*, December 29, 1937. This story originated as an editorial in the *Rocky Mountain News*, Denver, Colorado.

49. Michener, James A., *Centennial* (New York, NY: Random House, 1974), 765-767. An avid reader of newspapers, Michener dedicated *Centennial* to three friends, all editors of newspapers in northeastern Colorado: Floyd Merrill (*Greeley Tribune*); Clyde Stanley (*Keota News*) and Otto Unfug (*Sterling Journal-Advocate*). Michener also came to know

Charles Hansen, who invited him to attend lunches at "Angell's Tea Room" across 10ᵗʰ Avenue from the Colorado State College of Education (today the University of Northern Colorado). There Michener would join with the city's leadership as they met to discuss public affairs, among which was the campaign for the Colorado-Big Thompson project. Michener would write later that this stayed with him when he came back to Greeley in 1970 to conduct research on his novel.

50. Norris, Lee G., "William R. Kelly," *The Colorado Lawyer*, Vol. 13, No. 7, July 1984, 1173-1174; See also Brady, Richard P., "Weld County Bar Association" in "Histories of Local Bar Associations," *The Colorado Lawyer*, Vol. 26, No. 6, 100 Years of the Colorado Bar Association, Denver, Colorado, June 1997, 35-37.

51. *Rogers v. Letford*, 102 Colo. 284, 79 P. 2d, 274, (1938); Brady, "Weld County Bar Association," 35-37.

52. Kelly, William R., *The Greeley-Poudre Irrigation District*, July 15, 1964, 12.

53. Northern Colorado Water Users Organization Committee Documents, on file with Greeley Water and Sewer Department, Greeley, Colorado.

54. Ibid.

55. Schulte, Steven C., *As Precious as Blood, The Western Slope in Colorado's Water Wars, 1900-1970* (Boulder, CO: University Press of Colorado, 2016), 50-51.

56. Northern Colorado Water Users Organization Committee Documents, on file with Greeley Water and Sewer Department, Greeley, Colorado.

57. Sibley, George, *Water Wranglers, The 75-Year History of the Colorado River District: A Story About the Embattled Colorado River and the Growth of the West* (Glenwood Springs, CO: Colorado River Water Conservation District, 2012), 53-54.

58. Session Laws of Colorado, Second Extraordinary Session 1936, House Joint Resolution No. 1 at 94-96.

59. Ibid., 95.

60. Ibid., 94.

61. Kelly to Delaney, December 16, 1936; See also Northern Colorado Water Users Organization Committee Documents, on file with Greeley Water and Sewer Department, Greeley, Colorado.

62. Delaney to Nixon, Hansen and Kelly, December 24, 1936; See also Northern Colorado Water Users Organization Committee Documents, on file with Greeley Water and Sewer Department, Greeley, Colorado.

63. Sibley, 61.

64. Act of April 7, 1937.

65. Act of May 13, 1937.

66. Act of June 1, 1937.

67. See Cech, Thomas V. and McDonald, William J., *Defend and Develop, A Brief History of the Colorado Water Conservation Board's First 75 Years* (Ashland, OR: Wellstone Press, 2012), 52-66.

68. Section 13(b), Chp. 266, 1947 Colo. Sess. Laws, 1325.

69. *People v. Letford*, 79 P.2d, 280.

70. Ibid., 288-289.

71. Senate Document No. 80, 75th Congress, First Session.

72. Tyler, *The Last Water Hole in the West*, 94.

73. Ibid., 194-203.

74. "One-Third of Water Available On Diversion Project Has Been Applied for by Consumers," *Greeley Tribune*, February 10, 1938.

75. "Greeley Uses More Water But Pays Less," *Greeley Tribune,* April 19, 1938.

76. "15,000 Acre Feet To Be Asked from Diversion System," *Greeley Tribune*, January 6, 1939; "Special Council Meeting Will Consider Greeley Water To Be Contracted in Diversion Plan," *Greeley Tribune*, January 11, 1939.

Chapter Seven

1. Nash, Gerald D., *The American West Transformed: The Impact of the Second World War* (Bloomington, IN: University of Indiana Press, 1985), 3-14. Greeley had always taken pride in being self-reliant in planning and financing its municipal water development. In pushing for the C-BT project, Greeley's leaders instigated a controversial proposal that created a new statewide governance framework to develop Colorado's water compact allocations, reflecting Delph Carpenter's legacy of seeking cooperative and beneficial alliances and partnerships.

2. Ibid., 201-216.

3. "Keep Greeley's Water Supply Out Of Politics!" *Greeley Tribune,* March 29, 1941. The business group purchasing this advertisement included such luminaries as banker and cattle feeder W.D. Farr, *Tribune* publisher Charles Hansen, lawyer Charles E. Southard, mortician Fred J. Allnutt, college professor and former city councilor Ralph Bishop, and former councilor Lee B. Carrel.

4. Ibid.

5. Greeley City Council Meeting Minutes, January 30, February 6, 1940. As the farmers under the Greeley and Loveland looked forward to water via the C-BT tunnel, six "wind drying tunnels" debuted in Greeley as part of the war effort. Potatoes, Greeley's original "top crop," made a comeback during World War II when the Dehydrated Products Company of Colorado, Inc. opened its plant at 500-6th Avenue in June 1943. At peak

production, 60 tons of potatoes daily were dehydrated in these wind drying tunnels, yielding 15 pounds of dehydrated potatoes from 150 pounds of raw potatoes. Packed into five-gallon cans, the company's other products included dehydrated cabbage and carrots. Dehydration prevented spoilage and reduced the weight and space required for shipping food abroad to feed the troops. The company employed 210 people, including women, with 70 employees per eight-hour shift. [*Greeley Tribune,* October 5, 1942, "Dehydration Plant Set for Greeley," June 8, 1943, "Company Here Will Ship Car of Dehydrated Potatoes Last of Week, Manager Ruler Says—Plant Will Employ 210 in Three Shifts At Full Capacity."] The Fort Collins trip also would be one of Milton Seaman's last official functions for the City of Greeley.

6. Ibid., March 12, April 2, May 21, 1940; Letter of F.D. Healey, District Manager, District Three, Works Progress Administration, to the Director, Civilian Conservation Corps, Littleton, CO, April 22, 1940, Seaman Dam Final Report, 1942; Record Group (RG) 69, Records of the Works Project Administration and its Predecessors, ca. 1931-1944, National Archives and Records Administration, from microfilm at History Colorado, Denver, Colorado. Selander had built many concrete roads, overpasses, and underpasses in Colorado as well as a reservoir dam in 1931 for the Mountain and Plains Irrigation Company 60 miles west of Fort Collins.

7. "Greeley Will Return to Specified Watering Hours Next Saturday," *Greeley Tribune,* June 19, 1941.

8. Greeley City Council Meeting Minutes, June 25, July 16, 1940.

9. "Seaman, For 42 Years City Department Head, Dies After Long Illness," *Greeley Tribune,* September 19, 1940.

10. Greeley City Council Meeting Minutes, September 24, 1940.

11. Ibid.

12. *Greeley Tribune,* February 23, 1942.

13. "City Council Approves Milton Seaman Dam Enlargement for 15 Feet Higher if Required," *Greeley Tribune,* August 6, 1941.

14. Report of M.C. Hinderlider, State Engineer, to Roy Seaman, Superintendent, Greeley Water Works, September 26, 1941; "Specifications for the Construction of Milton Seaman Reservoir Dam," Seaman Dam Final Report, 1942.

15. Ibid.

16. Letter of Bennetts to Healey, October 15, 1941; Seaman Dam Final Report, 1942.

17. Ibid.

18. Ibid.

19. Greeley City Council Meeting Minutes, October 21, 1941; Letter of Bennetts to Healey, October 27, 1941; Seaman Dam Final Report, 1942.

20. "Water Department's Extension Bonds Sold at Lowest Interest Rate in History, 1.1 Per Cent," *Greeley Tribune,* November 26, 1941. The lack of workers was a chronic problem, and the closure of two laundries in Greeley in 1943 (the Greeley Laundry Company at 718-7th Street, established in 1894, and the O.K. Laundry) not because of a lack of water, but because of a lack of experienced workers, underscored the frustration experienced by municipal and business employers and farmers during World War II. ["Greeley's Oldest Laundry has Closed Due to Lack of Labor," *Greeley Tribune,* August 23, 1943.]

21. Greeley City Council Meeting Minutes, August 11, 1942.

22. Ibid.

23. *Greeley Tribune,* May 5, 1942.

24. *Greeley Tribune,* February 23, 1942.

25. Greeley City Council Meeting Minutes, October 28, 1941.

26. *Greeley Tribune,* February 23, 1943.

27. Greeley City Council Meeting Minutes, December 16, 1941; January 20, 1942.

28. "Victory Garden," cited in Wikipedia, the free encyclopedia, https://en.wikipedia.org/wiki/Victory_garden; accessed March 31, 2019; Greeley City Council Meeting Minutes, March 23, 1943.

29. *Greeley Tribune,* March 31, 1943, and correspondence with Peggy Ford Waldo, Development Curator, City of Greeley Museums, Greeley, Colorado, July 31, 2019.

30. Greeley City Council Meeting Minutes, February 15, 1943.

31. Ibid., May 4, 1943.

32. Ibid.

33. Ibid.

34. Paschell, Allen W., "The Enemy in Colorado: German Prisoners of War, 1943-46," *The Colorado Magazine,* Volume 56, Nos. 3 and 4, 1979, 119-142.

35. City of Greeley Council Meeting Minutes, August 31, 1942.

36. P.O.W. Camp, Greeley History, http://www.greeleyhistory.org/pages/pow_camp.html, accessed June 2019.

37. "Greeley Water for Garden City Menaces Local Development in Opinion of Dr. O.M. Dickerson," *Greeley Tribune,* December 28, 1943.

38. Ibid.

39. Greeley City Council Meeting Minutes, November 27, December 26, 1945.

40. Ibid., January 8, 15, 1946.

41. "District Refuses City's Demand To Cancel Water Contract; To Deliver Supply as It Specifies," *Greeley Tribune,* February 11, 1946.

42. Ibid.

43. "Some Aspects of Use of High-Range Lakes," *Greeley Tribune,* March 1, 1946.

44. Ibid. Davis was a community entrepreneur, farmer, cattle feeder, realtor, secretary of the Cache la Poudre Irrigation Company, and promoter of a new hospital for Greeley.

45. "Council Action Assures the City of Adequate Water Supply For Years; Purchase Advised by Engineering Firm," *Greeley Tribune,* July 4, 1947.

46. Greeley City Council Meeting Minutes, July 2, 1947. Roy Portner had started work on his system of high mountain reservoirs in 1906. T.E. Schuerman joined his company in 1920.

47. "U.P. Requests Greeley Sell Water to LaSalle to Make New Plant There Unnecessary," *Greeley Tribune,* February 25, 1948.

48. "Greeley May Sell Irrigation Water to Weld Farmers," *Greeley Tribune,* July 13, 1948.

49. Greeley City Council Meeting Minutes, August 17, 1948; "Greeley Council Sells 60 Million Feet Seaman Water to Save Thirsty Crops in Northern Weld," *Greeley Tribune,* July 28, 1948.

50. "Why the Water Restrictions?" *Greeley Tribune,* n.d.

51. Ibid.

52. "A New Pipe Line from Loveland," *Denver Post,* August 17, 1949.

53. Ibid.

54. "Greeley Has Plenty of Water But if Unlimited Use Allowed It Must Spend Heavily for New Pipe Line," *Greeley Tribune,* August 19, 1949.

55. "Mayor Names Committee of 25 To Draw Up Plan for Greeley Water System for General Discussion," *Greeley Tribune,* August 31, 1949.

56. Ibid.

CHAPTER EIGHT

1. Information on census data for the years 1950-1970 for Greeley and its neighbors has been taken from the Wikipedia pages for each community that are found on the Internet.

2. Mier, Sally and Monson, Jon, "Interview Two with William Daven Farr," Greeley, Colorado, December 28, 1999; Gregg Silkensen, Northern Colorado Water Conservancy District, Interview Four with William D. Farr, Greeley, Colorado, October 24, 1997.

3. "City Reservoir No. One Breaks Cutting Road, Flooding Schank's Yard; Now It is Being Drained," *Greeley Tribune,* May 17, 1951. City councilors would accept responsibility for the flooding of the farm owned by Mr. and Mrs. Thomas L. Schank, offering them the sum of $200 for their losses. Greeley City Council Meeting Minutes, Greeley, Colorado, March 18, 1952.

4. Ibid., May 18, July 13, November 16, 1954; January 11, May 31, 1955; "Greeley Water-Wastewater Plant," Undated File, Box 4, Colorado State University Water Archive, Fort Collins, Colorado. This document came from the W.D. Farr Collection.

5. Ibid., April 17, 1956; and "A History of Drought in Colorado," McKee, Thomas B., et al., Colorado Climate Center, Colorado State University, Fort Collins, Colorado, No. 9, 2nd Edition, February 2000, https://ccc.atmos.colostate.edu/pdfs/ahistoryofdrought.pdf, accessed January 2020.

6. Ibid., December 11, 1956; January 15, 1957; "Milton Gets Biggest Share of City Water," *Greeley Tribune,* January 14, 1957.

7. "City Manager Outlines Plans for Greeley," *Greeley Tribune*, December 7, 1951.

8. "First Report of Water Committee," City of Greeley Charter Convention, Greeley, Colorado, April 2, 1958, Greeley Water and Sewer Department Files.

9. Ibid., W.D. Farr interview, October 24, 1997.

10. Ibid.

11. "Water Board To Be Appointed Soon," *Greeley Tribune,* July 1, 1958.

12. Greeley Water Board Meeting Minutes, Greeley, Colorado, July 30, August 13, 1958, Greeley Water and Sewer Department Files. Farr would step down as water board chairman on January 26, 1998.

13. Ibid., August 27, 1958. A good source for understanding the demographic changes affecting the United States in the years after the Second World War, see Landon Y. Jones, *Great Expectations: America and the Baby Boom Generation* (New York, NY: Coward, McCann and Geoghegan, 1980). Jones is credited with creating the term "Baby Boom" to describe the youth phenomenon in the second half of the 20th century.

14. Greeley Water Board Meeting Minutes, Greeley, Colorado, August 27, 1958.

15. Ibid., August 29, 1960; "Kelly Named Attorney for Water Board," *Greeley Tribune,* September 2, 1960.

16. Greeley Water Board Meeting Minutes, October 3, 1960; "City Water Board Hires Commissioner for Report," *Greeley Tribune,* October 11, 1960.

17. Kelly, William R., "Greeley Water Board Report," October 3, 1960, Greeley Water and Sewer Department Files, Greeley, Colorado.

18. Ibid.

19. Greeley City Council Meeting Minutes, Greeley, Colorado, September 2, 1958.

20. Ibid.

21. Ibid., September 2, October 7, 1958.

22. Ibid.

23. Correspondence with Peggy Ford Waldo, City of Greeley Museums, Greeley, Colorado, November 5, 2019. The missile was transported to Greeley on June 21, 1961, and exhibited briefly at Lincoln Park prior to its installation. Made of thin stainless steel, it was 78-feet long, weighed 15 tons and cost $1.5 million. When loaded with fuel for launching, it weighed 130 tons. During fueling and launching, the area around the missile would be flooded with water. In October 1962, Greeley "Site L" was on national security alert in preparation to fire at the time of the Cuban missile crisis. The site and facility were short lived, however, as the Atlas Series E missile was soon rendered obsolete (replaced by the Titan Intercontinental Ballistic Missile). Greeley Missile Site L was later transformed into Weld County's first park, campground, and records storage facility by the mid-1970s—Missile Site Park.

24. "Cruce Thinks City Should Change Its 3-Mile Zone Policy," *Greeley Tribune,* April 13, 1961.

25. Ibid. Greeley's designated "three-mile zone" included lands three miles north of the Cache la Poudre River, three miles east of 1st Avenue, three miles west of 23rd Avenue, and three miles south of 24th Street, an area of approximately 64 square miles. Greeley's city limits in 1957 embraced approximately 4.6 square miles, but 1.5 square miles were annexed by January of 1962, for a total area of 6.1 square miles. ["Annexations Add About 1 ½ Square Miles to City," *Greeley Tribune,* May 5, 1962.] In 2019, Greeley's city limits encompassed 50 square miles.

26. W.D. Farr interview, Greeley, Colorado, October 24, 1997.

27. "Evans Prepares For Independent Water System," *Greeley Tribune,* November 22, 1961.

28. "Group to Consider Contract for Windsor," *Greeley Tribune,* May 10, 1961.

29. "Boyd Lake Contract Approved, Growth Potential Boosted," *Greeley Tribune,* July 1, 1961.

30. "Plan For Progress," *Greeley Tribune,* July 6, 1961. Once again history is a great teacher and can provide a glimpse into the future. In 1907, Mayor Henry Watson appointed a three-person water committee to investigate all aspects for obtaining mountain water on the Big Thompson River. This included the legal process for purchasing water rights, the design of diversion points, and determining the costs of a pipeline and storage reservoirs. A key member of the water committee was W.H. ("Billy") Farr, W.D. Farr's grandfather.

31. "Engineers Approve Boyd Lake," *Greeley Tribune,* May 8, 1962.

32. "Board Must Weigh Project's Value Against Higher Rates," *Greeley Tribune,* July 9, 1962.

33. "Text of Farr Letter to City Council," *Greeley Tribune,* September 12, 1962.

34. Ibid.

35. "Needs of Greeley Water System for 4 Years Outlined," *Greeley Tribune,* November 8, 1961.

36. "Water Use Nearing Capacity of City Transmission Lines," *Greeley Tribune,* May 21, 1964; "23rd Ave. Reservoir Usage Sets Record," *Greeley Tribune,* July 8, 1964; "Lawn Sprinkling May Be Banned 24 Hours a Week," *Greeley Tribune,* July 15, 1964; "Greeley Has Driest July In More Than 30 Years," *Greeley Tribune,* July 29, 1964; "Water Restrictions May Soon Be Lifted," *Greeley Tribune,* July 28, 1964.

37. "Says Greeley Rates In Line With Others," *Greeley Tribune,* December 8, 1964; "Cruce Will Compare Taxes, Water Rates," *Greeley Tribune,* January 8, 1965.

38. "Says Greeley Rates In Line With Others."

39. "Cruce Compares City's Rates With Those of its Neighbors," *Greeley Tribune*, January 13, 1965.

40. "Report Suggests 50% Boost in Flat Rate Water Charge," *Greeley Tribune,* July 7, 1962.

41. "Water and Sewer Collection," Greeley Museums, https://greeleymuseums.com/wp-content/uploads/2015/03/Water-and-Sewer-Collection-2013.81.pdf, accessed August 2019.

42. Greeley City Council Meeting Minutes, October 1, 15, 1963; January 7, February 18, 1964; "Pollution Problem Got its Start Years Ago as Area Was Settled," *Greeley Tribune,* March 11, 1964.

43. Greeley City Council Meeting Minutes, Greeley, Colorado, May 10, 1966.

44. "Water Board Told Rate Study Would Be Aid in Bond Issue," *Greeley Tribune,* June 14, 1967; Greeley Water Board Meeting Minutes, Greeley, Colorado, June 13, 1967.

45. "Water Board Told Rate Study Would Be Aid in Bond Issue," Greeley Water Board Meeting Minutes, Greeley, Colorado, December 12, 1967; "Council, Water Board Approve Sale of Lakes," *Greeley Tribune,* December 14, 1967.

46. "I-25 Community Leaders Meet With Eastman Officials," *Fort Collins Coloradoan,* Colorado, July 23, 1968.

47. W.D. Farr interview, Greeley, Colorado, December 21, 1997.

48. Ibid.

49. Ibid.

50. "St. Vrain Valley Welcomes New Neighbors," *Longmont Times-Call,* Longmont, Colorado, June 28, 1968.

51. "Eastman Makes Preliminary Proposal for Greeley Water," *Greeley Tribune,* September 12, 1968; "Kodak Presents Water Proposal," *Fort Collins Coloradoan,* September 15, 1968.

52. "City To Work With Kodak On Writing Water Contract," *Greeley Tribune,* September 23, 1968; "Water Plan for Kodak At Windsor Drafted," *Loveland Herald-Reporter,* Loveland, Colorado, September 25, 1968. Quirk also worked on the Boyd Lake Water Treatment Project.

53. Greeley Water Board Meeting Minutes, February 11, 1969; "Greeley Urged to Join West Slope Water Study," *Greeley Tribune,* February 15, 1969; "Six Cities Group Agrees to Form Water Sub District," *Fort Collins Coloradoan,* February 25, 1969; "Water Board Discusses Proposed Sub-District," *Greeley Tribune,* April 10, 1969; "Articles of Association Submitted For Northern Regional Plan Group," *Fort Collins Coloradoan*, May 12, 1969.

54. "Plan Seeks Thousands of Water Acres," *Longmont Times-Call,* December 17, 1969.

CHAPTER NINE

1. U.S. Census, 1970, 1980, 1990. By comparison, Denver's metropolitan area would grow by 45 percent between 1970 and 1990; a slower rate than Greeley's 55 percent. By 1990, the Denver area had 1,623,121 people, or slightly more than half of all Coloradans.

2. City Council Meeting Minutes, February 16, May 4, 1971; Greeley Water Board Meeting Minutes, January 4, May 3, September 27, November 10, 1971; "City Council Approves Water Dept. Projection," *Greeley Tribune,* May 7, 1971.

3. Thompson, Julius, "Meters for Conserving Water Here Advocated," *Greeley Tribune,* May 2, 1970.

4. "Sprinkling Ban Pondered," *Greeley Tribune,* June 29, 1971.

5. "Greeley has sufficient water for several hundred thousand," *Greeley Tribune,* February 1, 1973.

6. Greeley Water Board Meeting Minutes, August 7, 1972.

7. "Forward Together panel urges city go ahead on water plans," *Greeley Tribune,* February 13, 1973.

8. Greeley Water Board Meeting Minutes, March 12, 1973.

9. Dan Tyler interview of Hank Brown, February 1, 2009, 8-9.

10. Farr, W.D., *Greeley Water and Sewer Board (Its History, Purpose and Need),* March 23, 1981. The C-BT plan of development contained in Senate Document 80, June 15, 1937, had included the possibility of a canal running from the mouth of St. Louis Creek, near the town of Fraser, through a small regulating reservoir on Ranch Creek, to deliver Fraser River water into Lake Granby. See *Synopsis Of Report On Colorado-Big Thompson Project, Plan Of Development And Cost Estimate Prepared By The Bureau of Reclamation,* U.S. Department of Interior (Washington, D.C.: U.S. Government Printing Office, June 15, 1937), 19. This feature, to be located below Denver's Moffat Tunnel diversions from the Fraser River, was never built.

11. For a fine overview of efforts to build the Windy Gap Project, see Silkensen, Gregory M., *Windy Gap: Transmountain Water Diversion And The Environmental Movement,* Technical Report No. 61 (Fort Collins, CO: Colorado Water Resources Research Institute, Colorado State University, August 1994).

12. *Water Availability Study For The Windy Gap Water Supply Project Submitted to Six Cities Water Committee* (Denver, CO: ECI Engineering Consultants, Inc., October 1969), 2.

13. *Colorado River Water Conservation District* v. *Municipal Subdistrict, Northern Colorado Water Conservancy District,* 198 Colo. 352, 358 (1979).

14. *Agreement of February 24, 1969, by and between the City of Boulder, the Town of Estes Park, the City of Fort Collins, the City of Greeley, the City of Longmont, and the City of Loveland.*

15. *Waternews,* Northern Colorado Water Conservancy District, 50th Anniversary Edition, 1937-1987, Loveland, Colorado, 21.

16. *Greeley Water & Sewer Board Resolution No. 1*, February 20, 2008, honoring Bill Bohlender's service as the Water and Sewer Board's Attorney from January 1970 to January 1999.

17. *Agreement Concerning the Windy Gap Project and the Azure Reservoir and Power Project*, April 30, 1980.

18. Phipps, Earl, Manager Municipal Subdistrict, Northern Water Conservancy District, and Grieb, Jack R., Director, Colorado Division of Wildlife, *Memorandum of Understanding Between Municipal Subdistrict, Northern Colorado Water Conservancy District and Division of Wildlife, Colorado Department of Natural Resources, Relating to Minimum Stream Flow in Association with the Windy Gap Project*, June 23, 1980. Keeping a live stream intact through specified monthly releases from Granby Reservoir into the Colorado River first became operational through a January 19, 1961, directive of the U.S. Secretary of the Interior. *Principles to Govern the Release of Water at Granby Dam to Provide Fishery Flows Immediately Downstream in the Colorado River,* Fred A. Seaton, Secretary of the Interior, January 19, 1961.

19. On behalf of the Municipal Subdistrict, John Sayre and Larry Simpson appeared before the Colorado Water Conservation Board at its meeting of July 8, 1980, supporting these appropriations. David Robbins, who argued the instream flow case on behalf of the state successfully before the Colorado Supreme Court in 1979, was now a new member of the CWCB. He made the motion in favor of these water rights, but also commented on a letter of support ranchers below the Windy Gap diversion point had submitted in favor of these water rights. They supported the minimum flows to "protect their ranch values." Robbins observed, and the board agreed, that instream flow water rights are not riparian rights of landowners along the river. Instead, they are prior appropriation water rights for the preservation of the natural environment to a reasonable degree. *Reporter's Transcript of Public Hearing*, Colorado Water Conservation Board, July 8, 1980, 160-167.

20. The Division No. 5 Water Court entered final decrees for these instream water rights on October 29, 1982, in Cases No. 80CW446, 80CW447, and 80CW448, each with an appropriation date of July 8, 1980.

21. Sayre, John M., *The Windy Gap Project: A Case Study* (Boulder, CO: Natural Resources Law Center, University of Colorado School of Law, Short Course Relating to New Sources of Water for Energy Development and Growth: Interbasin Transfers, June 9, 1982), 6; Farr, W.D. and Barkley, J.R., *Progress Report On Subdistrict Activities And Windy Gap Project* (Loveland, CO: Municipal Subdistrict, Northern Colorado Water Conservancy District, March 1, 1973); Sayre, *The Windy Gap Project,* 7-8.

22. Silkensen, Technical Report No. 61, 84-86.

23. Ibid., 61, 86-87.

24. *2012 Annual Report*, 75th Anniversary, Northern Water (Berthoud, CO: Northern Colorado Water Conservancy District), 6. For a description and timeline of the Firming Project, see England, Dan, "The Evolving Process of Permitting," *Headwaters* (Denver, CO:

Water Education Colorado, Summer 2019), 15-25.

25. Tyler, *The Last Water Hole in the West*, 395.

26. Statement by Secretary of the Interior James Watt concerning Windy Gap Archeological Find, Denver, Colorado, December 22, 1981.

27. "Windsor approves plan to draw water from Horsetooth," *Fort Collins Coloradoan*, March 10, 1970.

28. "Size of Operation One Reason Kodak Not Moving to Colorado," *Greeley Tribune,* June 15, 1971.

29. Ibid.

30. News Release, George Bargelt and B.H. Cruce, "Deodorizer for Sewage Treatment Plants," January 26, 1970, in City Manager's Report, "Review of Comprehensive Survey Greeley's Wastewater Treatment Plant by Colorado Department of Health," 1970; Greeley Water and Sewer Department Files, January 5, 1971.

31. "New Monfort Feed Lot—It's a Computer World," *Greeley Tribune*, February 27, 1970.

32. "Study and Report, Municipal Treatment System," Greeley Water and Sewer Department Files, n.d.

33. "Lagoon Site Selection Is Termed 'Crisis' issue," *Greeley Tribune*, June 17, 1970.

34. Activity Report of Gregory T. Misbach, Colorado Department of Health, Water Pollution Control Commission, "Greeley Sewage Treatment Plant," December 17, 1970, Greeley Water and Sewer Department Files.

35. "City Needs Permit for Water Plants," September 29, 1971; Frank Rozich, Technical Secretary, Water Pollution Control Commission, Colorado Department of Health, Denver, Colorado, to C. Keith Eberhardt, Acting City Manager, City of Greeley, November 11, 1971, Greeley Water and Sewer Department Files.

36. "Monfort Lists Record Income," *Denver Post,* Denver, Colorado, June 27, 1972.

37. Greeley Water and Sewer Board Meeting Minutes, June 3, 1974.

38. Ibid.

39. Ibid.

40. Public Hearing, "The Wastewater Regional Facilities Plan," City Council Chambers, City of Greeley, Greeley Water Board Meeting Minutes, April 8, 1975. Colorado adopted its own Water Quality Control Act rather than leave the field of water quality regulation to the U.S. Environmental Protection Agency. See *Citizen's Guide To Colorado Water Quality Protection*, 3rd Edition (Denver, CO: Water Education Colorado, 2019); Mele, Jennifer; Oeth, Trisha; and Quill, Annette, *Intersection Of Water Quality and Water Rights*, 22 U. Denv. Water L. Rev. 437 (2019).

41. Ibid.

42. Ibid.

43. Greeley Water Board Meeting Minutes, Greeley, Colorado, January 5, 1976; "Inflation and CPI Consumer Price Index, 1970-1979;" accessed at https://inflationdata.com/articles/inflation-cpi-consumer-price-index-1970-1979/, August 11, 2019.

44. "Big Thompson Flood of 1976," *Denver Post*, July 31, 1976; "Water treatment costs triple," *Greeley Tribune*, August 31, 1976; "Flood damages city's mountain lakes," *Greeley Tribune*, September 1, 1976; Greeley Water and Sewer Board Meeting Minutes, August 31, 1976.

45. Stine, Jeffrey K., "Environmental Policy during the Carter Presidency," in Gary M. Fink and Hugh Davis Graham, eds., *The Carter Presidency: Policy Choices in the Post-New Deal Era* (Lawrence, KS: University of Kansas Press, 1998), 175-201; Greeley City Council Meeting Minutes, March 1, 1977.

46. Ibid., May 5, June 2, 1977; "City proposes $5.1 million water system expansion," *Greeley Tribune*, May 6, 1977.

47. Greeley Water and Sewer Board Meeting Minutes, July 7, August 4, 1977.

48. Greeley City Council Minutes, October 6, 1977.

49. Greeley Water and Sewer Board Meeting Minutes, February 2, 1978; "Water board pledges financing," *Greeley Tribune*, February 3, 1978.

50. Ibid., "Greeley ponders water sale," *Fort Collins Coloradoan*, February 1, 1978.

51. "Shared-use study of water likely," *Greeley Tribune*, February 3, 1978; Greeley Water and Sewer Board Meeting Minutes, February 2, 1978.

52. Greeley Water and Sewer Board Meeting Minutes, February 2, 1978.

53. "Windsor won't meet water deadline," *Greeley Tribune*, April 13, 1978; "Water pact squabbles persist," *Greeley Tribune*, April 27, 1978; "Windsor seeks own water source," *Loveland Reporter-Herald*, Loveland, Colorado, May 23, 1978.

54. "Windsor voters face water system choice," *Greeley Tribune*, August 7, 1978; "Windsor water system passes: Contract with Greeley to end," *Greeley Tribune*, August 9, 1978.

55. "State water unit approves Greeley sewer plans," *Greeley Tribune*, January 3, 1979.

56. Greeley Water and Sewer Board Meeting Minutes, March 1, 1979; April 5, 1979.

57. Planning Department of the City of Greeley, "North of Greeley Study: Feasibility of Greeley Growing Northward," Greeley Water and Sewer Board Files, December 1979.

58. Ibid.

59. "North of Greeley Study," W.D. Farr to Ms. Claire Zelle, Economic Planner, City of Greeley, April 17, 1979.

60. Ibid.

61. Ibid.

62. Correspondence with Peggy Ford Waldo, City of Greeley Museums, Greeley, Colorado, October 28, 2019.

Chapter Ten

1. For a discussion of the many factors shaping the Ronald Reagan presidency, see Woodard, J. David, *Ronald Reagan: A Biography* (Santa Barbara, CA: Greenwood Press, 2012), and Dallek, Robert, *Ronald Reagan: The Politics of Symbolism* with a new preface (Cambridge, MA: Harvard University Press, 1999).

2. Greeley Water and Sewer Board Meeting Minutes, January 17, 1980.

3. "City awaits response on sewer," *Greeley Tribune*, April 17, 1980.

4. Greeley Water and Sewer Board Meeting Minutes, June 12, 1980.

5. Ibid., November 5, 1981.

6. Greeley Water and Sewer Board Meeting Minutes, April 1, October 7, 1982; "Water panel Oks million-dollar sewer pipeline plan," *Greeley Tribune*, April 2, 1982.

7. "Greeley to pump $10 million into sewage treatment plant," *Greeley Tribune*, n.d.; also, correspondence with Joe Kunovic with assistance from Ted Vogel, Dennis Schump and Bruce Reed, City of Greeley, December 30, 2019.

8. Greeley Water and Sewer Board Minutes, December 1, 1983.

9. "Greeley, Fort Collins square off over Poudre," *Greeley Tribune*, December 9, 1983.

10. Greeley Water and Sewer Board Meeting Minutes, January 19, 1985.

11. Ibid.

12. An article about this unsuccessful bill appears in the Northern Colorado Water Conservancy District Fall 1984 edition of *WaterNews*.

13. Laflin, Rose and Werner, Brian, *Cache La Poudre River, Colorado's First Wild and Scenic River*, Citizen's Guide to Colorado's Environmental Era (Denver, CO: Colorado Foundation for Water Education, 2005), 20-23.

14. "Brown introduces compromise bill on Poudre River," *Greeley Tribune*, October 11, 1985; "Poudre compromise begins hearing process for wild designation," *Greeley Tribune*, October 31, 1985.

15. Tyler, Daniel, *WD Farr, Cowboy In The Boardroom* (Norman, OK: University of Oklahoma Press, 2011), 166.

16. Laflin, Rose and Werner, Brian, *Cache La Poudre River, Colorado's First Wild And Scenic River*, Citizen's Guide to Colorado's Environmental Era (Denver, CO: Colorado Foundation for Water Education, 2005), 20-23. For a fine overview of the origins and purposes of the 1968 Wild and Scenic Rivers Act, see Tarlock, Dan A., *Wild and Scenic Rivers Act of 1968*, 55 Cornell L. Rev. 707 (1970).

17. *Interview of Hank Brown* by Michael Welsh and Greg Hobbs, June 27, 2016, at City of Greeley Water and Sewer Department, Greeley, Colorado, 5, 144.

18. Ibid.

19. Hank Brown Interview, 40.

20. Ibid., 43.

21. Public Law 99-590, 99ᵗʰ Congress, Second Session, 100 Stat. 3330.

22. U.S. Senate Report 99-354, 4.

23. *In the Matter of the Application of the Cache La Poudre Water Users Association, et. al., Findings and Ruling of Referee and Decree of Court*, Case No. W-8086-75, Water Division No. 1, Greeley, Colorado.

24. Public Law 99-590, Section 102.

25. *Revised Findings of Fact, Conclusions of Law and Decree, Concerning the Application of the United States of America for Reserved Water Rights for the Cache La Poudre Wild and Scenic River in Larimer County (Rocky Mountain National Park and Roosevelt National Forest)*, Case No. 86CW367, District Court, Water Division No. 1, Greeley, Colorado.

26. Greeley Water and Sewer Board Meeting Minutes, January 2, 1986.

27. Ibid.

28. Ibid.

29. "Thornton buys area farm land, water rights," *Greeley Tribune*, April 9, 1986.

30. "Deal prevents city purchase of more water," *Greeley Tribune*, April 16, 1986.

31. Ibid.

32. "Breaking water story caused deadline havoc," *Greeley Tribune*, April 14, 1986.

33. "Water district opposes Thornton plan," *Greeley Tribune*, May 9, 1986.

34. Greeley Water and Sewer Board Meeting Minutes, July 16, 1986; "Greeley seeks water rights of GW Sugar," *Greeley Tribune*, June 27, 1986; "Water dispute begins to spurt," *Greeley Tribune*, June 27, 1986.

35. Ibid.

36. Greeley City Council Meeting Minutes, July 22, 1986; "Reservoir deal needs more work, council says," *Greeley Tribune*, July 23, 1986.

37. "Petitions decry lake sale plan," *Greeley Tribune*, August 4, 1986.

38. Greeley City Council Meeting Minutes, August 5, 1986.

39. "Council delays vote on sale of reservoirs," *Greeley Tribune*, August 6, 1986.

40. "Council nixes reservoirs sale," *Greeley Tribune*, August 20, 1986.

41. Ibid.

42. Ibid., August 6, 1987; "Four studies for Poudre project to start this year," *Greeley Tribune*, March 25, 1987; "Cache la Poudre Basin Study Extension, Status of Project Studies, October 1987," Poudre Basin Extension Study: Poudre Project Status of Present Studies, October 1987 File, Northern Colorado Water Conservancy District Archives, Berthoud, Colorado.

43. Quoted in Witwer, James S., *The Renewal Of Authorizations To Divert Water On National Forests*, 24 Colo. Law. 2363 (Denver, CO: Colorado Lawyer, Colorado Bar Association, Denver, Colorado, 1995).

44. See Greeley Water Resources Map in *City of Greeley Water Fact Book*, August 2015, Greeley, Colorado, 11-12.

45. See *Greeley Water History Timeline* at www.greeleygov.com/services/ws/sysem/water-history.

46. *United States v. New Mexico*, 438 U.S. 696, 718 (1978).

47. *United States v. City and County of Denver*, 656 P.2d 1, 23 (1983).

48. Ibid., Greeley Water and Sewer Board Meeting Minutes, December 5, 1985.

49. *In the Matter of the Amended Application of the United States of America for Reserved Water Rights in the Platte River in Boulder, Clear Creek, Douglas, El Paso, Gilpin, Jefferson, Larimer, Park and Teller Counties (Arapaho, Pike, Roosevelt and San Isabel National Forests)*, Case No. W-8439-76 (W-8977-77, W-9052-77, W-9064-77 and W-9065-77), District Court, Water Division No. 1, State of Colorado, Decree dated July 22, 1993.

50. Greeley Water and Sewer Board Meeting Minutes, January 4, May 3, June 7, August 2, October 4, December 6, 1990. (W.D. Farr somewhat facetiously called them the "Family Jewels.")

51. Ibid., January 3, 1991.

52. Ibid., August 22, 1991.

53. Ibid., September 5, October 3, October 28, December 5, 1991; December 3, 1992.

54. Witwer, "The Renewal Of Authorizations To Divert Water On National Forests."

55. Senate Joint Resolution No. 92-17, Colo. Session Laws 1992.

56. Letter dated August 14, 1992, to Skip Underwood, Forest Supervisor, Arapaho/Roosevelt National Forest, from W.D. Farr, President, Municipal Subdistrict, Northern Colorado Water Conservancy District and William E. Bohlender, President, Northern Colorado Water Conservancy District, regarding Forest Plan Revision Arapaho/Roosevelt National Forest.

57. Letter dated September 21, 1992, from Senator Hank Brown to Secretary Edward R. Madigan enclosing letters to Senator Brown from Roger A. Bates, Mayor, City of Loveland, dated September 15, 1992; from Frank J. Stephens, P.E., Director Water and Sewer Department, City of Greeley, dated September 17, 1992; and from Dennis Ducommun, Grand County Water and Sanitation District No. 1, dated September 21, 1992.

58. Letter dated October 22, 1993, to M.M. Underwood, Forest Supervisor, Arapaho & Roosevelt National Forests from Kenneth L. Salazar, Executive Director, Colorado Department of Natural Resources, regarding NEPA Scoping Comments On Special Use Permit Applications For Existing Water Supply Projects.

59. Greeley City Council Minutes, February 7, 1995.

60. U.S. Department of Agriculture, Forest Service, Water Facility Easement dated January 4, 1995, issued to City of Greeley, Colorado, Grantee. Incorporated into the easement is the Revised Joint Operations Plan dated May 18, 1994, addressed to M.M. Underwood, Forest Supervisor, Arapaho/Roosevelt National Forest and signed by Michael B. Smith, Water and Wastewater Utility Director, City of Fort Collins, Frank J. Stephens, P.E., Water and Sewer Director, City of Greeley, and Thomas K. Moore, President, Water Supply and Storage Company.

61. Greeley Water and Sewer Board Meeting Minutes, October 1, December 3, 1992, September 2, 1993, August 11, 1994; Greeley City Council Meeting Minutes, September 6, 1994. This would be the fourth major expansion project related to wastewater treatment in the history of Greeley. The first was in 1955, the second was in 1964, and the third in 1984. The original plant was constructed in 1935.

62. Greeley Water and Sewer Board Meeting Minutes, March 23, September 28, October 26, November 16, 1995.

63. Ibid., November 21, 1996, September 25, November 21, 1997, April 23, August 25, 1998, May 27, 1999.

64. Greeley City Council Meeting Minutes, May 6, 1997. The council named Farr "chairman emeritus" of the water and sewer board, which permitted him to participate in board activities as an "*ex-officio*" member. W.D. Farr represented the best of those who came before him, and served as a model for water leaders who would emerge and plan for the future.

65. Cache La Poudre River Corridor Act, Public Law 104-323, 104th Congress, October 19, 1996, 110 Stat. 3889.

66. Hank Brown Interview, Welsh and Hobbs, 116-117.

Chapter Eleven

1. See *Simpson v. Bijou Irrigation Co.*, 69 P.3d 50 (Colo. 2003); *Well Augmentation Subdistrict of Central Colorado Water Conservancy Dist. v. City of Aurora*, 221 P.3d 399 (Colo, 2009); discussed in Jones, Andrew P. and Cech, Tom, *The South Platte Well Crisis and Beyond: Evolving Alluvial Groundwater Regulation*, 22 Univ. Denv. Water Law Rev. 161 (2019). A descendent of Governor Benjamin Eaton vividly describes the devastating impacts of aridity and the well crisis. See D'Elgin, Tershia, *The Man Who Thought He Owned Water, On the Brink with American Farms, Cities and Food* (Boulder, CO: University Press of Colorado, 2016). An augmentation plan places water into a river, with sufficient quantity and timing, to prevent injury to downstream senior water rights, allowing wells to pump without curtailment. The Water Court Division

No. 1 in Greeley and the Colorado Supreme Court upheld the Colorado Constitution's prior appropriation provisions.

2. Greeley City Council Meeting Minutes, May 5, 2000.

3. Greeley Water and Sewer Board Meeting Minutes, July 27, 2000.

4. Ibid., April 17, May 15, June 19, September 18, November 20, 2002; Greeley City Council Meeting Minutes, July 2, 2002.

5. Greeley City Council Meeting Minutes, July 2, 2002, January 21, 2003; Greeley Water and Sewer Board Meeting Minutes, February 19, March 19, April 16, 2003.

6. City Council Meeting Minutes, April 1, 15, 2003.

7. Greeley Water and Sewer Board Meeting Minutes, June 18, July 16, September 17, October 15, 2003; Greeley City Council Meeting Minutes, May 20, July 15, 2003.

8. "Water Master Plan," Greeley Water and Sewer Department, Greeley, Colorado, October 1, 2003. All of this would be accomplished through the expenditure of $574,656,000 (a 2019 estimate).

9. Ibid.

10. Greeley City Council Meeting Minutes, June 15, 2004; Greeley Water and Sewer Board Meeting Minutes, March 17, May 19, August 18, October 20, 2004, April 20, 2005.

11. "2005 Water Master Plan Annual Review," 1-4, Greeley Water and Sewer Department files, 7.

12. Greeley Water and Sewer Board Meeting Minutes, January 18, December 13, 2006; March 21, June 20, 2007.

13. Ibid., November 1, 2007.

14. "2007 Water Master Plan Annual Review," Greeley Water and Sewer Department files, 1-3.

15. "2016 Water Master Plan Review," Greeley Water and Sewer Department Files, 10-14.

16. Greeley Water and Sewer Board Meeting Minutes, January 18, 2006; March 21, 2007.

17. "2016 Water Master Plan Review," Greeley Water and Sewer Department Files, 1.

18. Greeley City Council Meeting Minutes, June 15, 2004; Greeley Water and Sewer Board Meeting Minutes, March 17, May 19, August 18, October 20, 2004, April 20, 2005.

19. Greeley Water and Sewer Board Meeting Minutes, November 19, December 17, 2003; Greeley City Council Meeting Minutes, January 6, 2004.

20. Greeley Water and Sewer Board Meeting Minutes, June 18, July 16, September 17, October 15, 2003; Greeley City Council Meeting Minutes, May 20, July 15, 2003, 2-4.

21. "2007 Water Master Plan Annual Review," Greeley Water and Sewer Department files, 5.

22. "2005 Water Master Plan Annual Review," 1-4; Greeley Water and Sewer Department files, 7.

23. Ibid., May 16, June 20, 2012.

24. Ibid., February 20, March 20, April 17, May 13, June 19, 2013.

25. Greeley Water and Sewer Board Meeting Minutes, June 18, July 16, September 17, October 15, 2003; Greeley City Council Meeting Minutes, May 20, July 15, 2003, 6.

26. "2005 Water Master Plan Annual Review," Greeley Water and Sewer Department files, 6-7.

27. "2019 Water Master Plan Review," Greeley Water and Sewer Department Files, 5.

28. Ibid., 5.

29. Email Correspondence of Adam Prior, Chief Engineer, Greeley Water and Sewer Department, to Harold Evans, Chairman, Greeley Water and Sewer Board, and Michael Welsh, University of Northern Colorado, January 17, 2020.

30. "2019 Water Master Plan Review," Greeley Water and Sewer Department Files, 5.

31. Executive Summary, "Water Pollution Control Facility Treatment and Nutrient Master Plan," City of Greeley, November 2018, Greeley Water and Sewer Department files.

32. Ibid. The Leprino cheese factory, built in 2013, generated five times as much solid waste as did the entire city's population. Similar conditions prevailed at the JBS meat processing plant.

33. Ibid.

34. Greeley Water and Sewer Board Meeting Minutes, June 18, July 16, September 17, October 15, 2003; Greeley City Council Meeting Minutes, May 20, July 15, 2003, 4.

35. "2004 Water Master Plan Annual Review," 1-3, Greeley Water and Sewer Department files.

36. "2006 Water Master Plan Annual Review," 1-7, Greeley Water and Sewer Department files.

37. Ibid., November 1, November 14, 2007.

38. Ibid., 6-7.

39. Ibid., 6.

40. *GUIDEBOOK 2011, Cache la Poudre River National Heritage Area* (Fort Collins, CO: Poudre River Heritage Alliance, 2011), 5. www.PoudreHeritage.org.

41. Cache la Poudre River National Heritage Area, H.R. 146, 111th Congress, First Session 2009, Omnibus Public Land Management Act of 2009, Sec. 8002, pp. 239-245, Public Law 111-11.

42. Poudre Heritage Alliance Homepage, https://poudreheritage.org/about-pha/, accessed January 19, 2020.

43. *GUIDEBOOK*, 54.

CHAPTER TWELVE

1. Watson, a member of the Union Colony, and one of its first arrivals at the new town site of Greeley, was a prosperous farmer, produce dealer, businessman and civic leader. Frank Green was three years old when he arrived in Greeley with his parents, William and Anna Green, also members of the Union Colony.

Acknowledgments

WE, THE CO-AUTHORS, have many people to thank for making this book possible. In our research and writing, we have benefitted immensely from the Greeley City Council's support and the talent and energy of the Water and Sewer Department board and staff members. We have gained a much better understanding of Greeley and the Cache la Poudre River's role in western and U.S. history.

From its cradle high up in the seeps and bogs of the Continental Divide, the Poudre River forms and flows as snowmelt. It courses through forested lands, is stored in high mountain reservoirs, then released and diverted again for farms, cities and commerce. This trickle of a mountain stream grows and builds, working its way towards the Eastern Plains, beyond Fort Collins and Greeley, to meet the South Platte River downstream of Greeley.

The Poudre Basin also receives waters diverted across the Divide from the Colorado, Michigan and Laramie Rivers. These combine to provide an important source of water for everyone who lives and works in Greeley. In addition, the community depends on the Big Thompson River as it runs from Estes Park, through Loveland to Boyd Lake, where water is treated and delivered into Greeley's water system.

Up and down the Front Range, ditches and reservoirs interlace with farms and cities where so many families look to water for jobs, recreational pursuits, and the environment Coloradans cherish. Through the Great Divide, the Adams Tunnel of the Colorado-Big Thompson Project delivers water into northern Colorado through a 13.1-mile-long borehole beneath the lofty summits of Rocky Mountain National Park. On June 15, 1940, President Franklin D. Roosevelt pushed a switch in Washington, D.C., igniting the first blast to begin this great work. Greeley water leaders had long supported this effort in prolonged negotiations with Colorado's Western Slope.

Of course, in researching this book, we had to see for ourselves the lay of the land and its waters. We journeyed especially with Randy Gustafson, Greeley's long-time water operations manager, on memorable excursions up the Cache la Poudre Wild and Scenic River. Over the course of springs, summers and autumns, Gustafson led us to Seaman Reservoir on the Poudre's North Fork, as well as to the City's high mountain reservoirs on the South Fork and Mainstem, including Peterson, Twin Lake, Hourglass, Comanche, and Barnes Meadow Reservoirs.

Dennis Harmon of the Water Supply and Storage Company accompanied us to Chambers Lake, the Grand River Ditch, Long Draw Reservoir, and the Laramie-Poudre Tunnel. Randy also made sure that the Michigan River and Rawah Ditches, which carry waters of the North Platte River system into the Upper Poudre River, were on the traveling agenda. He took us through Greeley's water treatment plants at Bellvue on the Poudre River, just below the mouth of the canyon, and the Boyd Lake treatment plant at Loveland, on the Big Thompson side of the City's water works.

Much of what became the narrative of operations, maintenance, funding, and policy for the story of the Greeley water and wastewater system came from sources beyond the city itself. For that reason, several individuals and institutions deserve recognition, for guiding the researchers and writers, as they designed a strategy to demonstrate to the citizenry the value of water to their daily lives.

Brian Werner and his staff of Chris Pigg and Alyssa Alpe at the Northern Colorado Water Conservancy District and its Municipal Subdistrict spent long days making sure we understood the operations of the Colorado-Big Thompson Western Slope and Eastern Slope storage, hydropower generation, and delivery facilities for Colorado River water. They also offered invaluable assistance with their files and newspaper clippings. Holly Geist of the Denver Water Archives helped with documents and images of Greeley's interaction with that city's water officials. So, too, did the staff of the Water Resources Archive at Colorado State University, led by Patricia Rettig, who provided essential materials from their collections of public and private papers about water in northern Colorado. Files from the National Archives and Records Administration in Broomfield, Colorado, likewise expanded the story of Greeley Water through the lens of federal project development.

With Burt Knight, Greeley's former water and sewer department director, and Harold Evans, chair of Greeley's Water and Sewer Board, the authors inhaled the birds' eye view of Greeley's water system by helicopter, overflying the Poudre and the Big Thompson Rivers—circling from Bellvue to the Great Divide, and around back through Greeley. On other days, we traveled with Tom Selders up the Poudre River Trail from Greeley to the former Kodak plant; then with Robert Ward along the trail through Fort Collins to the Watson Fish Hatchery. We also visited the Jackson Ditch location of Ralph Parshall's flume measurement design experiments, and the old Fort Collins water treatment works near the site of the fur trappers' powder cache!

We videotaped interviews with highly knowledgeable persons, now preserved in the City of Greeley Archives. These included Hank Brown, Bob Ruyle, Dick Boettcher, Stow Witwer, Jr., Jim Witwer, Harold Evans, Jon Monson, Burt Knight, Roy Otto, Randy Gustafson, George Hall, Eric Reckentine, Eric Wilkinson, Greg Hobbs, Brian Werner, Ed Young, Fred Otis, Jim Hall, Manuel Sisneros, Mick Todd, Norm Dean, Ruth Quade, Sam Boone, Tom Cech, Tom Norton, Tom Selders, Pete Morrell, Leonard Wiest, and Tony Miller. Shannon Metcalf, Lory Stephens, and videographer Natalie Stevens provided indispensable support for arranging and conducting these interviews.

Former Water Division No. 1 Engineer Dick Stenzel supplied us with original books, manuscripts, reports, and circulars he and Tom Cech used in researching and publishing *Water, Colorado's Real Gold* (2013). Brent Schantz of Water Division No. 1 lent us his original 1902 first edition of *Colonial Days* signed by its author J. Max Clark. Colorado Supreme Court Law Librarian Chris Hudson and his colleagues opened-up the courts' extensive collection of early water codes, statutes and U.S. Supreme Court briefs and transcripts in the Arkansas River, Laramie River, and Colorado River equitable apportionment and compact negotiation proceedings.

The University of Northern Colorado, the City's largest customer in the early years of the Greeley Water Works, extended the support of Jay Trask and his staff at the University Archives. Student researchers found much in the microfilm collections of the *Greeley Tribune*, the city archives, and the city council meeting minutes; they included Jamie Fogg, Tracy Briggs, Justin Steele, and Tom Schemp. From these sources came the unique database Tishana Cano developed for the city's water and sewer department. We have used it to help explain the history and maturation of Greeley's water system.

Peggy Ford Waldo, of the City of Greeley Museums, brought to bear her incomparable knowledge of the Union Colony and Greeley's water people, facilities, maps, photographs and historic artifacts of significant importance. Others from the museums who provided valuable assistance were Katalyn Lutkin, Katie Ross, and Lenore Harriman.

Thank you Roy Otto, Greeley City Manager, for your insightful Preface; Reagan Waskom of Colorado State University, for your expansive Foreword; and Harold Evans for your memorable summary of Greeley water epochs. Doug Marek, Greeley City Attorney and his staff; Betsy Holder and the City Clerk's staff; Director Andy

McRoberts, Jason Evenson, and Kim Snyder from the City of Greeley Culture, Parks and Recreation Department; Lisa Peterson of the City of Greeley GIS Department; and Tom Dingeman, City of Greeley, retired, all provided valuable assistance.

To Stephanie Burchett, photographer, and Jay Moore, the extraordinary artist who painted the cover for the book—our sincere thanks. Water and Sewer Department Director Sean Chambers, you have helped us greatly to the finish line.

Professor Dan Tyler's books serve as guideposts and bulwarks to our narrative: *The Last Water Hole in the West, Silver Fox of the Rockies, Love In An Envelope, and W.D. Farr, Cowboy in the Boardroom.* No other person has better surveyed the legacy of Greeley's Delph Carpenter, first generation descendant of the Union Colony, and those who have followed him so well in extending the art of diplomacy to water conflicts. We are very grateful to Tom Cech, project manager and copy editor; Peggy Ford Waldo, researcher, editor and contributor; and Emmett Jordan, graphic designer and production manager, for bringing this book together for publication on the 150th anniversary of the Union Colony.

We are most indebted to our wives, Bobbie Hobbs and Cindy Welsh. They are the stars we steer by!

This project had its origins in 2015 and began with Harold Evans, who diligently pursued funding, and organized a team of dedicated authors, editors and production professionals to make the vision a reality. We acknowledge the indispensable help of:

Greeley City Council

Greeley Water and Sewer Board

City of Greeley Arts Commission and the 1% for Art Program

Achieving Community Excellence Board

Additional private financial support was provided by:

Union Colony Company of Colorado

The Farr Family – Greeley, Colorado

Todd Family Foundation

Harold and Carol Evans

This book would not have been possible without their generous support.

—*Greg Hobbs and Michael Welsh*

Index

CPSIA information can be obtained
at www.ICGtesting.com
Printed in the USA
BVHW071129200720
584131BV00003B/7/J